G000113030

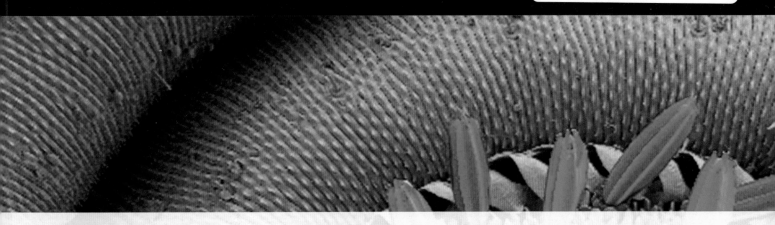

Project Directors

Angela Hall   Emma Palmer

Robin Millar   Mary Whitehouse

Editors

Emma Palmer   Carol Usher

Anne Scott   Mary Whitehouse

Authors

Ann Fullick   Andrew Hunt   Emily Perry   Elizabeth Swinbank

Helen Harden   Neil Ingram   Jacqueline Punter   Vicky Wong

Maria Pack   David Sang

THE UNIVERSITY *of York*

THE SALTERS' INSTITUTE

Nuffield Foundation

OCR
RECOGNISING ACHIEVEMENT

OXFORD
UNIVERSITY PRESS

Official Publisher Partnership

Contents

How to use this book

Welcome to Twenty First Century Science. This book has been specially written by a partnership between OCR, The University of York Science Education Group, The Nuffield Foundation, and Oxford University Press.

On these two pages you can see the types of page you will find in this book, and the features on them. Everything in the book is designed to provide you with the support you need to help you prepare for your examinations and achieve your best.

Module Openers

Why study?: This explains how what you're about to learn is relevant to everyday life.

Find out about: Every module starts with a short list of the things you'll be covering.

Ideas about Science: Here you can read about the key ideas about science covered in this module.

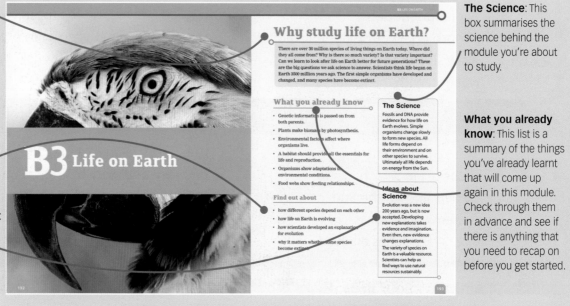

The Science: This box summarises the science behind the module you're about to study.

What you already know: This list is a summary of the things you've already learnt that will come up again in this module. Check through them in advance and see if there is anything that you need to recap on before you get started.

Main Pages

Find out about: For every part of the book you can see a list of the key points explored in that section.

Worked examples: These help you understand how to use an equation or to work through a calculation. You can check back whenever you use the calculation in your work to make sure you understand.

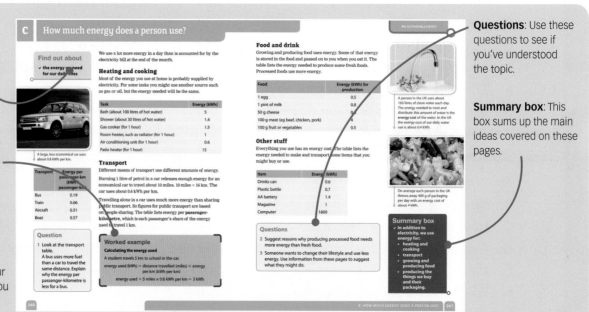

Questions: Use these questions to see if you've understood the topic.

Summary box: This box sums up the main ideas covered on these pages.

You should know: This is a summary of the main ideas in the unit. You can use it as a starting point for revision, to check that you know about the big ideas covered.

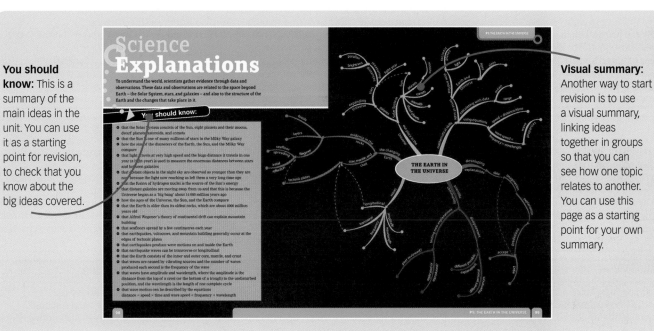

Visual summary: Another way to start revision is to use a visual summary, linking ideas together in groups so that you can see how one topic relates to another. You can use this page as a starting point for your own summary.

Ideas about Science: For every module this page summarises the ideas about science that you need to understand.

Review Questions: You can begin to prepare for your exams by using these questions to test how well you know the topics in this module.

Structure of assessment

Matching your course

What's in each module?

As you go through the book you should use the module opener pages to understand what you will be learning and why it is important. The table below gives an overview of the main topics each module includes.

B1
• What are genes and how do they affect the way that organisms develop? • Why can people look like their parents, brothers and sisters, but not be identical to them? • How can and should genetic information be used? How can we use our knowledge of genes to prevent disease? • How is a clone made?

C1
• Which chemicals make up air, and which ones are pollutants? How do I make sense of data about air pollution? • What chemical reactions produce air pollutants? What happens to these pollutants in the atmosphere? • What choices can we make personally, locally, nationally or globally to improve air quality?

P1
• What do we know about the place of the Earth in the Universe? • What do we know about the the Earth and how it is changing?

B2
• How do our bodies resist infection? • What are vaccines and antibiotics and how do they work? • What factors increase the risk of heart disease? • How do our bodies keep a healthy water balance?

C2
• How do we measure the properties of materials and why are the results useful? • Why is crude oil important as a source of new materials such as plastics and fibres? • Why does it help to know about the molecular structure of materials such as plastics and fibres? • What is nanotechnology and why is it important?

P2
• What types of electromagnetic radiation are there? • Which types of electromagnetic radiation harm living tissue and why? • What is the evidence for global warming, why might it be occuring? How serious a threat is it? • How are electromagnetic waves used in communications?

B3
• Systems in balance – how do different species depend on each other? • How has life on Earth evolved? • What is the importance of biodiversity?

C3
• What were the origins of minerals in Britain that contribute to our economic wealth? • Where does salt come from; why is it important? • Why do we need chemicals such as alkalis and chlorine and how do we make them? • What can we do to make our use of chemicals safe and sustainable?

P3
• How much energy do we use? • How can electricity be generated? • Which energy sources should we choose?

How do the modules fit together?

The modules in this book have been written to match the specification for GCSE Science. In the diagram to the right you can see that the modules can also be used to study parts of GCSE Biology, GCSE Chemistry, and GCSE Physics courses.

	GCSE Biology	GCSE Chemistry	GCSE Physics
GCSE Science	B1	C1	P1
	B2	C2	P2
	B3	C3	P3
GCSE Additional Science	B4	C4	P4
	B5	C5	P5
	B6	C6	P6
	B7	C7	P7

GCSE Science assessment

The content in the modules of this book matches the modules of the specification.

Twenty First Century Science offers two routes to the GCSE Science qualification, which includes different exam papers depending on the route you take.

The diagrams below show you which modules are included in each exam paper. They also show you how much of your final mark you will be working towards in each paper.

	Unit	Modules Tested			Percentage	Type	Time	Marks Available
Route 1	A161	B1	B2	B3	25%	Written Exam	1 h	60
	A171	C1	C2	C3	25%	Written Exam	1 h	60
	A181	P1	P2	P3	25%	Written Exam	1 h	60
	A144	Controlled Assessment			25%		9 h	64

	Unit	Modules Tested			Percentage	Type	Time	Marks Available
Route 2	A141	B1	C1	P1	25%	Written Exam	1 h	60
	A142	B2	C2	P2	25%	Written Exam	1 h	60
	A143	B3	C3	P3	25%	Written Exam	1 h	60
	A144	Controlled Assessment			25%		9 h	64

Command words

The list below explains some of the common words you will see used in exam questions.

Calculate
Work out a number. You can use your calculator to help you. You may need to use an equation. The question will say if your working must be shown. (Hint: don't confuse with 'Estimate' or 'Predict'.)

Compare
Write about the similarities and differences between two things.

Describe
Write a detailed answer that covers what happens, when it happens, and where it happens. Talk about facts and characteristics. (Hint: don't confuse with 'Explain'.)

Discuss
Write about the issues related to a topic. You may need to talk about the opposing sides of a debate, and you may need to show the difference between ideas, opinions, and facts.

Estimate
Suggest an approximate (rough) value, without performing a full calculation or an accurate measurement. Don't just guess – use your knowledge of science to suggest a realistic value. (Hint: don't confuse with 'Calculate' and 'Predict'.)

Explain
Write a detailed answer that covers how and why a thing happens. Talk about mechanisms and reasons. (Hint: don't confuse with 'Describe'.)

Evaluate
You will be given some facts, data, or other kind of information. Write about the data or facts and provide your own conclusion or opinion on them.

Justify
Give some evidence or write down an explanation to tell the examiner why you gave an answer.

Outline
Give only the key facts of the topic. You may need to set out the steps of a procedure or process – make sure you write down the steps in the correct order.

Predict
Look at some data and suggest a realistic value or outcome. You may use a calculation to help. Don't guess – look at trends in the data and use your knowledge of science. (Hint: don't confuse with 'Calculate' or 'Estimate'.)

Show
Write down the details, steps, or calculations needed to prove an answer that you have given.

Suggest
Think about what you've learnt and apply it to a new situation or context. Use what you have learnt to suggest sensible answers to the question.

Write down
Give a short answer, without a supporting argument.

Top Tips

Always read exam questions carefully, even if you recognise the word used. Look at the information in the question and the number of answer lines to see how much detail the examiner is looking for.

You can use bullet points or a diagram if it helps your answer.

If a number needs units you should include them, unless the units are already given on the answer line.

Making sense of graphs

Scientists use graphs and charts to present data clearly and to look for patterns in the data. You will need to plot graphs or draw charts to present data and then describe and explain what the data is showing. Examination questions may also give you a graph and ask you to describe and explain what a graph is telling you.

Reading the axes

Look at these two charts, which both provide data about daily energy use in several countries.

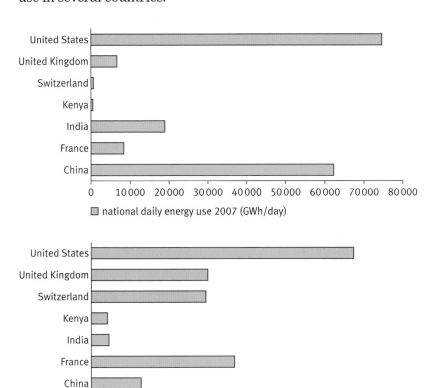

Graphs to show energy use in a range of countries, total and per capita.

Why are the charts so different if they both represent information about energy use?

Look at the labels on the axes.

One shows the **energy use per person per day**, the other shows the **energy use per day by the whole country**.

For example, the first graph shows that China uses a similar amount of energy to the US. But the population of China is much greater – so the energy use per person is much less.

First rule of reading graphs: read the axes and check the units.

Describing the relationship between variables

The pattern of points plotted on a graph shows whether two **factors** are related. Look at this scatter graph.

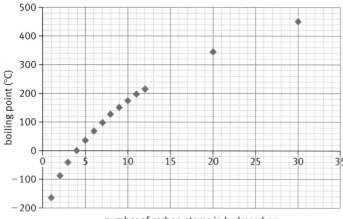

number of carbon atoms in hydrocarbon

Graph to show the relationship between the number of carbon atoms in a hydrocarbon and the boiling point.

There *is* a pattern in the data; as the number of carbon atoms increases, the boiling point increases.

But it is not a straight line, it is quite a smooth curve, so we can say more than that. When the number of carbon atoms is small the boiling point increases quickly with each extra carbon atom. As the number of carbon atoms gets bigger, the boiling point still increases, but less quickly. Another way of describing this is to say that the slope of the graph – the **gradient** – gets less as the number of carbon atoms increases.

Look at the graph on the right, which shows how the number of bacteria infecting a patient changes over time.

How many different gradients can you see?

There are three phases to the graph, each with a different gradient. So you should describe each phase, including **data** if possible:

- The number of bacteria **increases rapidly** for the first day until there are about **4.5 million** bacteria.
- For about **the next three days** the number remains steady at about 4.5 million.
- After the **fourth** day the number of bacteria declines to less than a **million** over the following **two to three days**.

Second rule of reading graphs: describe each phase of the graph, and include ideas about the **gradient** and **data**, including **units**.

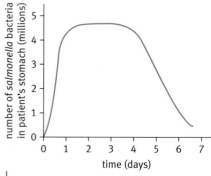

Graph of bacteria population against time.

Is there a correlation?

Sometimes we are interested in whether one thing changes when another does. If a change in one factor goes together with a change in something else, we say that the two things are **correlated**.

The two graphs on the right show how global temperatures have changed over time and how levels of carbon dioxide in the atmosphere have changed over time.

Is there a correlation between the two sets of data?

Look at the graphs – why is it difficult to decide if there is a correlation?

The two sets of data are over different periods of time, so although both graphs show a rise with time, it is difficult to see if there is a correlation.

It would be easier to identify a correlation if both sets of data were plotted for the same time period and placed one above the other, or on the same axes, like this:

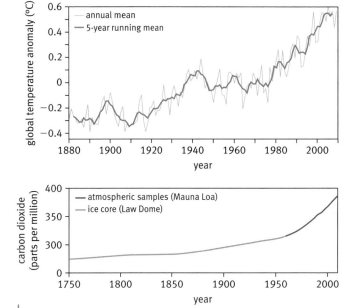

Graphs to show increasing global temperatures and carbon dioxide levels. Source: NASA.

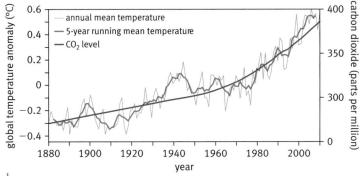

Graph to show the same data as the above two graphs, plotted on one set of axes.

When there are two sets of data on the same axes take care to look at which axis relates to which line.

Third rule for reading graphs: when looking for a correlation between two sets of data, read the axes carefully.

Explaining graphs

When a graph shows that there is a correlation between two sets of data, scientists try to find out if a change in one factor causes a change in the other. They use science ideas to look for an underlying mechanism to explain why two factors are related.

Controlled assessment

In GCSE Science the controlled assessment counts for 25% of your total grade. Marks are given for a case study and a practical data analysis task.

Your school or college may give you the mark schemes for this.

This will help you understand how to get the most credit for your work.

Tip

The best advice is 'plan ahead'. Give your work the time it needs and work steadily and evenly over the time you are given. Your deadlines will come all too quickly, especially if you have coursework to do in other subjects.

Case study (12.5%)

Everyday life has many questions science can help to answer. You may meet these in media reports, for example, on television, radio, in newspapers, and in magazines. A case study is a report that weighs up evidence about a scientific question.

OCR will provide a news sheet with a variety of articles about some of the science topics you have studied in this course.

You will choose an issue from the news sheet as the basis for your case study, and identify a question that you can go on to answer. Your question will probably fit into one of these categories:

- a question where the scientific knowledge is not certain, for example, 'Does using mobile phones cause brain damage?'
- a question about decision making using scientific information, for example, 'Should cars be banned from a shopping street to reduce air pollution?' or 'Should the government stop research into human cloning?'
- a question about a personal issue involving science, for example, 'Should my child have the MMR vaccine?'

You should find out what different people have said about the issue. Then evaluate this information and reach your own conclusion.

You will be awarded marks for:

Selecting information

- Collect information from different places – books, the Internet, newspapers.
- Say where your information has come from.
- Choose only information that is relevant to the question you are studying.
- Decide how reliable each source of information is.

Understanding the question

- Use scientific knowledge and understanding to explain the topic you are studying.
- When you report what other people have said, say what scientific evidence they used (from experiments, surveys, etc.).

Reaching your own conclusion

- Compare different evidence and points of view.
- Consider the benefits and risks of different courses of action.
- Say what you think should be done, and link this to the evidence you have reported.

Presenting your study

- Make sure your report is laid out clearly in a sensible order – use a table of contents to help organise your ideas.
- You may use different presentation styles, for example, a written report, newspaper article, PowerPoint presentation, poster or booklet, or web page.
- Use pictures, tables, charts, graphs, and so on to present information.
- Take care with your spelling, grammar, and punctuation, and use scientific terms where they are appropriate.

Creating a case study

Where do I start?

Read the news sheet you are given and think of a question you want to find the answer to.

Sources of information could include:

- Internet
- school library
- local public library
- your science textbook and notes
- TV
- radio
- newspapers and magazines
- museums and exhibitions.

When will I do my controlled assessment?

Your case study will be written in class time over a series of lessons.

You may also do some research out of class.

Your practical data analysis task will be done in class time over a series of lessons.

Your school or college will decide when you do your controlled assessment. If you do more than one case study or practical data analysis, they will choose the one with the best marks.

Practical data analysis (12.5%)

Scientists collect data from experiments and studies. They use this data to explain how something happens. You need to be able to assess the methods and data from scientific experiments. This will help you decide how reliable a scientific claim is.

A practical data analysis task is based on a practical experiment that you carry out. The experiment will be designed to test a hypothesis suggested by your teacher. You may do the experiment alone or work in groups and pool all your data. Then you interpret and evaluate the data.

You will be awarded marks for:

Choosing how to collect the data

- Carry out the experiment in ways that will give you high-quality data.
- Explain why you chose this method.
- Explain how you worked safely.

Interpreting data

- Present your data in tables, charts, or graphs.
- Say what conclusions you can reach from your data.
- Explain your conclusions using your scientific knowledge and understanding.

Evaluating the method and quality of data

- Look back at your experiment and say how you could improve the method.
- Explain how confident you are in your evidence. Have you got enough results? Do they show a clear pattern? Have you repeated measurements to check them? Would you get the same results if you repeated the experiment?
- Comment on the repeatability of your data, account for any outliers in the data, or explain why there are no outliers.
- Suggest some improvements or extra data you could collect to be more confident in your conclusions.

Reviewing the hypothesis

- Use your scientific knowledge to decide whether the hypothesis is supported by your data.
- Suggest what extra data could be collected to increase confidence in the hypothesis.

Presenting your report

- Make sure your report is laid out clearly in a sensible order.
- Use diagrams, tables, charts, and graphs to present information.
- Take care with your spelling, grammar, and punctuation, and use scientific terms where they are appropriate.

B1 You and your genes

Why study genes?

What makes me the way that I am? How are features passed on from parents to children? Your ancestors probably asked the same questions. You may look like your relatives, but you are unique. Only in the last few generations has science been able to answer questions like these.

What you already know

- In sexual reproduction fertilisation happens when a male and female sex cell join together. Information from two parents is mixed to make a new plan for the offspring. The offspring will be similar but not identical to their parents.

- There are variations between members of the same species that are due to environmental as well as inherited causes.

- Clones are individuals with identical genetic information.

- The science of cloning raises ethical issues.

Find out about

- how genes and your environment make you unique

- how and why people find out about their genes

- how we can use our knowledge of genes

- whether we should allow this.

The Science

Your environment has a huge effect on you, for example, on your appearance, your body, and your health. But these features are also affected by your genes. In this Module you'll find out how. You'll discover the story of inheritance.

Ideas about Science

In the future, science could help you to change your baby's genes before it is born. Cloned embryos could provide cells to cure diseases. But, as new technologies are developed, we must decide how they should be used. These can be questions of ethics – decisions about what is right and wrong.

15

Find out about

- ✓ **what makes us all different**
- ✓ **what genes are and what genes do**

Both the information you inherit and your environment affect most of your features.

Summary box

- ✓ **You inherit genes from your parents.**
- ✓ **Your genes and your environment make you unique.**
- ✓ **The nuclei of your cells contain chromosomes. Chromosomes are made of DNA.**
- ✓ **A gene is a section of DNA.**
- ✓ **Genes have the information to make proteins.**
- ✓ **Structural proteins make up the fabric of your body.**
- ✓ **Enzymes are proteins; they control chemical reactions in the body.**

Children look like their parents. They **inherit** information from them. This information is in **genes**. Genes control how new organisms develop and function.

All people are very similar. Look at the people around you – the differences between us are very small. But they are interesting because they make us unique.

These sisters have some features in common.

Environment makes a difference

The information you inherited from your parents affects almost all of your features. For example, your blood group depends on this information. Some features are the result of only your **environment**, such as scars and tattoos.

But most of your features are affected by both your genes and your environment. For example, your weight depends on inherited information. But if you eat too much, you will become heavier.

Questions

1 Choose two of the students in the photograph on the left. Write down five ways they look different.

2 What two things can affect how you develop?

3 Explain what is meant by inherited information.

Where is all the information kept?

Living organisms are made up of cells. Most cells contain **nuclei**. Inside each nucleus are long threads called **chromosomes**. Each chromosome has thousands of genes. Genes control how you develop.

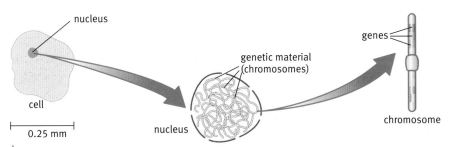

The nucleus of a cell has all the information to make a whole human being. The nucleus is just 0.006 mm across!

What are chromosomes made of?

Chromosomes are made of very long molecules of **DNA**. DNA is short for deoxyribonucleic acid. A gene is a section of a DNA molecule.

How do genes control your development?

Genes are instructions for making proteins. Each gene is the 'recipe' for making a different protein.

What's so important about proteins?

There are many different proteins in the body, and each one has an important job. They may be:

- **structural** proteins – to build the body, eg collagen (the protein found in tendons)
- **functional proteins** – to take part in the chemical reactions of the body, eg enzymes such as amylase

Genes control which proteins a cell makes. This is how they direct what the cell does and how an organism develops.

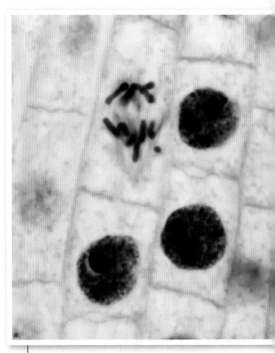

Scientists have stained these plant cells to show up their nuclei. One cell is dividing. The separating chromosomes can be seen.

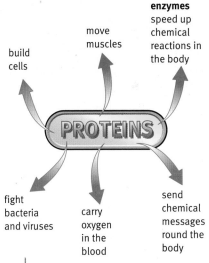

build cells

move muscles

enzymes speed up chemical reactions in the body

PROTEINS

fight bacteria and viruses

carry oxygen in the blood

send chemical messages round the body

There are about 50 000 types of proteins in the human body.

Questions

4 Write these cell parts in order starting with the smallest:
chromosome, gene, cell, nucleus

5 Explain how genes control what a cell does.

6 a List two kinds of job that proteins do in the human body.

b Name two proteins in the human body and say what they do.

Find out about

- why identical twins look like each other
- why identical twins do not stay identical
- what a clone is

Summary box

- **Identical twins have the same genetic information.**
- **There may be differences in some characteristics because of the environment.**
- **A clone is a living organism with the same genetic information as another living organism.**

Questions

1 How are dimples, green eyes, and being 2 m tall inherited differently?

2 Why do scientists find studying identical twins so useful?

Genes decide a lot about how a baby will grow and develop. A few characteristics, like dangly earlobes or dimples, are decided by one pair of genes only. Mostly several different genes work together. In this way they decide characteristics such as your height, your weight, and your eye colour. But your genes don't tell the whole story.

Twins and the environment

Identical twins have the same genes but they don't look exactly the same.

Sometimes a fertilised egg starts to divide and splits to form two babies instead of one. These are identical twins. Each baby has the same genes. Any differences between them must be because of the environment.

Most identical twins grow up in the same family. Their environment is very similar. But sometimes twins are separated after birth and adopted by different parents. Then scientists can find out what difference the environment makes to the twins' characteristics.

Often the separated twins are still very alike. Genes have a very strong influence. But some things, like weight, are more different in twins who grow up apart than twins who live in the same environment.

Cloning

We call any genetically identical organisms **clones**. So identical twins are human clones! Scientists can use clones to find out the effect of the environment on growth and development. But it would be wrong for scientists to separate babies. For this reason scientists often study plants.

Plant clones are quite common. For example, strawberry plants and spider plants make plant clones at the end of runners. Bulbs, like daffodils, also produce clones.

Cloning plants

It is easy for people to clone plants artificially. A piece of the adult plant is cut off. It soon forms new roots and stems to become a small plant. The new plant is a clone. It has the same genes as the parent plant and is identical.

You can also place tiny pieces of a plant on special jelly, called agar. They grow into plants, which are all clones. In this way, you can make hundreds of clones from a single plant.

Cloned plants are useful

You can use clones to look at how the environment affects them. If the parent plant grew very tall, that will be partly down to its genes. But what happens if it doesn't get enough nutrients or water? Will it still grow tall?

We can look at the effects of different factors on the characteristics of cloned plants. This helps us to understand how genes and the environment interact.

Each of these baby spider plants is a clone of its parent plant and of all the other baby plants.

You may make cauliflower clones like these.

Questions

3 What is a clone?

4 Why are cloned plants so useful to scientists?

5 The environment affects the appearance of plants. Describe how you could use cloned plants to show this.

People in a family look like each other. You may have inherited a feature you don't like, such as your dad's big ears. But family likenesses can be very serious.

Robert's story

I'm so frustrated. I can't sit still in a chair. I'm more and more forgetful and I fall over. The doctor has said it might be **Huntington's disease**. She said I can have a blood test to find out.

Huntington's disease

You can't catch Huntington's disease. It's an inherited disorder. Parents pass the disease on to their children. The symptoms of Huntington's disease don't happen until middle age. They are:

- difficulty controlling muscles, which shows up as twitching
- becoming forgetful
- difficulty understanding things and concentrating
- mood changes.

After a few years, sufferers can't control their movements. Sadly, the condition is fatal.

Robert and his grandson Craig.

Questions

1 List the symptoms of Huntington's disease.

2 Explain why Huntington's disease is called an inherited disorder.

Robert, 56
I've been forgetting things and stumbling.

Eileen, 58
Robert's mum was just the same. David looks just like his father.

Sarah, 32
I'm definitely having the test if Dad's got it. I need to know so I can plan my life.

David, 35
I'm not having a test. It won't change what happens to me.

Clare, 33
David's got the right idea, just getting on with his life. Mind you, I'm really worried about him now – and Craig and Hannah.

Craig, 16
It's not fair. I want to find out but they won't let me. They think I'm too young to understand.

Hannah, 14
No-one seems to want to tell me anything about it at all.

Craig's family.

How do you inherit your genes?

In some families brothers and sisters look like each other. In others they look very different. They may also look different from their parents. This is because of genes.

Parents pass on genes in their **sex cells**. In animals these are sperm and egg cells. Sex cells have copies of half the parent's chromosomes. When a sperm cell fertilises an egg cell, the fertilised egg cell gets a full set of chromosomes. It is called an **embryo**.

The number of chromosomes in each cell

Chromosomes come in pairs. Every human body cell has 23 pairs of chromosomes. The chromosomes in most pairs are the same size and shape. They carry the same genes in the same place. So your genes also come in pairs.

Sex cells have single chromosomes

Sex cells are made with copies of half the parent's chromosomes. This makes sure that the fertilised egg cell has the right number of chromosomes – 23 pairs. One chromosome came from the egg cell. The other came from the sperm cell. Each chromosome carries thousands of genes. Each chromosome in a pair carries the same genes along its length. So the fertilised egg cell has a mixture of the parents' genes.

Half of the new baby's genes are from the mother. Half are from the father. This is why children resemble both their parents.

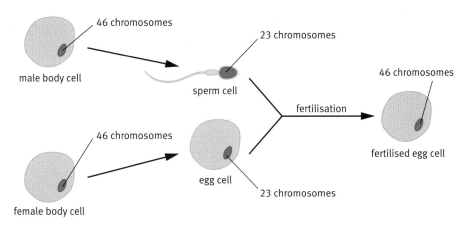

The cells in this diagram are not drawn to scale. A human egg cell is 0.1 mm across. This is 20 times larger than a human sperm cell.

Questions

3 a Draw a diagram to show a sperm cell, an egg cell, and the fertilised egg cell they make.

  b Explain why the fertilised egg cell has pairs of chromosomes.

4 Explain why children may look a bit like each of their parents.

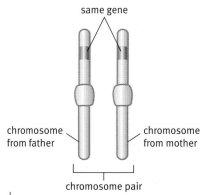

These chromosomes are a pair.

Summary box

✓ Your **sex cells** only have one of each chromosome pair.
✓ An egg cell and a sperm cell join to form an **embryo**.
✓ You inherit half of your genes from your mother and half from your father.
✓ Huntington's disease is caused by a faulty gene. It is passed on or inherited from one of your parents.

Find out about

✔ **what decides if you are male or female**
✔ **how a Y chromosome makes a baby male**

Question

1 What sex chromosome(s) would be in the nucleus of:
   a a man's body cell?
   b an egg cell?
   c a woman's body cell?
   d a sperm cell?

What decides an embryo's sex?

A fertilised human egg cell has 23 pairs of chromosomes. Males have an X chromosome and a Y chromosome – **XY**. Females have two X chromosomes – **XX**.

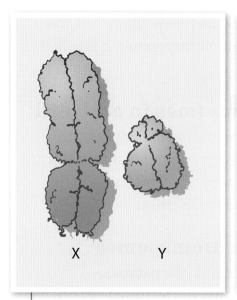
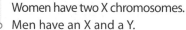

Women have two X chromosomes. Men have an X and a Y.

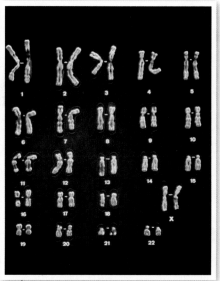

These chromosomes are from the nucleus of a woman's body cell. They are lined up in pairs.

What's the chance of being male or female?

A parent's chromosomes are in pairs. When sex cells are made they only get one chromosome from each pair. So half a man's sperm cells get an X chromosome and half get a Y chromosome. A woman's egg cells all get an X chromosome.

When a sperm cell fertilises an egg cell the chances are 50% that it will be an X sperm and 50% that it will be a Y sperm. This means that there is a 50% chance that the baby will be a boy and 50% chance a girl.

Summary box

✔ **Males have XY chromosomes.**
✔ **Females have XX chromosomes.**

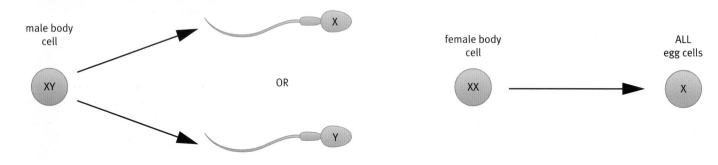

Will this baby be tall and have red hair? Will she be good at music or sport? Both her environment and her genes will affect these features. A few features are controlled by just one gene. We can understand these more easily.

Find out about

- ✓ how pairs of genes control some features
- ✓ cystic fibrosis (an inherited illness)
- ✓ testing a baby's genes before they are born

This baby has inherited a unique mix of genetic information.

Genes come in different versions

Both chromosomes in a pair carry genes that control the same features. Each pair of genes controlling a feature is in the same place on the chromosomes.

But genes in a pair can be slightly different versions. You can think about it like football strips. A team's home and away strips are both based on the same pattern, but they're not the same. Different versions of the same genes are called **alleles**.

The gene that controls dimples has two alleles. The D allele gives you dimples. The d allele won't cause dimples.

Do you have dimples when you smile?

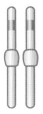

This diagram shows one pair of chromosomes. The gene controlling dimples is coloured in.

Question

1 Write down what is meant by the word 'allele'.

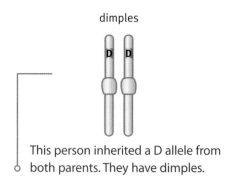

dimples

This person inherited a D allele from both parents. They have dimples.

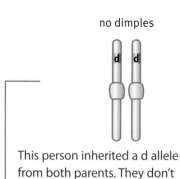

no dimples

This person inherited a d allele from both parents. They don't have dimples.

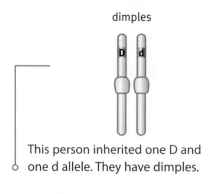

dimples

This person inherited one D and one d allele. They have dimples.

Dominant alleles – they're in charge

The D allele is **dominant**. You only need one copy of a dominant allele to have its feature. The d allele is **recessive**. You must have two copies of a recessive allele to have its feature – in this case no dimples.

Which alleles can a person inherit?

Sex cells get one chromosome from each pair of their parents' chromosomes. If a parent has two D or two d alleles, they can only pass on a D or a d allele to their children.

But a parent could have one D and one d allele. Then half of their sex cells will get the D allele and half will get the d allele.

The human lottery

We don't know which egg and sperm cells will meet at fertilisation. This genetic diagram is called a Punnett square. It shows all the possibilities for one couple.

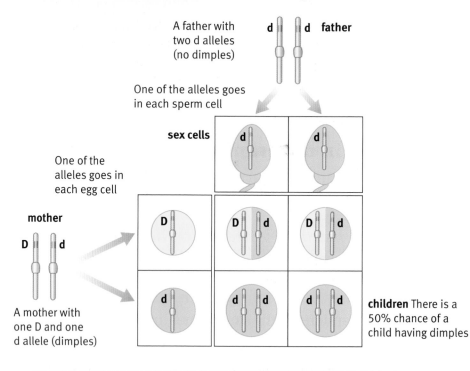

A father with two d alleles (no dimples)

One of the alleles goes in each sperm cell

sex cells

One of the alleles goes in each egg cell

mother

A mother with one D and one d allele (dimples)

children There is a 50% chance of a child having dimples

Questions

2 Explain how you inherit two alleles for each gene.

3 Explain the difference between a dominant and a recessive allele.

Why don't brothers and sisters look the same?

Human beings have about 23 000 genes. Each gene has different alleles. Both of the alleles you inherit can be the same or different.

Brothers and sisters are different because they each get a different mixture of alleles from their parents. Except for identical twins, each one of us has a unique set of genes.

Summary box
- ✓ There are different versions of genes—they are called **alleles**.
- ✓ If you have one copy of a **dominant** allele, you will have that feature.
- ✓ You have to have two copies of a **recessive** allele to show that feature.

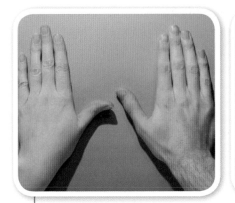

The allele that gives you straight thumbs is dominant (T). The allele for curved thumbs is recessive (t).

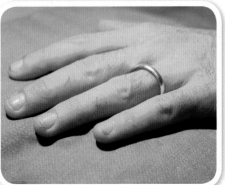

The allele that gives you hair on the middle of your fingers is dominant (R). The allele for no hair is recessive (r).

What about the family?

A small number of disorders are caused by faulty alleles of a single gene. Huntington's disease is caused by a dominant allele. You only need to inherit the allele from one parent to have the condition. Craig and Hannah's grandfather, Robert, has Huntington's disorder. So their dad, David, may have inherited this faulty allele. At the moment he has decided not to have the test to find out.

I'm not having the test. It won't change what happens to me.

<hr>

Questions

4 What are the possible pairs of alleles a person could have for:
  a dimples?
  b straight thumbs?
  c no hair on the second part of their ring finger?

5 Use a diagram to explain why a couple who have dimples could have a child with no dimples.

6 Use a diagram to work out the chance that David has inherited the Huntington's disease allele.

Dear Clare,

Please help us. My husband Huw and I have just been told that our first child has cystic fibrosis. No one in our family has ever had this disease before. Did I do something wrong during my pregnancy? I'm so worried.

Yours sincerely

Emma

Dear Emma,

What a difficult time for you all. First of all, nothing you did during your pregnancy could have affected this, so don't feel guilty. Cystic fibrosis is an inherited disorder ...

Cystic fibrosis — in depth

We've had a huge postbag in response to last month's letter from Emma. So this month we're looking in depth at cystic fibrosis, a disease that one in 25 of us carries in the UK.

What is cystic fibrosis?

You can't catch cystic fibrosis. It is a genetic disorder. It is passed on from parents to their children.

The cells that make mucus in the body are faulty. The mucus is too thick. This causes problems for breathing, digestion, and reproduction. There is no cure at the moment. But treatments are getting better and life expectancy is increasing.

Problem	Symptom	Treatment
Mucus blocks up lungs.	• Difficult to breathe. • People with CF get breathless. • Lots of chest pains.	• Physiotherapy. • Use of enzyme spray thins out mucus in the lungs. This makes it easier to clear mucus. • Antibiotics.
Mucus blocks up tubes that take enzymes from the pancreas to the gut.	• Shortage of enzymes in the gut. • Food is not digested properly. • People with CF can be short of nutrients.	• Take tablets of missing gut enzymes.
Mucus blocks up tubes in reproductive system.	Can't have children.	

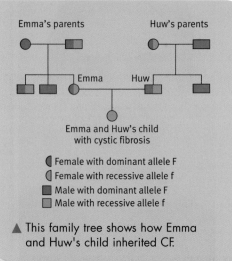

Emma's parents   Huw's parents

Emma   Huw

Emma and Huw's child
with cystic fibrosis

◖ Female with dominant allele F
◖ Female with recessive allele f
◼ Male with dominant allele F
◻ Male with recessive allele f

▲ This family tree shows how Emma and Huw's child inherited CF.

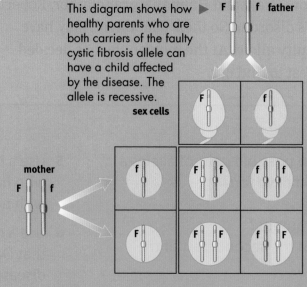

This diagram shows how healthy parents who are both carriers of the faulty cystic fibrosis allele can have a child affected by the disease. The allele is recessive.

F   f   father

sex cells

mother
F   f

children There is a 25% chance that a child from the carrier parents will have cystic fibrosis.

26

How do you get cystic fibrosis?

Most people who have CF can't have children. Babies with CF are usually born to healthy parents. How can this be?

The CF gene has two versions. One is dominant. It tells cells to make normal mucus. The other is a faulty recessive gene. There are errors in the DNA. It instructs cells to make thick mucus.

A person with one normal (F) dominant allele and a faulty (f) recessive allele will not have CF. But they can pass the faulty gene on to their children. They are carriers.

Half the sex cells of CF carriers contain the normal allele and half contain the faulty allele. If two faulty alleles meet at fertilisation, the baby will have CF. One in 25 people in the UK carry the CF allele.

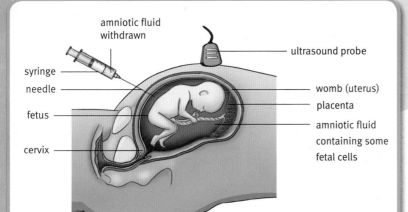

- 1% miscarriage risk
- results at 15–18 weeks
- very small risk of infection
- results not 100% reliable

What are the options?

If a couple know there is a risk they could have children with cystic fibrosis, they could have tests. During pregnancy, doctors can collect cells from the developing fetus. The couple should be aware of the following about the tests:

- there is a risk of up to 1% that they could lose the baby (miscarriage)
- there is a very small risk of infection
- the results are not 100% reliable.

◀ Amniocentesis test.

The results of the tests

Doctors examine the genes. If the fetus has two faulty (ff) CF alleles, the child will have cystic fibrosis. Then the parents may choose to end the pregnancy. This is done with a medical operation called a termination (abortion).
The fetal cells for the genetic test can be collected in an amniocentesis test.

Questions

7 The magazine doctor is sure that nothing Emma did during her pregnancy caused her baby to have cystic fibrosis. How can she be so sure?

8 People with cystic fibrosis make thick, sticky mucus. Describe the health problems that this may cause.

9 Explain what it means when someone is a 'carrier' of cystic fibrosis.

Summary box

✓ **A recessive allele causes cystic fibrosis. It causes a person to have thick mucus. If a person has only one faulty CF allele, they have normal mucus. They are carriers. A genetic test of a fetus may show two faulty CF alleles. The baby would have cystic fibrosis. A couple could have a termination.**

Find out about

- ✓ **how people make ethical decisions**
- ✓ **how genetic information could be used**

'We had a test for each of my pregnancies,' says Elaine. 'Sadly we felt we had to terminate the first one, because the fetus had CF. We are lucky enough now to have two healthy children – and we know we haven't got to watch them suffer.'

Elaine's nephew has cystic fibrosis. When they found out, Elaine and Peter became worried about any children they might have. They both had a **genetic test**. The tests showed that they were both carriers for cystic fibrosis.

Elaine and Peter decided to have a prenatal genetic test of the fetus when Elaine was pregnant. The test was positive.

Elaine and Peter's unborn child would have cystic fibrosis. They decided to end the pregnancy. This was a very hard decision.

When a person has to make a decision about what is the right or wrong thing to do, they are thinking about **ethics**. Deciding whether to have a termination is an example of an ethical question.

Ethics – right and wrong

For some ethical questions, the right answer is clear. For example, should you feed your pet? But in some situations there may not be one right answer. People think about ethical questions in different ways.

Summary box
- ✓ **Ethics is about deciding whether something is right or wrong**

Weighing up the consequences

Elaine and Peter had to decide to either continue with the pregnancy or have a termination. They thought about how each choice would affect all the people involved. They judged the problems their unborn child would face.

Elaine and Peter also had to think about:

*   the effects that an ill child would have on their lives and also on the lives of any other children they might have
*   whether they feel they could cope with caring for a child with a serious genetic disorder.

Different choices

Not everyone weighing up the consequences of each choice would have come to the same decision as this couple did.

Some people feel that any illness would make a person's quality of life terrible. But some people lead very happy, full lives with very serious disabilities.

When you believe that an action is wrong

For some people having a termination is completely wrong in itself. They believe that an unborn child has the right to life. Other people believe that terminating a pregnancy is unnatural, and that we should not interfere. These viewpoints could be their own personal beliefs or their religious beliefs.

Elaine and Peter may have felt that termination was wrong. They could have decided not to have children at all. This would mean that they could not pass on the faulty allele. Or they could decide to have children, and to care for any child that did inherit the disease.

Jo has a serious genetic disorder. Her parents believe that termination is wrong. They decided not to have more children, rather than use information from a test.

Questions

1   Explain what is meant by 'an ethical question'.

2   Describe three different points of view that a couple in Elaine and Peter's position might take.

Find out about

- ✓ what a genetic test is
- ✓ what genetic screening is

This couple are both carriers of cystic fibrosis. They had an amniocentesis test during their pregnancy. The results showed that the baby did not have CF. When their daughter was born she was completely healthy.

Questions

1 What are 'false negative' and 'false positive' results?

2 Why is it important for people to know about false results?

3 Explain what is meant by the term 'genetic screening'.

How reliable are genetic tests?

Some alleles cause genetic disorders. A genetic test can spot the faulty alleles. People like Elaine and Peter have to decide about having children. They can use the information from genetic tests to help. Genetic tests helped Elaine and Peter to decide whether to continue with the pregnancy or not.

It is important to realise that the tests are not completely reliable.

- In a very few cases it will not detect CF. Then the test will show the baby to be healthy. But it would be born with CF. This is called a **false negative**. The test only looks for common DNA errors in the faulty CF gene.
- **False positive** tests are even less common. But they can happen due to technical failure of the test. Then a baby, who tested positive for CF, is healthy.

Why do people have genetic tests?

Some people, like Elaine and Peter, know they have a genetic disorder in their family. They might have a genetic test. Most people who are carriers of CF do not know. They only find out when their child has CF. So, they would not have had a genetic test during pregnancy.

Every baby in the UK is now screened for cystic fibrosis at birth. They have a blood test. This does not test genes. If the blood test is positive for CF, the baby will be genetically tested to confirm CF.

Treatment can start before the lungs are too badly damaged. The blood test does not show up babies who are carriers of the CF allele.

Genetic testing the whole population or large groups for a genetic disease is called **genetic screening**.

Genetic screening of adults for diseases

Tay-sachs

Rabbi Joseph Ekstein had four children. They all died from Tay-Sachs disease. This is a severe genetic condition. A recessive allele causes it. In the general population Tay-Sachs is very rare. But in the 1980s, it was quite common in European Jewish families. One in every 3600 babies was affected and died.

In 1983 Rabbi Ekstein set up a genetic screening programme. Some couples, who were planning to marry, had a genetic test. If both carried the recessive allele for Tay-Sachs, they were advised not to marry. If they married, they could have their unborn baby screened and terminate affected pregnancies. Tay-Sachs has almost disappeared from Jewish communities worldwide because of genetic screening.

Testing your genes

You can buy DNA testing kits now. They can tell you if you are carrying faulty alleles that cause over 100 genetic diseases, like cystic fibrosis and Tay-Sachs. Some scientists hope these tests will help to prevent many genetic diseases. Other scientists think that screening is not worthwhile. The risk of being affected by these rare genetic diseases is low. It costs money and may cause people to worry.

Scientists can already work out the complete DNA sequence (the genome) of anyone who has enough money to pay thousands of pounds. In five years' time it may be so cheap that everyone will be able to have it done. The genome of every newborn baby may be worked out. How can we use this information?

DNA testing can be done at home with simple kits like this.

Summary box

- ✔ Genetic tests look for faulty alleles that cause diseases. Genetic screening tests a large group of people.
- ✔ Sometimes faulty alleles are found, and the person is healthy. This is a false positive. In other cases the test could show the alleles are normal, but the person has the disorder. This is a false negative.

Question

4 Babies are born with terrible genetic diseases. How can the genetic testing of adults prevent them being born?

Carolyn had a dangerous reaction to drugs. Genetic testing may help to avoid this.

Questions

5 How might genetic testing make medicines more effective?

6 What problems might genetic testing for effective medicines cause?

7 What do you think are the advantages and disadvantages of testing adults?

Summary box

✓ **Genetic screening of adults can give people the information to:**
- **choose whether to have children**
- **decide whether to have pre-natal genetic testing**
- **have the best medicine and dose for them.**

Finding the right medicine

In 2009 Carolyn Major had cancer. She started to take medicine that she hoped would help cure her. Four days later she was in an intensive care ward. Her heart was struggling to keep going. Carolyn's body reacted very badly to the anti-cancer drug. This only happens to a small group of people. Luckily, she recovered with no permanent damage done to her heart – the cancer hasn't returned either!

Genetic testing before prescribing drugs

Taking the wrong medicine may be a thing of the past. We can use genetics to match medicines to patients. Some people have enzymes that break down drugs very quickly. They need higher doses of a medicine than most of us. Other people can't break down certain drugs in their body. So medicines that are meant to help them poison them instead. In future, genetic testing may mean we can all be given the drugs that work best for our bodies.

Helping us to help ourselves?

You may have inherited genes that increase your risk of heart disease or different types of cancer. Genetic screening may be able to tell you this in the future. But remember, your genes and your lifestyle affect these diseases.

This information could be very helpful. For example, you find out that you have a higher-than-average risk of developing heart disease because of your genes. You might decide to not smoke, to eat a healthy diet, and to take lots of exercise. Then you would lower your environmental risk of heart disease. This might help to balance your increased genetic risk.

Your genes may mean you have an increased risk of getting a particular type of cancer. Regular screening will help to catch the disease as early as possible if it develops.

Who decides about genetic screening?

NHS trusts are responsible for the healthcare of their local people. The government's Department of Health give funds to local NHS trusts. They decide if they should use genetic screening.

Local NHS trusts might consider:

- the costs of testing everyone for the allele
- the benefits of testing everyone for the allele
- whether it is better to spend the money on other things, such as hip-replacement operations and treating people who already have cystic fibrosis.

Is it right to use genetic screening?

It is easy to see why people may want genetic screening. A couple's children may be at risk of inheriting a disorder. Genetic screening would help them find out. It may seem like the best course of action for everyone.

What is the right decision?

But the best decision for most people is not always the right decision. There are ethical questions to consider about genetic screening for cystic fibrosis and other disorders. These include:

- who should know the test results
- what effect could the test result have on people's future decisions
- should people be made to have screening
- should they be able to opt out
- is it right to interfere?

About 1 in 25 people in the UK carries the allele for cystic fibrosis. Having this information might be useful. But there are good reasons why not everyone agrees. A decision may benefit many people. But it could harm a few people. Then it may be the wrong decision.

It's very dangerous. People shouldn't have to worry about this information. There's nothing wrong in having a child with an illness.

We shouldn't interfere with having children. It's a natural process. So there's no point in testing for a disease.

We should give people all the information we can about their health. Then they can make an informed decision.

I want to choose my medical treatments—not have them forced upon me!

What if my husband and I both had the faulty allele? We'd be very worried about having children.

People have different ideas about whether genetic screening for cystic fibrosis would be a good thing.

Question

8 Give two arguments for and two against genetic screening for cystic fibrosis.

Find out about

✓ **how new techniques can allow people to select embryos**

Sally takes a 'fertility drug' so that she releases several eggs. The doctor collects the eggs. Bob's sperm fertilise the eggs in a Petri dish.

When the embryos reach the eight-cell stage, one cell is removed from each.

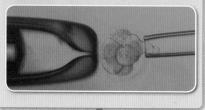

The cells are tested. Only embryos without the Huntington's allele are implanted in Sally's uterus.

Summary box

✓ **Eggs are fertilised outside the womb by sperm. The embryos are then screened for genetic diseases. Healthy embryos are implanted into the woman's womb, so they can develop.**

Many people do not agree with termination. If they are at risk of having a child with a genetic disease, what can they do? They may decide not to have children, or they can now have another treatment. It uses in vitro fertilisation (IVF). In this treatment the mother's egg cells are fertilised outside her body. This treatment is also used to help couples who cannot conceive a child naturally.

Embryo selection

Bob and Sally want children, but Bob has the allele for Huntington's disease. Sally has become pregnant twice. Tests showed that both the fetuses had the Huntington's allele. The pregnancies were terminated.

Their doctor suggested that they should use IVF. Doctors select fertilised eggs or **embryos** without the Huntington's allele. These are put back or **implanted** into Sally's womb so they can develop. Sally's treatment is explained in the flow chart.

This procedure was first carried out in 1989. At the moment, **embryo selection** is only allowed for families with particular inherited conditions.

New technology – new decisions

In the UK, Parliament makes laws to control research and technologies to do with genes. Scientists cannot do research on whatever they like. From time to time Parliament updates the law. But Parliament can't make decisions case by case. So the Government has set up groups of people to decide which cases are within the law on reproduction. The groups also decide when embryo selection can be used.

Question

1 Everyone who has embryo selection has to use IVF treatment in order to become pregnant. Explain why.

Cloning: a natural process

Many living things only need one individual to reproduce. This is called **asexual reproduction**. Single-celled organisms like the bacterium in the picture use asexual reproduction.

The bacterium divides to form two new cells. The two cells have identical genes to each other. They are clones. All of the differences between them will be caused by their environment.

Asexual reproduction

Larger plants and animals have different types of cells for different jobs. As an embryo grows, cells become **specialised**. Some examples are blood cells, muscle cells, and nerve cells.

Plants keep some unspecialised cells all their lives. These cells can become anything that the plant may need. For example, they can make new stems and leaves if the plant is cut down. These cells can also grow whole new plants. So they can be used for asexual reproduction.

Some simple animals, like the *Hydra* in the picture opposite, also use asexual reproduction. Cloning is very uncommon in animals.

Sexual reproduction

Most animals use **sexual reproduction**. The new offspring have two parents so they are not clones. But clones are sometimes produced – we call them identical twins.

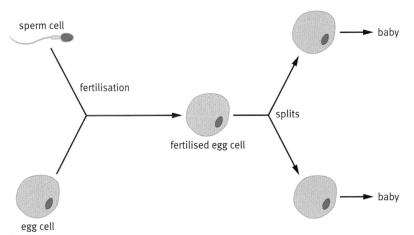

Identical twins have the same genes. But their genes came from both parents. So they are clones of each other, but not of either parent.

Find out about

✔ **asexual reproduction**
✔ **cloning and stem cells**

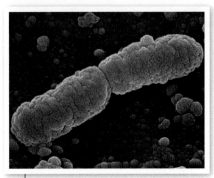

A bacterium cell grows and then splits into two new cells. (Mag: × 7500 approx.)

Hydra.

Questions

1 What is asexual reproduction?

2 What do plants use unspecialised cells for?

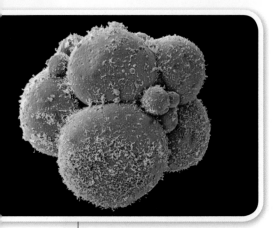

Cells from eight-cell embryos like this one can develop into any type of body cell. They start to become specialised when the embryo is five days old.
(Mag: × 500 approx)

Questions

3 How are stem cells different from other cells?

4 Explain why scientists think stem cells would be useful in treating Parkinson's disease.

5 For each of these cells, say whether or not your body would reject it:
   a bone marrow from your identical twin
   b your own skin cells
   c a cloned embryo stem cell.

6 For embryo cloning to make stem cells:
   a describe one viewpoint in favour
   b describe two different viewpoints against.

Cloning human embryos

Most scientists don't want to clone adult human beings. But some scientists do want to clone human cells. They think that some cloned cells could be used to treat diseases. The useful cells are called **stem cells**.

What are stem cells?

Stem cells are **unspecialised** cells. All the cells in an early embryo are stem cells. These embryonic cells can grow into any type of cell in the human body.

Adults do have stem cells. They have them in many tissues like the heart, bone marrow, and brain. Those unspecialised cells can develop into many types of cell. But it is difficult to do this. Bone marrow cells are already used in transplants to treat leukaemia.

Stem cells can be taken from embryos that are a few days old. Researchers use human embryos that are left over from fertility treatment.

Stem cell treatment

Scientists want to grow stem cells to make new cells to treat patients with some diseases. For example, new brain cells could be made for patients with Parkinson's disease.

These new cells would need to have the same genes as the person getting them as a treatment. When someone else's cells are used in a transplant they are rejected.

Cloning to make stem cells

Embryos have stem cells. Scientists may be able to produce an embryo that is a clone of the patient. Stem cells from this embryo would have the same genes as the patient. So cells produced from the embryo could be used to treat their illness. They would not be rejected by the patient's body.

Doctors have only just started to explore this. Success is still years away. Millions of people could benefit if it is made to work.

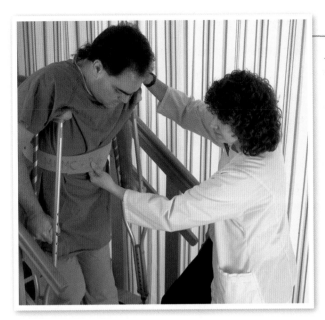

James has Parkinson's disease. His brain cells do not communicate with each other properly. He cannot control his movements.

Should human embryo cloning be allowed?

With some things there's no argument. Murder is just wrong – in the same way that lying and stealing are wrong. Killing an embryo at any age is as wrong as killing a child or an adult.

Research on embryos is legal up to 14 days. If something is 'legal' it can't be wrong.

Whether it's right or not depends on how much good it does versus how much harm. If your best friend was paralysed in an accident, you wouldn't think it was wrong to sacrifice a five-day-old embryo made of 50 cells. Not if those cells could be used to make nerve tissue to repair your friend's damaged nerves.

An embryo is human so it has human rights. Its age doesn't make any difference. You can't experiment on a child or an adult.

Creating embryos for medical treatments is wrong. It's creating a life that is then destroyed. This lowers the value of life.

If research on cloning is allowed, it could lead to reproductive cloning. Once the technology to produce a human clone is developed, it will be difficult to stop someone using it to produce a cloned adult human.

Science
Explanations

In this module, you will learn about inheritance, that genes are the units of inheritance, the relationship between genes and the environment, and that sexual reproduction is a source of variation.

You should know:

- that genes are sections of DNA and form part of chromosomes; they are found in cells' nuclei and instruct cells to make proteins
- how single genes can determine some human characteristics, such as dimples; several genes working together determine many characteristics, such as eye colour; features such as scars are determined by the environment; other characteristics, such as weight, are determined by both genes and the environment
- that a pair of chromosomes carries the same gene in the same place; alleles are different versions of the same gene
- about the difference between dominant and recessive alleles
- how sex cells contain one chromosome from each pair and how genes from both parents come together during sexual reproduction
- why offspring are similar to both parents but are not the same because they inherit genes from both parents
- that genetic diagrams are used to show inheritance
- that the symptoms of Huntington's disease appear later in life and include clumsiness, tremors, memory loss, and mood changes
- that Huntington's disease is caused by a faulty dominant allele
- that a faulty recessive allele causes cystic fibrosis
- that cystic fibrosis is a condition where cells produce thick mucus that causes chest infections and difficulties breathing and digesting food
- how genetic testing is used to screen adults, children, and embryos for faulty alleles
- how the information from genetic testing is used to make decisions and why this has implications
- that clones are organisms with identical genes; there are also natural clones
- about unspecialised cells, called stem cells, that can develop into other types of cell and how they can be used to treat some illnesses.

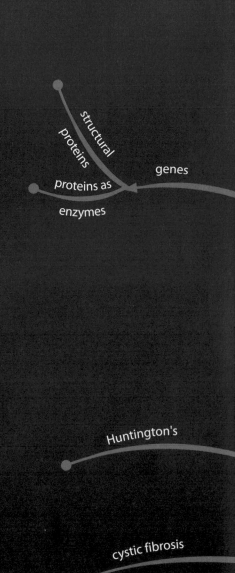

structural proteins

genes

proteins as enzymes

Huntington's

cystic fibrosis

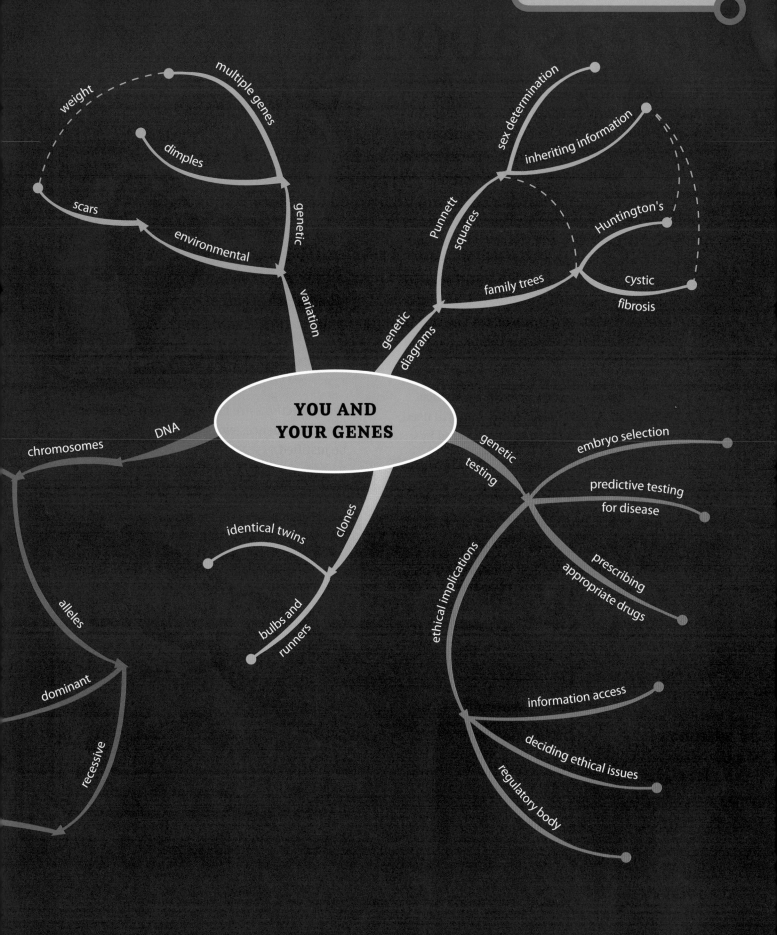

YOU AND
YOUR GENES

weight

multiple genes

dimples

scars

environmental

genetic

variation

sex determination

inheriting information

Punnett squares

Huntington's

family trees

cystic fibrosis

genetic diagrams

DNA

chromosomes

alleles

dominant

recessive

clones

identical twins

bulbs and runners

genetic testing

embryo selection

predictive testing for disease

prescribing appropriate drugs

ethical implications

information access

deciding ethical issues

regulatory body

Ideas about Science

The application of science and technology has many implications for society. Ethical issues are often raised by science. The scientific approach cannot always answer these questions and society as a whole needs to discuss these issues and reach a decision together.

Often the development and application of science is regulated. You will need to be able to discuss examples of when this happens, for example:

- the role of the regulatory body for UK embryo research
- making decisions about genetic testing on adults and selecting embryos before implantation.

Some questions cannot be answered by science, for example, those involving values. You will need to recognise questions that can be answered by using a scientific approach from those that cannot, such as:

- is it right to test embryos for genetic diseases?
- should a pregnancy be terminated or not?

Some forms of scientific work have ethical implications that some people will agree with and others will not. When an ethical issue is involved, you need to be able to:

- state clearly what the issue is
- summarise the different views that people might hold.

When discussing ethical issues, you will need to be able to identify examples of common arguments based on the ideas that:

- the right decision is the one that leads to the best outcome for the majority of the people involved

- certain actions are right or wrong whatever the consequences; wrong actions can never be justified.

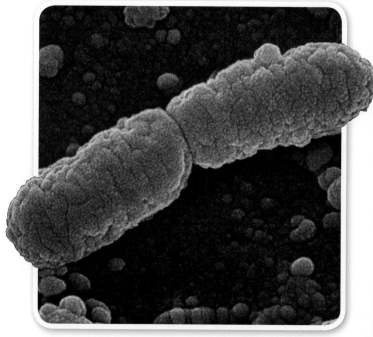

Review
Questions

1 Cystic fibrosis is a genetic disorder.

a Choose the **two** words that describe the allele that causes cystic fibrosis:

faulty   **normal**

dominant   **recessive**

○ Female without cystic fibrosis ● Female with cystic fibrosis
□ Male without cystic fibrosis ▪ Male with cystic fibrosis

b The family tree shows the inheritance of cystic fibrosis.

 i Which person, **A**, **B**, **C**, or **D**, is a female who has inherited two faulty cystic fibrosis alleles?

 ii Which people from **A**, **B**, **C**, and D are carriers?

 iii Person **B** has a daughter. We cannot tell from the family tree if the daughter is a carrier. Explain why.

2 Science can show how genetic testing can be carried out. It cannot explain whether it should be carried out.

a Describe some implications of carrying out genetic testing on human beings.

b Explain some ethical issues involved.

c State the different views that might be held, including at least one argument for genetic testing and one against.

3 Clones can be produced artificially.

a Which of the examples below are natural clones?

 A Two plants made by asexual reproduction from the same parent.

 B Two bacteria produced from one bacterium.

 C Identical twins.

 D Two sperm cells from the same man.

b Clones can look different.

Which factors can cause clones to look different? Choose the correct answer.

genetic factors only

environmental factors only

both genetic and environmental factors

neither genetic nor environmental factors

C1 Air quality

Why study air quality?

We breathe air every second of our lives. If it contains any pollutants they go into our lungs. Poor-quality air can affect people's health.

Chemicals that harm air quality are called atmospheric or air pollutants. To improve air quality we need to understand how atmospheric pollutants are made.

What you already know

- A mixture is made of two or more chemicals mixed together but not chemically combined.

- During a chemical change a new product is formed.

- Coal and natural gas are fossil fuels.

- Elements are made up of just one type of atom.

- Compounds are made of two or more elements that are chemically combined.

- Data is used to provide evidence for scientific explanations.

Find out about

- 'good-quality' and 'poor-quality' air

- where the chemicals that harm air quality come from

- what can be done to improve air quality

- how scientists collect and use data on air quality

- how scientists investigate links between air quality and certain illnesses.

The Science

Most air pollutants are made by burning fossil fuels. When a fuel burns, the chemicals in the fuel combine with oxygen from the air. Some of the new chemicals are air pollutants, which escape into the atmosphere.

Ideas about Science

Scientists who are trying to improve air quality measure the amounts of pollutants in the air. They must make sure their data is as accurate as possible. Some scientists use their data to see if they can find a link between air quality and health problems. They publish their findings so that other scientists can evaluate their claims.

Find out about

- ✓ **the gases that make up air**
- ✓ **the atmosphere that surrounds Earth**
- ✓ **how other gases may be added to the atmosphere by human activity or natural processes**

oxygen molecule containing two oxygen atoms

nitrogen molecule containing two nitrogen atoms

Nitrogen and oxygen make up 99% of the air.

What do you know about air?

The air

Air is all around us. You cannot see the air but if you wave your hand you can feel it.

You may think that a can of fizzy drink is empty once you have drunk it, but look what happens if all the air is then removed from inside the can. The can collapses.

If you remove the air from inside a can, it collapses.

Air is made up of small **molecules** with large spaces in between. Molecules are groups of atoms joined together.

The atmosphere

An astronaut in space needs an air supply in order to breathe. A mountaineer climbing Everest feels that the air is becoming 'thinner' as he climbs. Where does our air stop?

The Earth from space. White clouds of water vapour can be seen in the atmosphere.

The **atmosphere** is the layer of gases that surrounds the Earth. It is about 15 km thick. That sounds a lot but the diameter of the Earth is over 12 000 km. The atmosphere is like a very thin skin around the Earth.

What gases are found in the air?

Air contains the gas oxygen. Oxygen is the gas we need to breathe but air is not just made of oxygen.

Air is a **mixture** of oxygen and nitrogen, with a small amount of argon plus tiny amounts of carbon dioxide, water vapour, and other gases.

Human activity has released a whole variety of different gases into the air. Many of these gases affect the quality of the air we breathe. Unfortunately, gases released in one part of the world will slowly spread through the atmosphere and can affect the air quality of people many miles away.

Some gases are naturally released into the air by volcanoes. These gases include sulfur dioxide, carbon dioxide, carbon monoxide, nitrogen dioxide, and water vapour. Volcanoes also produce solid particles called **particulates** in the form of smoke and ash. These tiny specks of solid are small enough to stay suspended in the air.

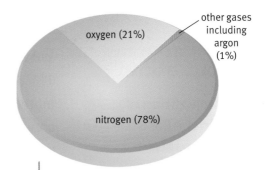

other gases including argon (1%)

oxygen (21%)

nitrogen (78%)

This pie chart shows the percentages of the main gases in clean air.

This geologist is working upwind of a volcano. She is wearing a gas mask to protect her from breathing in sulfur dioxide gas.

Questions

1 Copy and complete:
Air is a _____ of gases made up of small _____ with large _____ between them.

2 List the main gases that are found in air.

3 In 2010 a volcano in Iceland erupted, releasing huge quantities of volcanic ash and particulates. Explain why it was not only local people in Iceland who were affected by this eruption.

Summary box

✓ The main gases in the air are nitrogen 78%, oxygen 21%, and argon 1%.

✓ The Earth's atmosphere is a thin layer of gases surrounding the Earth.

✓ Other gases have been added to the atmosphere by human activity and natural processes.

Find out about

- ✓ **the composition of gases in the Earth's early atmosphere**
- ✓ **evidence for an increase in oxygen in the atmosphere**
- ✓ **why scientists sometimes need to change their explanations**

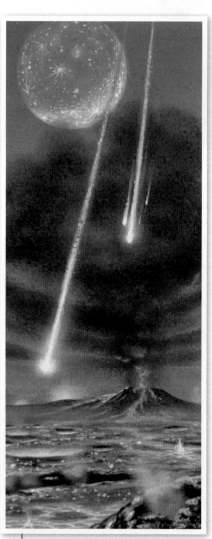

An artist's impression of early Earth.

Early Earth

The early Earth was a violent place, constantly bombarded by meteors and covered with active volcanoes. The atmosphere consisted mainly of carbon dioxide and water vapour. These gases probably came from volcanoes, which belched huge quantities of carbon dioxide and water vapour, and also some nitrogen and methane, into the atmosphere.

The temperature on the surface of Earth was very high. If it had stayed that way, human life would not be present on Earth today.

However, temperatures began to cool. This caused the water vapour to gradually **condense** and form the oceans. Some of the carbon dioxide began to dissolve in the oceans and later became incorporated into **sedimentary rocks**.

Exactly what happened next is less certain. Scientists are still investigating when and how the Earth's atmosphere changed from being mostly carbon dioxide, to containing oxygen and just a little carbon dioxide.

Finding out about Earth's changing atmosphere

Of course, scientists can't directly measure the composition of Earth's very early atmosphere. They have to use indirect evidence instead.

For example, the chemicals that make up rocks can give scientists clues about the atmosphere when the rocks were formed. So if they know the age of the rocks they find out something about the composition of the atmosphere at that time.

Scientists also look at fossil evidence of early life. Early plants used up carbon dioxide and released oxygen during **photosynthesis**. Evidence suggests that this caused the first rise in the level of oxygen and a fall in the level of carbon dioxide. Much of the carbon dioxide was removed from the atmosphere for a long time as it was trapped underground as the coal and oil that we now use as fuels.

Scientists still discuss the details of exactly when and how fast the atmosphere changed. Sometimes new evidence is found that means that scientists have to change their explanations.

For example, in 2010 some fossils of simple early animals were found in Australia. These fossils are 50–100 million years older than any other known fossils of animals. New discoveries like this mean that scientists have to rethink their ideas and come up with new explanations to account for the fresh data.

Iron pyrite is made up of iron sulfide, which only forms if there is *no* oxygen present.

Red iron oxide rocks only form if there is oxygen present.

Air bubbles trapped in ice cores drilled in Antarctica allow scientists to analyse the composition of the air from hundreds of thousands of years ago. However, the Earth is about 4.5 billion years old. Ice cores don't go back far enough in time to provide evidence of the earliest atmosphere.

Questions

1 What happened when the temperatures on Earth began to cool?

2 Explain how over time the amount of oxygen in the atmosphere increased and the carbon dioxide was removed.

3 Rocks made of iron oxide have been dated to two billion years ago. What does this tell you about when oxygen first appeared in Earth's atmosphere?

Summary box

✓ **The Earth's early atmosphere was made up mainly of carbon dioxide and water vapour.**

✓ **Early plants added oxygen to the atmosphere and removed carbon dioxide by photosynthesis.**

✓ **New data can mean that scientists have to rethink their explanations.**

Find out about

- ✔ **the most important air pollutants**
- ✔ **the problems pollutants cause**
- ✔ **what can influence air quality in different locations**

Every time you are driven somewhere by car, or when you switch on the lights at home, new gases are made. They are released by the car, or from the power station where electricity is generated. Some of these chemicals are harmful and are called air **pollutants**. These pollutants can harm us directly by affecting our health, or harm us indirectly by affecting our environment.

The table lists some of the air pollutants that scientists are concerned about.

The clouds coming from the cooling towers may look like pollutants, but are just harmless water vapour. There may be invisible pollutants coming out of the tall chimney.

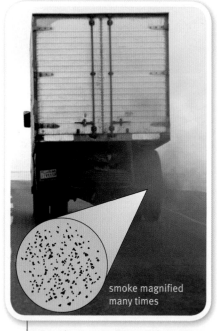

smoke magnified many times

Smoke is a pollutant that can be easily seen. It contains microscopic particles of carbon. Some of these are just 10 micrometres (10 millionths of a metre) in size. Although they are very small, they are very much bigger than atoms or molecules. Each particle contains billions of carbon atoms.

Pollutant		Effects
sulfur dioxide SO_2		Reacts with water and oxygen to produce acid rain. This can damage buildings and harm trees and plants.
carbon monoxide CO		A poisonous gas. Changes the amount of oxygen in the blood. This can make people's existing heart conditions worse.
carbon dioxide CO_2		Dissolves in rain water and sea water. Used by plants in photosynthesis. Excess levels of CO_2 can give rise to global warming.
nitrogen monoxide NO		Reacts in the atmosphere to form nitrogen dioxide.
nitrogen dioxide NO_2		Reacts with water and oxygen to produce acid rain. Can cause breathing problems and can make asthma worse.
particulates (tiny bits of solid suspended in the air)	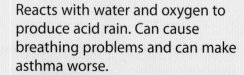	Is deposited on surfaces, making them dirty. Can be breathed into the lungs and can make asthma and lung infections worse.

How can you find out about air quality?

Some people suffer from asthma or hayfever. They may be able to feel when the air quality is poor. But most people do not know whether the air quality is good or bad.

Automatic instruments collect air samples, measure the concentrations of pollutants, and record the data. Much of the data is published on websites. Newspapers and TV stations summarise the data in reports, which may give the day's air quality as a number or describe it as low, medium, or high quality.

Does it matter where you live?

Some people live in cities. Other people live in the countryside. Will they all have air of the same quality to breathe?

The bar chart shows the concentration of nitrogen dioxide on the same day in three different places. The concentration of nitrogen dioxide depends a lot on the level of human activity and road traffic in the area.

Mace Head, in Ireland, has very pure air when the wind blows in from across the Atlantic Ocean. Most of us live in places where the air quality is much poorer than at Mace Head.

Measuring the concentration of a pollutant

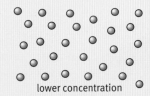

A low concentration of pollutants. There are very few pollutant molecules in a certain volume of air. This is an indication of good air quality.

lower concentration

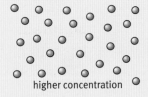

A high concentration of pollutants. There is a large number of pollutant molecules in a certain volume of air. This shows that the air quality is poor.

higher concentration

○ molecules of pollutant
○ other molecules in air

Concentration is the amount of pollutant in a certain volume of air.

(Note: the air molecules are normally much more spread out than shown in the diagrams.)

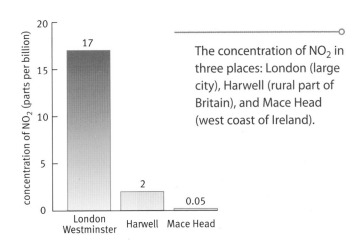

The concentration of NO_2 in three places: London (large city), Harwell (rural part of Britain), and Mace Head (west coast of Ireland).

Questions

1 Write down one problem that can be caused by each of these air pollutants:
   a SO_2 b NO_2 c particulates

2 A newspaper article on air quality included a photograph of white clouds coming out of a power station's cooling towers. Write a note to the paper explaining why the clouds are not polluting the atmosphere.

Human activity adds pollutants directly to the atmosphere. Some pollutants can chemically reacts in the air to produce other pollutants.

Summary box

- ✓ Carbon monoxide, nitrogen oxides, sulfur dioxide, carbon dioxide, and particulates are all air pollutants.
- ✓ Air pollutants can be harmful to our health and our environment.
- ✓ Air quality is affected by emissions of pollutants into the atmosphere from nearby industry or vehicles and the weather (wind moves pollutants around).

What influences air quality?

The quality of the air where you live depends mostly on weather and emissions. **Emissions** are gases released into the atmosphere by vehicles, power stations, and other sources. Emissions can spread through the atmosphere and change its composition. Winds can move pollutants many miles and even carry them from one country to another.

Question

3 The weather moves air pollutants from one place to another. If we reduce emissions of air pollutants in our own town, we can still get pollution from other areas. Explain why it is still important to try to reduce emissions.

Crucial data

Quantities of air pollutants are measured using a network of monitoring stations all around the country. The information is useful, as it allows people to check the air quality in their area. It is also used by the government to check whether air pollution is reaching dangerous levels anywhere.

Scientists use data to help answer questions such as 'How do pollutants travel?' or 'How do air pollutants interact with other chemicals in the atmosphere?' Scientists put forward answers to the questions and use data to check their explanations.

Making measurements

If you measure the concentration of nitrogen dioxide (NO_2) in the same sample of air several times, you will probably get different results. This is because:

- you used the equipment differently
- there were differences in the equipment itself.

If you take just one reading, you cannot be sure it is very accurate. So it is better to take several measurements. Then you can use them to estimate the true value.

The true value is what the measurement should really be. The **accuracy** of a result is how close it is to the true value.

How can you make sure your data is accurate?

The table on page 52 shows what you should do to get a measurement of the level of nitrogen oxide that is as accurate as possible.

The table on page 52

Find out about

- ✔ **measurement of air pollutants**
- ✔ **how data about air quality is checked and used**

Air pollution monitoring station. This station monitors and records air pollution. It measures particulates, carbon monoxide, nitrogen dioxide, and sulfur dioxide levels. There are more than 1500 monitoring sites across the UK measuring air quality.

Question

1 Why do scientists collect data?

What you do	Data	Describing what you do
Take several measurements from the same air sample. Not all the measurements will be the same.	Concentration of NO_2 in parts per billion (ppb) 18.8, 19.1, 18.9, 19.4, 19.0, 19.2, 19.1, 19.0, 18.3, 19.3	The measurements (10 in this case) are called the data set.
Plot the results on a number line. This shows that the 18.3 ppb measurement is very different from the others.	this result is an outlier	A result that is very different from the others is called an **outlier**. Decide whether to ignore this reading. Ignore this result only if you can think of a reason why it is so different (eg you made a mistake when you took the measurement).
Add the other nine results together. Divide the total by 9. The answer is 19.1 ppb of NO_2.	Total of nine readings = 171.8 $$\frac{171.8}{9} = 19.1 \text{ ppb}$$	19.1 is called the **mean value** of the nine measurements.
You can use the mean value rather than any of the nine measurements.	The best estimate for the concentration of NO_2 is 19.1 ppb	The mean value is used as the **best estimate** of the true value.
When you write down the mean value you also record: • the lowest, 18.8 ppb, • and the highest, 19.4 ppb, measurements.	The range is 18.8 ppb – 19.4 ppb	18.8 ppb – 19.4 ppb is called the **range** of the measurements.

The mean value is 19.1 ppb. This is the best estimate of the concentration of nitrogen dioxide in the sample of air. You cannot be absolutely sure that it is the true value. But you can be sure that:

• the true value is within the range 18.8 – 19.4 ppb
• the best estimate of the true value is 19.1 ppb.

If you had taken only one measurement, you wouldn't have been sure it was accurate. If the range had been narrower, say 19.0 – 19.3 ppb, you would have been even more confident about your best estimate of the true value.

Questions

2 Jess measured the nitrogen dioxide concentration in the middle of a town. She took six readings: 22 ppb, 20 ppb, 18 ppb, 24 ppb, 21 ppb, 23 ppb. Jess used new equipment and was careful taking her measurements.
   a Add the six readings together and write down your answer.
   b Calculate the mean value of the six readings.
   c Look at the measurements for the nitrogen dioxide concentration in Jess's sample. Write down:
     i the best estimate
     ii the lowest value
     iii the highest value
     iv the range of the measurements.

3 Why do scientists take several measurements of a quantity instead of just one measurement?

4 Repeat measurements on an air sample produced these results for the nitrogen dioxide concentration:
   Reading 1 – 39.4 ppb   Reading 2 – 45.8 ppb
   Reading 3 – 42.3 ppb   Reading 4 – 38.7 ppb
   Reading 5 – 39.7 ppb   Reading 6 – 32.7 ppb

   There had been some problems with the equipment that day.
   a Plot these six results on a number line.
   b Work out the mean nitrogen dioxide concentration and range for this sample.

This map shows the concentration of NO_2 over parts of England. It is based on measurements from government monitoring sites. Red shows the highest levels of NO_2. Why do you think the high levels follow motorway routes?

Summary box

- ✔ Data is very important to science.
- ✔ Data is used to check scientific explanations.
- ✔ A single measurement may not be the true value of the quantity you are measuring.
- ✔ It is better to make at least three or four measurements and work out the mean to use as the best estimate of the true value.

Find out about

- ✓ **what fuels are made from**
- ✓ **the products that result from burning fuels**
- ✓ **how burning fuels can make atmospheric pollutants**

A hydrocarbon molecule. Natural gas, petrol, diesel, and fuel oil are all mainly made up of hydrocarbon molecules.

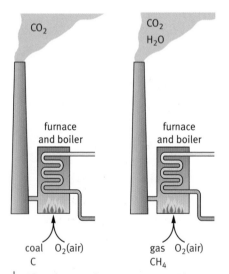

The chemicals going into and coming out of power station furnaces.

Many air pollutants are made by burning fossil fuels. This happens in power stations and in the engines of vehicles, for example, cars, buses, and aeroplanes.

What happens when fuel burns in a power station?

Most power stations are fuelled by either coal or natural gas. Coal is mainly carbon **atoms**. Natural gas is mainly methane (CH_4). Methane is a **hydrocarbon**. It is made of carbon (C) and hydrogen (H) atoms.

Fuels such as coal need oxygen to burn. Oxygen is found in the air. Fuel and air go into the furnace and new waste chemicals come out of the chimney.

Any change that forms a new chemical is called a **chemical change** or a **chemical reaction**.

Products from burning fuels in a power station

The chemicals going into and out of power station furnaces are summarised below. Chemicals going into the power station are called **reactants**. Chemicals going out of the power station are called **products**.

Power station	Chemicals going in (reactants)	Chemicals going out (products)
coal-fired	coal (carbon), C oxygen (air), O_2	carbon dioxide, CO_2
gas-fired	methane, CH_4 oxygen (air), O_2	carbon dioxide, CO_2 water, H_2O

Burning coal and gas can also produce smaller amounts of these air pollutants:

- particulates – small pieces of unburned carbon
- carbon monoxide (CO) – formed when there is not enough oxygen to turn all of the carbon into carbon dioxide

- nitrogen oxides (NO and NO_2) – formed when some of the nitrogen in the air reacts with oxygen at the high temperatures in the furnace
- sulfur dioxide (SO_2) – formed if the fuel contains some sulfur atoms.

What happens when fuel burns in a car engine?

Vehicle engines burn petrol or diesel. These are made up of hydrogen and carbon atoms (in hydrocarbon molecules). A chemical reaction takes place in a car engine. Atoms from the fuel react with oxygen atoms from the air.

Use the diagram to compare what goes into a car engine with what comes out.

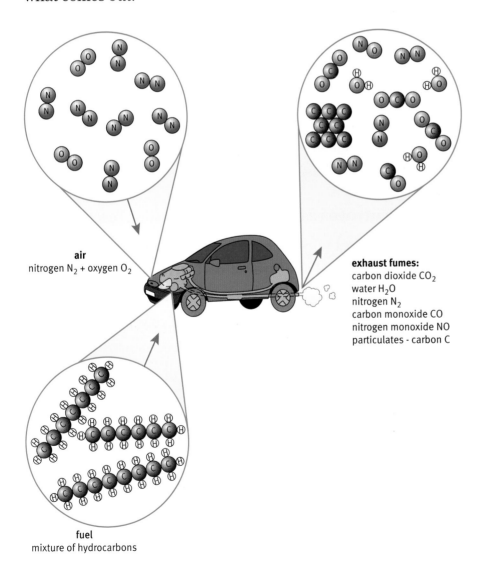

air
nitrogen N_2 + oxygen O_2

exhaust fumes:
carbon dioxide CO_2
water H_2O
nitrogen N_2
carbon monoxide CO
nitrogen monoxide NO
particulates - carbon C

fuel
mixture of hydrocarbons

Summary box

- ✓ Coal is mainly carbon. Many other fuels are made up of hydrocarbon molecules.
- ✓ When hydrocarbon fuels burn the main products are carbon dioxide and water.
- ✓ Burning fuels can also make air pollutants such as carbon dioxide, sulfur dioxide, carbon monoxide, small pieces of unburned carbon (particulates), and nitrogen oxides.

Questions

1 Which two elements mainly make up the molecules in petrol, diesel, and fuel oil?

2 List the air pollutants that can be released from a coal-burning power station.

3 List the air pollutants that can be released from a car petrol engine.

4 Explain how nitrogen oxides in a car exhaust are formed.

Find out about

- ✔ **how atoms are rearranged during combustion reactions**
- ✔ **different ways of representing chemical changes**

Reactions where a chemical joins with oxygen are called **oxidation** reactions.

Some chemicals can react quickly with oxygen to give out energy and possibly light. This type of oxidation reaction is called **combustion** or burning.

Fuel has escaped during this racing car crash. An uncontrolled combustion reaction is happening. The fuel and air mixture has been heated by either a spark or the hot engine.

Combustion is a chemical reaction. In a chemical reaction atoms are rearranged.

Burning charcoal

Burning charcoal on a barbeque is a combustion reaction.

Charcoal is almost pure carbon. You can picture the surface of a piece of charcoal as a layer of carbon atoms tightly packed together.

Oxygen is a gas found in air. A molecule of oxygen is two oxygen atoms joined together.

During a combustion reaction, the atoms of carbon and oxygen are rearranged.

Fuel burns more rapidly in pure oxygen than in air. Oxygen from the atmosphere is used in this oxy-fuel welding torch.

Air contains oxygen gas. One molecule of oxygen is two oxygen atoms joined together ⚬⚬. Oxygen molecules split and react with carbon atoms in the charcoal. This forms carbon dioxide gas ⚬⚬⚬.

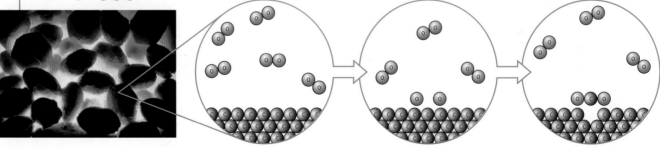

Describing combustion reactions

You can use pictures to describe the chemical change that happens when carbon burns.

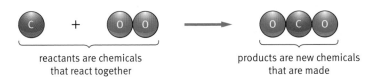

reactants are chemicals that react together

products are new chemicals that are made

It would be time consuming if you always had to draw pictures to describe chemical reactions. So scientists use equations to summarise the pictures.

The combustion of charcoal can be summarised in this **word equation**:

> carbon + oxygen $\longrightarrow$ carbon dioxide

When methane (CH_4) burns, carbon dioxide and water are formed.

The combustion of methane can be summarised in this word equation:

> methane + oxygen $\longrightarrow$ carbon dioxide + water

The products are formed by the carbon atoms and hydrogen atoms in methane separating. The carbon atoms combine with oxygen atoms to form carbon dioxide. The hydrogen atoms combine with oxygen atoms to form water.

H — hydrogen atom

O — oxygen atom

C — carbon atom

H O H — water molecule

H H — hydrogen molecule

O O — oxygen molecule

H C H / H H — methane molecule

Atoms and molecules.

Questions

1 For a combustion reaction to take place oxygen is needed. Where could the oxygen come from?

2 What are the reactants and what are the products in each of the following chemical changes:
   a carbon combines with oxygen to form carbon dioxide
   b a hydrocarbon in petrol burns in oxygen to form carbon dioxide and water.

Summary box

✔ **Combustion is a chemical reaction.**
✔ **In a chemical reaction atoms are rearranged: molecules of the reactants split into atoms and combine together to form the products.**

G | Where do all the atoms go?

Find out about

- ✔ **what happens to atoms during chemical reactions**
- ✔ **how the properties of reactants and products are different**

When you have had a bonfire, some of the atoms that made up the rubbish are in the ashes left on the ground. The others are in the products released into the air.

Question

1 Burning rubbish gets rid of it forever. Is this a true statement? Think about the atoms in the rubbish. Explain your answer.

Look at the picture below. How many atoms of hydrogen (H) are there before and after the reaction? Count the atoms of oxygen (O) before and after. What does this show?

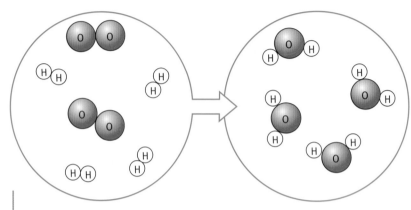

The reaction of hydrogen and oxygen to form water.

Conservation of atoms

All the atoms present at the beginning of a chemical reaction are still there at the end. No atoms are destroyed and no new atoms are formed. They rearrange to form new chemicals but they are still there. This is called **conservation of atoms**.

Look again at the picture of hydrogen reacting with oxygen to form water. We can represent this change by:

There are the same numbers of each kind of atom on each side of the equation. All the atoms that are in the reactants end up in the products. The atoms are conserved.

Properties of reactants and products

The **properties** of a chemical are what make it different from other chemicals.

For example, some chemicals are solids, some are liquids, and some are gases at normal temperatures. Some are coloured, some burn easily, some smell, some react with metals, some dissolve in water, and so on. Each chemical has its own set of properties.

The table compares the properties of the reactants and products of the reaction between sulfur and oxygen.

Chemical	Properties
sulfur (reactant)	yellow solid
oxygen (reactant)	colourless gas; no smell; supports life
sulfur dioxide (product)	colourless gas; sharp, choking smell; harmful to breathe; dissolves in water to form an acid

In any chemical reaction, all the atoms you start with are still there at the end. But they are combined in a different way. So the properties of the products are different from the properties of the reactants.

This is very important for air quality. You can have a piece of coal that is a harmless black stone. But the coal may contain a small amount of sulfur. When it burns the sulfur will react with oxygen to form the harmful gas sulfur dioxide.

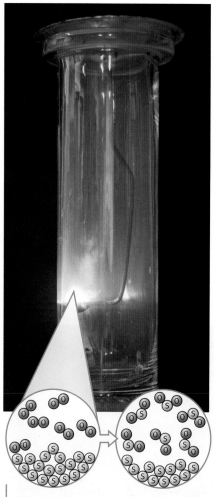

The atoms and molecules involved in the burning of sulfur.

Questions

2
 + →  +

methane   oxygen   carbon dioxide   water

This reaction is the burning or combustion of methane (a fossil fuel).
a Write down the number of each type of atom in the reactants.
b Write down the number of each type of atom in the products.
c What do you notice about your answers to a and b?

3 Look at the table and list the properties of:
a sulfur (the reactant)
b sulfur dioxide (the product).

Are the properties of the reactant and the product the same or different?

Summary box
In a chemical reaction:
- the properties of the reactants and products are different
- all the atoms that are present at the beginning of the reaction are still there at the end
- the atoms are rearranged but no new atoms are made and no atoms are destroyed.

Find out about

- **how to look for links between air-quality data and the symptoms of an illness**
- **how pollen causes hayfever**
- **the link between asthma and air quality**

Hayfever

Do you suffer from a runny nose, sneezing, and itchy eyes in the summer? This could be hayfever.

Hayfever got its name because people noticed that it happens in the summer. This is when grass is being cut to make hay. It is also the time when pollen from plants is at its highest.

To find out what causes hayfever it is important to first look at what **factors** are linked with hayfever. In this case hayfever is the outcome and pollen is a factor that may affect the **outcome**.

Pollen traps collect pollen grains so that they can be counted using a microscope. This gives the 'pollen count'.

Is there a link between hayfever and pollen?

If an outcome increases (or decreases) as a particular factor increases this is called a **correlation**. So, do more people get hayfever when the pollen count gets higher?

Pollen is released by plants and may travel many kilometres on the wind. Pollen grains are in the air that we breathe.

Pollen grains under the microscope. (Magnification approximately: × 1360.)

Looking at thousands of medical records shows that more people suffer from hayfever in the summer. It is important to look at a randomly selected sample of medical records so that the data is representative of the whole population.

This evidence shows that there is a correlation between pollen levels and hayfever attacks. But does this mean that pollen is the **cause** of hayfever?

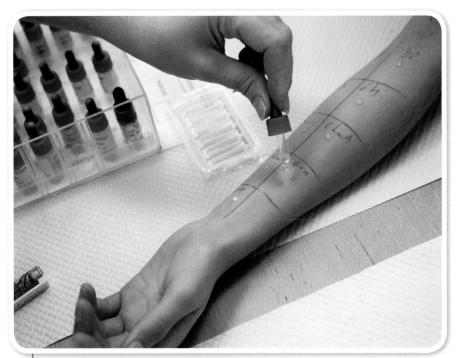

During a skin-prick test, drops of solution are placed on the skin. The skin beneath is pricked. If the patient is allergic to the substance in the solution (eg pollen), their skin will turn red and itchy.

Does pollen cause hayfever?

To say that pollen causes hayfever you need some evidence. You need show that there is a correlation and you need to be able to explain *how* pollen causes hayfever.

Different types of pollen are relased at different times of year. Some people have hayfever in months that correlate with particular types of pollen being released. This is strong extra evidence for the correlation between pollen and hayfever.

Skin-prick tests show that people who suffer from hayfever are allergic to pollen. Hayfever is an allergic reaction caused by pollen. So there is a correlation between hayfever and pollen, because pollen causes hayfever.

Summary box
- If an outcome increases (or decreases) when a factor increases this is called a correlation.
- Pollen grains are released by plants into the air.
- People who get hayfever are allergic to the pollen in the air that they breathe.
- There is a correlation between hayfever and pollen because pollen causes hayfever.

Questions

1 Why is it useful to know the levels of pollen in the air during the summer?

2 Why do some people get hayfever?

3 What is meant by 'there is a correlation between levels of pollen and hayfever symptoms'?

Asthma and air quality

Asthma is a common problem. During an asthma attack, a person's chest feels very tight. They find it difficult to breathe.

Asthma attacks are treated using inhalers.

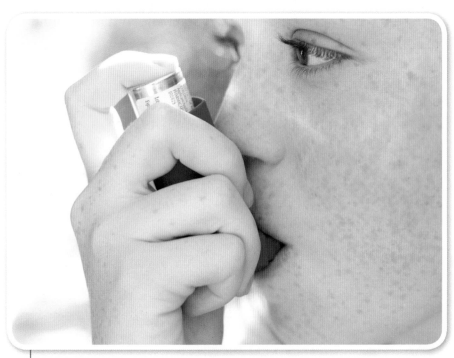

Inhalers are used to treat asthma attacks and to keep the condition under control. They contain medicines that help people's airways 'open up', allowing them to breathe more freely.

Medical evidence shows that asthma attacks may be triggered by different factors.

People who have asthma have sensitive lungs. Air pollutants may irritate a person's lungs, particularly if their lungs are sensitive.

Nitrogen dioxide is an air pollutant found in vehicle exhausts. Large-scale studies have shown that if nitrogen dioxide levels are high, people with asthma are more more likely to suffer from asthma attacks. This is a correlation.

When nitrogen dioxide levels are high there is an increased chance of people suffering asthma attacks but it does not mean for sure that all people with asthma will suffer an attack. Even so, the link between the factor (exposure to polluted air) and the outcome (an asthma attack) is still described as a correlation.

Things that can trigger asthma attacks in people who have asthma.

tree or grass pollen

animal skin flakes

dustmite droppings

air pollution

nuts, shellfish

food additives

dusty materials

strong perfumes

getting emotional

stress

exercise (especially in cold weather)

colds and flu.

Studying asthma

The causes of asthma are not fully understood. Evidence shows that many different factors may be involved.

Scientists who study asthma publish their findings at conferences and in journals. This means that other scientists can evaluate their claims by looking at the method of investigation, at the presentation of data, and at the way the data is interpreted.

Some scientists claim they have evidence to show that stress is a factor that increases the chance of an asthma attack. A theory like this is more likely to be accepted if scientists can understand how it works. For example, if stress changes the way that the lungs react to pollutants, this is an explanation that would support the theory.

The number of people affected by asthma has increased across the world. The stress theory is just one explanation for this increase. The data is complex and so different scientists can quite reasonably reach different conclusions about the causes of asthma.

Exposure of children to high levels of traffic pollution may lead to an increased chance of their developing asthma.

Summary box

✓ Scientists are still investigating the link between air quality and asthma. These studies are very complicated as there are many factors that may affect the results. They look for correlations in the data then try to explain them.

Questions

4 a Write down a list of factors that might cause asthma.

b Why do scientists find it hard to work out why more and more people are suffering from asthma?

5 Why is it important that scientists publish their data and explanations?

Find out about

- ✔ **how laws and regulations can help improve air quality**
- ✔ **how new technology can reduce harmful emissions from cars and power stations**
- ✔ **what we can all do to reduce air pollution**

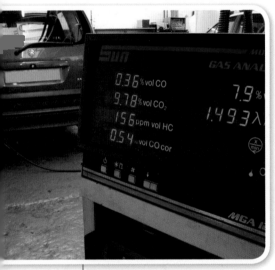

MOT exhaust emission analysis. Exhaust emissions are tested for carbon monoxide and unburnt fuel.

Reducing pollutants from cars

There are many different ways in which governments and individuals can reduce pollutants from cars and other vehicles.

Individuals can use cars less often and take public transport, or walk or cycle instead. Fifty people travelling by bus use a lot less fuel than if they each travel by car. Less fuel burned means fewer pollutants released. Governments can help by making it easier for people to use buses and trains.

Governments can also set legal limits on exhaust emissions. In Britain all vehicles must pass an MOT test to be allowed on the roads. This includes an emissions test. If the amount of pollutants in the **exhaust emissions** is too high, the vehicle fails the MOT.

Efficient engines and catalytic converters

Technological solutions can also be used to reduce emissions of pollutants from cars.

Engineers try to design **efficient** engines. A more efficient engine means that a car will burn less fuel to travel the same distance. This is good for car owners because they do not need to buy so much fuel. It is also good for air quality because fewer pollutants are released.

Another solution is to use a **catalytic converter**. All new cars have catalytic converters fitted to their exhaust systems. A catalytic converter changes the pollutants carbon monoxide and nitrogen monoxide into less harmful gases.

Questions

1 State one thing that individuals can do to reduce air pollution from cars.

2 State one thing that governments can do to reduce air pollution from cars.

3 An MOT test includes an exhaust emissions test. Name one gas that is measured by the emissions test.

4 Which two pollutants are removed by catalytic converters?

5 Using low-sulfur fuel helps to reduce emissions of which pollutant?

6 Write a letter to your local councillor suggesting how people living in your area could reduce air pollution.

The chemical reactions that occur in a catalytic converter are:

carbon monoxide + oxygen $\longrightarrow$ carbon dioxide

nitrogen monoxide $\longrightarrow$ nitrogen + oxygen

Carbon monoxide gains oxygen. This is called oxidation.

Nitrogen monoxide loses oxygen. This is called **reduction**.

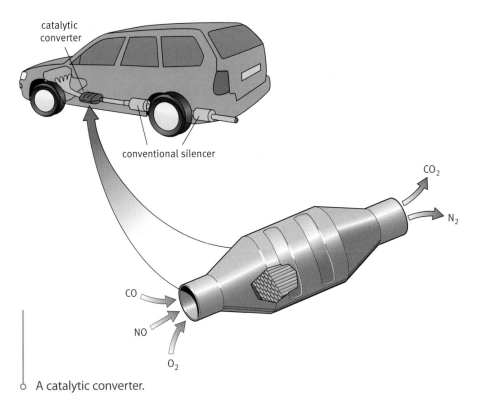

A catalytic converter.

This hybrid car runs on both electricity and petrol. The electricity comes from power stations through the national grid. By choosing a car that can use electricity, drivers can reduce the amount of petrol they use.

Even with a catalytic converter, carbon dioxide is released. Carbon dioxide levels are a concern due to the link with global warming. The only way to reduce the amount of carbon dioxide being added to the atmosphere is to burn less fossil fuels.

Cleaner transport

Diesel fuel contains small amounts of sulfur. This means sulfur dioxide forms when it burns. Sulfur can be removed from fuels before they are used to make low-sulfur fuels. These low-sulfur fuels produce much less sulfur dioxide when they burn.

Some new cars and buses have been designed to run using electricity. Electric vehicles do not produce waste gases, but the electricity may have been generated by burning fossil fuels.

Summary box

- ✓ **Governments and individuals can reduce emissions of air pollutants from vehicles.**
- ✓ **Low-sulfur fuels, catalytic converters and efficient engines are examples of how technology can reduce emissions from vehicles.**
- ✓ **In a catalytic converter carbon monoxide is oxidised and nitrogen monoxide is reduced.**
- ✓ **The only way of producing less carbon dioxide is to burn less fossil fuel.**

Trees killed by acid rain in the Czech Republic. Sulfur dioxide is a waste gas produced by power stations. It reacts with water and oxygen to form acid rain.

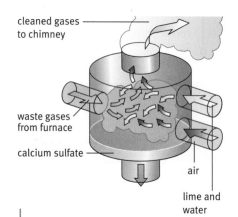

cleaned gases to chimney

waste gases from furnace

calcium sulfate

air

lime and water

Removing sulfur dioxide to prevent it escaping from power-station chimneys.

Questions

7 Name three types of fossil fuel that are burned in power stations.

8 What problems are caused by sulfur dioxide in the atmosphere?

Reducing pollutants from power stations

There are also many ways in which governments and individuals can reduce pollutants from power stations.

Everyone can contribute towards a reduction in pollutants released from power stations by using less electricity. However, even if people do use less electricity, it is still good to reduce the amount of air pollutants that are made in producing the electricity we do use.

Most power stations burn coal, natural gas, or fuel oil to produce electricity. When these fossil fuels are burned waste gases and particulates are produced.

If the fuel contains sulfur, the pollutant sulfur dioxide is produced. This can go on to produce acid rain.

Sulfur dioxide

One way of reducing the amount of sulfur dioxide released into the atmosphere is to remove sulfur from fuels before they are burnt.

Natural gas and fuel oil can be refined to remove sulfur. This means that less sulfur dioxide is formed when they are burnt.

Scientists have also devised a way of removing the harmful sulfur dioxide gas from power station chimneys before it can reach the atmosphere.

Waste gases pass through a spray of powdered lime (calcium oxide), water, and air. The sulfur dioxide in the gases combines with the mixture to form a new solid chemical, calcium sulfate. The solid is collected and removed and the cleaned gases continue up the chimney.

Particulates

Particulates are also found in power-station flue gases. These are tiny particles of carbon and ash. They can make surfaces of buildings dirty and cause breathing problems. Particulates can be removed from power station waste gases by passing them through an electrostatic precipitator. This contains electrically charged plates. The particulates are attracted to the charged plates and removed from the waste gases.

The particulates pick up a negative charge, are attracted to the positive plate, and are then collected and removed.

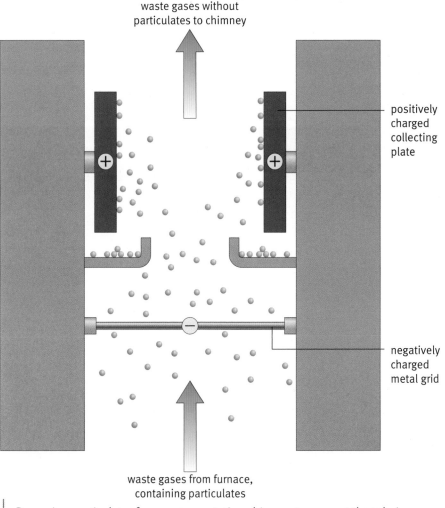

waste gases without particulates to chimney

positively charged collecting plate

negatively charged metal grid

waste gases from furnace, containing particulates

Removing particulates from a power-station chimney to prevent them being released into the atmosphere.

Polluted water can be purified and delivered to people. Air is all around us. You do not get it out of a tap. So everyone should try to reduce pollutants getting into the air.

Questions

9 Describe one way of stopping sulfur dioxide being formed in power stations, and another way of removing it from waste gases if it is formed.

10 Describe how particulates are removed from power-station waste gases.

Summary box
- ✓ **Individuals can reduce pollutants from power stations by using less electricity.**
- ✓ **Sulfur can be removed from natural gas and fuel oil before they are burned to reduce the amount of sulfur dioxide that forms.**
- ✓ **Sulfur dioxide and particulates can be removed from the waste gases from a power station to stop them from reaching the atmosphere.**

Science Explanations

Air pollution can affect people's health and the environment. In order to improve air quality it is important to understand where air pollutants come from and how they are made.

You should know:

- how the Earth's early atmosphere was formed
- how oxygen was added to the atmosphere and carbon dioxide was removed as a result of the evolution of organisms that photosynthesise
- the importance of the oceans in removing carbon dioxide from the atmosphere and how this has led to the formation of sedimentary rocks and fossil fuels
- which gases now make up the Earth's atmosphere
- that burning fossil fuels changes the atmosphere by adding extra carbon dioxide (contributing to global warming) and smaller amounts of other pollutant gases as well as tiny particles of solids (such as particulate carbon)
- that natural events (such as volcanoes) add gases and particulates to the air
- that the reactions when fuels burn are oxidation reactions
- that hydrocarbons are made from carbon and hydrogen atoms only
- that, when a hydrocarbon burns, the carbon atoms combine with oxygen atoms from the air to form carbon dioxide and the hydrogen atoms combine with oxygen atoms from the air to form water
- why some pollutants are directly harmful to humans and some are harmful to the environment
- that in any chemical reaction the number of each kind of atom is the same in the products as in the reactants
- that conservation of atoms means that fuels do not just disappear when they burn but produce products that can pollute the air
- that the properties of the reactants and products of chemical changes are different
- that the incomplete burning of fuels produces particulate carbon and a poisonous gas, carbon monoxide
- why some fuels produce sulfur dioxide gas when they burn, and why this gas gives rise to acid rain if released into the air
- why the waste gases from fuels burning inside a furnace or engine produce nitrogen oxide gas
- that technological developments such as catalytic converters can reduce the amounts of pollutants released into the atmosphere.

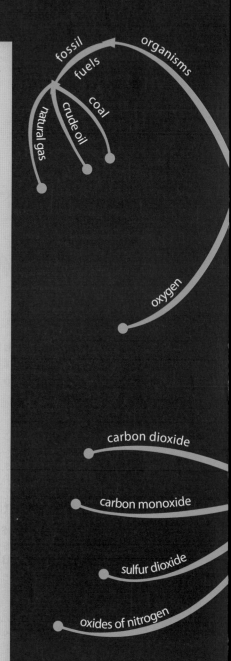

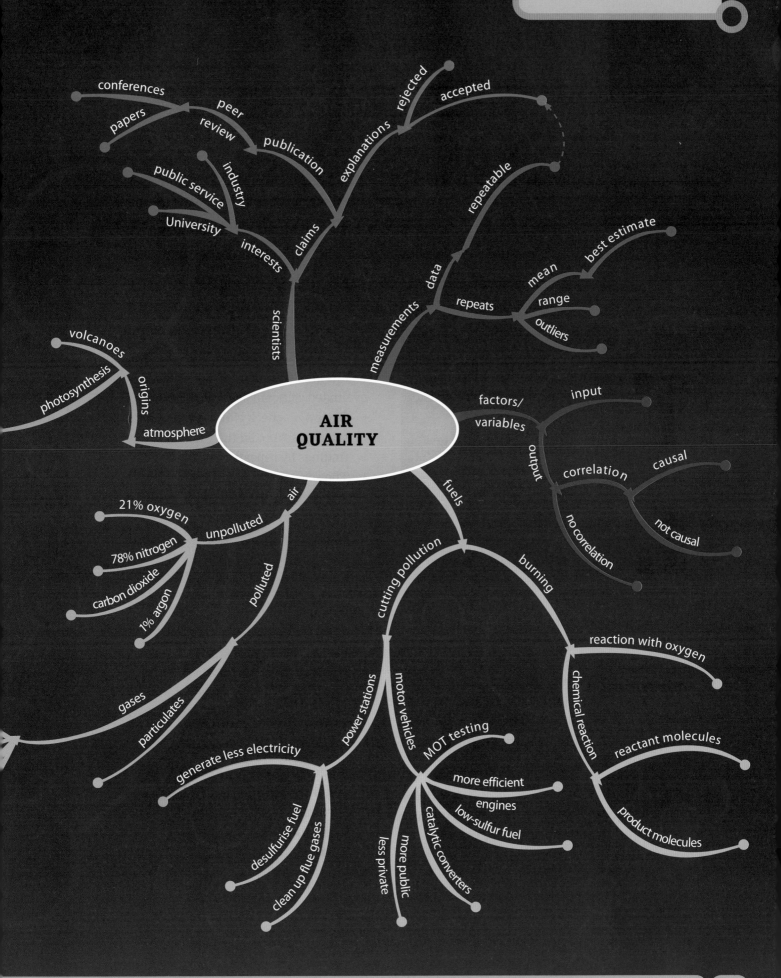

AIR QUALITY

conferences
papers
peer
review
publication
explanations
rejected
accepted
repeatable
claims
industry
public service
University
interests
scientists
measurements
data
repeats
mean
best estimate
range
outliers

volcanoes
photosynthesis
origins
atmosphere

factors/
variables
input
output
correlation
causal
no correlation
not causal

air
21% oxygen
unpolluted
78% nitrogen
carbon dioxide
1% argon
polluted
gases
particulates

fuels
cutting pollution
burning
reaction with oxygen
chemical reaction
reactant molecules
product molecules

power stations
motor vehicles
MOT testing
more efficient
engines
low-sulfur fuel
generate less electricity
desulfurise fuel
clean up flue gases
catalytic converters
less private
more public

Ideas about Science

Scientists use data, rather than opinions, to justify their explanations. They collect large amounts of data when they investigate the causes and effects of air pollutants. They can never be sure that a measurement tells them the true value of the quantity being measured.

If you take several measurements of the same quantity, the results are likely to vary. This may be because:
* you have to measure several individual examples, for example, exhaust gases from different cars of the same make
* the quantity you are measuring is varying, for example, the level of nitrogen oxides in exhaust gases
* the limitations of the measuring equipment or because of the way you use the equipment.

The best estimate of the true value of a quantity is the mean of several measurements. The true value lies in the spread of values in a set of repeat measurements.

* A measurement may be an outlier if it lies outside the range of the other values in a set of repeat measurements.
* An outlier should be treated as data unless you have a reason to doubt its accuracy.
* A correlation shows a link between a factor and an outcome, for example, as the level of particulates in the air goes up the number of people suffering from lung disease goes up.
* A correlation does not always mean that the factor causes the outcome.

Scientists publish their results so that their data and claims can be checked by others. Scientific claims are only accepted once they have been evaluated critically by other scientists.
* Reviewers check claims to make sure the scientists who did the work have checked their findings by repeating them.
* The scientific community generally does not accept new claims unless they have been reproduced by other scientists.
* Scientists may come to different conclusions about the same data.

Some applications of science, such as the use of fuels, can have a negative impact on the quality of life or the environment.
* The only way of producing less carbon dioxide is to burn less fossil fuel.
* Pollution caused by power stations that burn fossil fuels can be reduced by using less electricity, removing sulfur from natural gas and fuel oil, and by removing sulfur dioxide and particulates (carbon and ash) from flue gases.
* Pollution caused by vehicles can be reduced by burning less fuel in more efficient engines, using low-sulfur fuels, and using catalytic converters.

Review Questions

1 The table shows the percentage of gases in dry air. Copy and complete the table by writing the correct gas next to each percentage. Choose from these gases.

argon	hydrogen
nitrogen	oxygen

Gas	Percentage
	1
	21
	78

2 Fossil fuels are burned in some power stations and motor vehicles. The table is to show how the burning of fossil fuels changes the proportion of different gases in the air.

Copy and complete the table by putting a tick (✓) in the correct box for each gas.

Gas	Increases	No change	Decreases
sulfur dioxide	✓		
oxygen			
carbon monoxide			
carbon dioxide			

3 Ethanol can be used as a fuel for cars.

The diagram represents a molecule of ethanol.

a i How many different elements are in a molecule of ethanol?

ii How many atoms are in a molecule of ethanol?

b When ethanol burns completely, it reacts with oxygen (O_2) and produces carbon dioxide (CO_2) and water (H_2O). Copy and complete this diagram to show the products of the reaction when ethanol is burned completely.

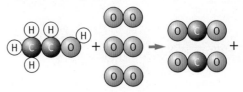

4 Students measured the pH of rain falling on their school playground. They collected and tested six samples of water on the same day. To get a best estimate, they worked out an average pH from their results. Their results are shown in the table.

Sample	1	2	3	4	5	6
pH	5.8	5.6	5.8	4.2	5.7	5.6

a Why did the students collect and test six samples? Choose the best answer:

1 To get a better estimate of the pH.

2 So that they could each have a sample to test.

3 So that they could test samples from different places.

4 So that they could take samples at different times of the day.

b When the students worked out the average value for their results, why did they not include the value for sample 4? Choose the best answer:

1 It is above the mean.

2 It is the highest value.

3 It is an outlier.

c Ignoring the value for sample 4, work out the following for the students' results:

i the range

ii the mean.

P1 The Earth in the Universe

Why study the Earth in the Universe?

Many people want to understand more about the Earth and its place in the Universe. The Earth is a very, very small place in a huge and almost empty Universe. How did the substances we are made of come to be here? What is the history of the Universe itself? Natural disasters, such as earthquakes and volcanic eruptions, can be life-threatening. Why do they happen? Can anything be done to predict them?

What you already know

- The solar system includes planets, asteroids, minor planets, and comets, all orbiting the Sun.

- Some of the planets have moons orbiting them.

- The Sun is a star, one of a vast number of stars in space.

- The speed of a moving object can be calculated using speed = distance / time.

Find out about

- the history of the Universe

- how scientists develop explanations of the Earth and space

- evidence of the Earth's history found in the rocks

- the movement of the Earth's continents

- what seismic waves can tell us about the Earth.

The Science

Science can explain change. Changes in stars and galaxies can take millions of years. Other changes, such as earthquakes, happen very quickly.

Ideas about Science

Can scientists be sure? They depend on carefully collected data. Scientists must use their imaginations to interpret the data they collect. How are scientific ideas tested? Scientists often argue before new data and explanations are accepted.

Find out about

✓ **what is known about the Earth and the Universe**

Our rocky planet was made from the scattered dust of old stars. We don't know if it is the only place in the whole **Universe** with life.

This diagram shows some of the things scientists know about where and how the **Earth** moves through space.
But there are many things that we still do not know.
Somethings we may never know.

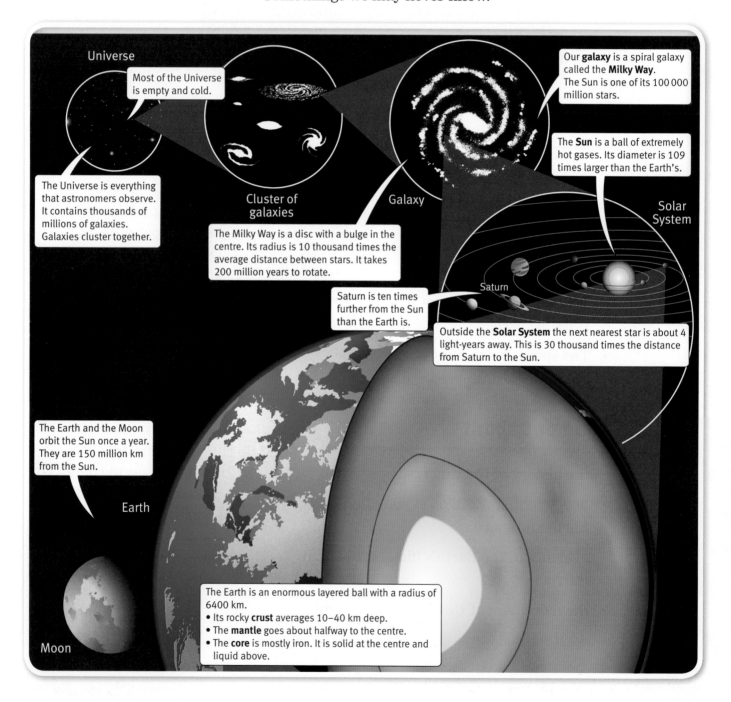

Universe

Most of the Universe is empty and cold.

The Universe is everything that astronomers observe. It contains thousands of millions of galaxies. Galaxies cluster together.

Cluster of galaxies

The Milky Way is a disc with a bulge in the centre. Its radius is 10 thousand times the average distance between stars. It takes 200 million years to rotate.

Galaxy

Our **galaxy** is a spiral galaxy called the **Milky Way**. The Sun is one of its 100 000 million stars.

The **Sun** is a ball of extremely hot gases. Its diameter is 109 times larger than the Earth's.

Solar System

Saturn is ten times further from the Sun than the Earth is.

Saturn

Outside the **Solar System** the next nearest star is about 4 light-years away. This is 30 thousand times the distance from Saturn to the Sun.

The Earth and the Moon orbit the Sun once a year. They are 150 million km from the Sun.

Earth

Moon

The Earth is an enormous layered ball with a radius of 6400 km.
• Its rocky **crust** averages 10–40 km deep.
• The **mantle** goes about halfway to the centre.
• The **core** is mostly iron. It is solid at the centre and liquid above.

Timeline: The history of the Earth

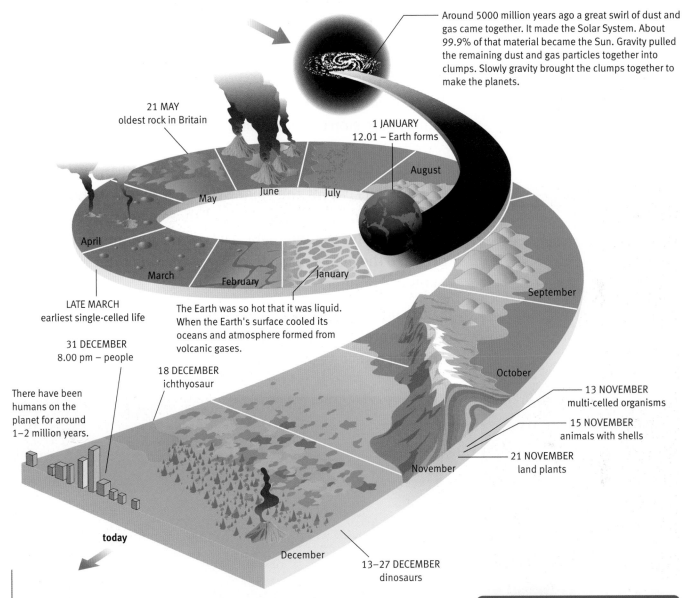

Around 5000 million years ago a great swirl of dust and gas came together. It made the Solar System. About 99.9% of that material became the Sun. Gravity pulled the remaining dust and gas particles together into clumps. Slowly gravity brought the clumps together to make the planets.

21 MAY
oldest rock in Britain

1 JANUARY
12.01 – Earth forms

August

May

June

July

April

March

February

January

September

LATE MARCH
earliest single-celled life

The Earth was so hot that it was liquid. When the Earth's surface cooled its oceans and atmosphere formed from volcanic gases.

31 DECEMBER
8.00 pm – people

18 DECEMBER
ichthyosaur

There have been humans on the planet for around 1–2 million years.

October

13 NOVEMBER
multi-celled organisms

15 NOVEMBER
animals with shells

21 NOVEMBER
land plants

November

today

December

13–27 DECEMBER
dinosaurs

Timeline: The history of the Earth, scaled as if it took place in one year.

Questions

1 Using the illustration on the previous page as a source, make a list of seven astronomical objects, in order of size. Start with the Moon and end with the Universe.

2 The timeline above shows the age of the Earth.
   a Redraw it as if it happened over a period of 12 years.
   b On this scale, when did life first appear on Earth? When did the dinosaurs die out?

Summary box
- ✓ **The Solar System was formed about 5000 million years ago.**
- ✓ **The Sun is one of thousands of millions of stars in the Milky Way.**
- ✓ **The Universe contains thousands of millions of galaxies.**

Find out about

- ✔ **what makes up the Solar System**
- ✔ **the process that releases energy in the stars and produces new elements**

Astronomers use telescopes to observe the night sky. A telescope gathers radiation, such as light, from distant stars. This radiation carries information, which helps us to build up our understanding of the Universe and everything in it.

In some places **light pollution**, dust and dampness in the atmosphere stop the radiation getting through.

Solar System

The Earth is part of the Solar System. It is one of eight planets that orbit the Sun. Most of these planets have smaller moons in orbit around them. The **dwarf planets** have similar orbits to the planets. Small, rocky **asteroids** orbit between Mars and Jupiter.

The orbits of the planets and asteroids are roughly circular. **Comets** are large balls of ice and dust. They have very different orbits, as shown in this diagram of the Solar System.

Astronomers prefer to work in dark places where they have a clear view of the night sky. They analyse light from stars to discover how hot they are and what they are made of.

Comets spend a lot of time far from the Sun. They rush inwards to pass around the Sun before returning to the cold outer reaches of the Solar System.

Question

1 Draw a diagram to compare the orbits of the Earth and a comet around the Sun.

The Sun

The Sun is the biggest object in the Solar System. It has 99.9% of the mass. It is the only object that produces its own light. We see everything else by reflected light.

Scientists knew the Sun could not be a great ball of fire, because fire needs fuel and oxygen and these would have run out long ago.

They found that atoms have a central core, called a nucleus. Joining small nuclei together releases energy and creates new elements. This process is called **nuclear fusion**.

Nuclear fusion happens only at extremely high temperatures – millions of degrees. This is the temperature inside a star. Hydrogen nuclei fuse to make helium in the Sun, and other stars.

Heavy elements are made in stars

The most common elements in the Universe are hydrogen and helium. All the heavier elements are made by other fusion reactions in stars, or by big stars exploding.

The age of the Solar System

As you saw on page 75, the Solar System formed about 5000 million years ago. This process took millions of years.

The swirling cloud of dust and gas that formed the Solar System came from the remains of dead stars. Except for hydrogen and helium, the chemical elements that make up everything on Earth come from stars. We are made of stardust.

The remains of a star that exploded spreading out into space. One day, this material may be part of new stars and planets.

An artist's impression of the Solar System as it formed, 5 billion years ago. The Sun's gravity pulled in most of the material. The rest formed the planets and everything else.

Questions

2 Put these objects in order of size, from the smallest to the biggest:
a comet   the Moon   the Sun   an asteroid   the Earth

3 Why do scientists believe that there must have been stars that existed and died before the Solar System formed?

Summary box

✓ **The Solar System is eight planets orbiting the Sun, together with asteroids, dwarf planets, and comets.**
✓ **Nuclear fusion inside stars releases energy and forms new elements.**

Find out about

- ✓ **ways of measuring the distance to stars**
- ✓ **how astronomers see into the past**

The stars we see in the night sky have a fixed pattern. The Sun, Moon, and planets appear to move against this fixed pattern. This shows that the stars are not part of the Solar System.

Star distances

Here are two ways of measuring the distances to stars.

Measuring star distances

Method 1: *Parallax*

In six months, the Earth moves from one side of the Sun to the other. A nearby star will shift its position against the background of more distant stars. The nearer a star is, the more it shifts.

Astronomers look through telescopes on Earth and work out the distance to the nearest stars by measuring the shift. The shift is measured as the angle between the two directions.

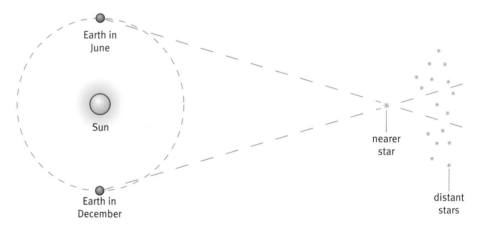

To see the parallax effect, hold up your thumb and look at it with each eye in turn. Your left eye represents the position of the Earth in June, your right eye is the Earth in December.

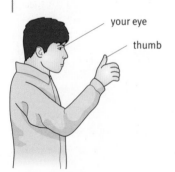

Look at the diagram that shows how to see the **parallax** effect with your thumb.

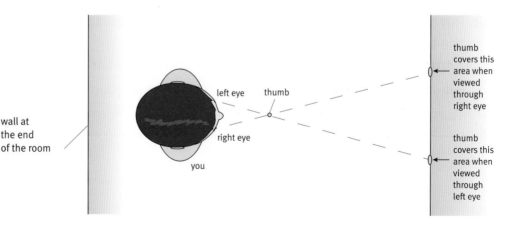

Method 2: *Brightness*

Look at the photograph of streetlights. They all shine with the same brightness but the ones that are further away appear fainter.

We can use this to work out which of two stars is nearest. The brighter a star appears to be, the nearer it must be.

But there is a problem with this. The two stars must be shining with equal brightness. Astronomers can analyse the light from the stars to work out what kind of star they are. Then we can say that, if two stars are the same kind, the one that appears fainter must be further away.

The speed of light

Light moves fast. Its speed is 300 000 km/s through empty space. But light still needs time to travel from place to place.

It takes light:

- 6 millionths of a second to travel the length of Britain
- about 8 minutes to travel from the Sun to the Earth
- about 4 years to travel to the nearest star
- about 100 000 years to travel right across our galaxy, the Milky Way.

Light-years away

Light from the closest star outside the Solar System takes 4.22 years to reach Earth. We say that it is 4.22 light-years away.

A **light-year** is a unit of distance used by astronomers. It is the distance travelled by light in one year.

Looking back in time

Light from the Sun takes just over eight minutes to reach Earth. This means that you see the Sun as it was eight minutes ago. You see the stars now as they were many years ago.

All the streetlights shine with the same brightness, so the ones that look fainter must be further away.

Questions

1 It takes light from the Moon 1.3 seconds to reach the Earth. Calculate the distance from the Moon to the Earth.
2 Some light from a star six light-years away is reaching Earth as you read this. How old were you when that light left the star?

Summary box

- ✔ Brightness of stars and parallax are used to measure their distance away.
- ✔ The star light we see left the stars many years ago.

Find out about

- ✔ **our galaxy, the Milky Way**
- ✔ **objects beyond the Milky Way**

An artist's impression of the Milky Way galaxy, built up from observations of many millions of stars. The bright yellow dot in the lower arm is the Sun, although really the Sun is no brighter than other stars.

Our galaxy

Our galaxy is called the Milky Way because it looks like a bright band across the night sky. A galaxy is a collection of thousands of millions of stars, held together by gravity. To see it you need to be in a place where there is little light pollution.

For over 2000 years, astronomers thought that the Milky Way was made up of large numbers of stars. This was confirmed in 1610, when Galileo first used a telescope to look at the sky.

Astronomers have built up a picture of the galaxy by counting the numbers of stars in different directions and estimating their distances. The illustration gives an idea of its shape.

- The Milky Way has several arms spiralling out from the centre.
- It has a bulge at the centre.
- The Sun is about half-way out from the centre, in one of the spiral arms.

More than one galaxy

The Andromeda Galaxy is a faint smudge of light in the constellation of Andromeda. It used to be called the Andromeda Nebula. **Nebula** is the Latin word for a cloud.

Astronomers wanted to know what nebulae were.

- Were they clouds of gas inside the Milky Way?
- Or, were they star clusters, far outside the Milky Way?

Edwin Hubble was an American astronomer. In 1925 he studied the Andromeda nebula. The result was surprising. It was more than a million light-years away, far outside the Milky Way.

Today's space telescopes show that the Andromeda Galaxy is a spiral galaxy, similar to the Milky Way.

Questions

1 What is the name of the galaxy in which the Solar System is found?

2 What new observation showed that there were objects outside the Milky Way?

Billions of billions

We now know that there are thousands of millions of galaxies in the Universe, each made up of thousands of millions of stars – perhaps 10 thousand billion billion stars in total.

The Hubble Space Telescope image (below) shows some very distant galaxies. The light that made this image left its stars over 10 thousand million years ago. That was long before the Sun and the rest of the Solar System existed.

Measurement uncertainties

Measuring the distances to the stars was difficult. First astronomers measured the diameter of the Earth's orbit around the Sun. Then they used the parallax method to measure the distance to nearby stars. After that astronomers used the brightness method to estimate the distance to further stars. Then another method, using variable stars whose brightness varies was used to measure distances beyond the Milky Way.

Astronomers have to make some **assumptions** in their work – for example, the brightness method assumes that two stars that look the same really are the same kind of star.

Each method depends on the results of the previous one, so the final results were, to start with, very **uncertain**. By making many different measurements and comparing the results, astronomers eventually estimated the size of the Universe. And it's very, very big!

A photograph of the Andromeda galaxy. You can see two other galaxies. One is the bright blob above Andromeda and one is the smear below it.

An image of distant galaxies, made by light at the end of a long, long journey.

Questions

3 Roughly how many galaxies are there in the Universe?

4 Draw a flow chart to show the steps in measuring the size of the Universe. Start with the diameter of the Earth's orbit.

5 Explain why there are uncertainties about the actual size of galaxies.

Summary box

✓ **Astronomers are uncertain about the distances to stars and galaxies because of:**
- **difficulty in observation**
- **assumptions made.**

The Universe is everything. It is stars and galaxies. It is clouds and oceans. It is bacteria and birds. You are part of the Universe.

The exploding Universe

Until the 20th century, most people thought that the Universe never changed. Bigger and better telescopes that could see distant galaxies changed all that.

Astronomers discovered that clusters of galaxies are all moving away from each other. Look at the diagram of the expanding balloon. Scientists believe that galaxies are all moving apart because the Universe is expanding. The Universe is big and getting bigger.

The big bang theory

Picture the expanding Universe – all the galaxies are spreading apart. Now run this imaginary 'film' backwards and the galaxies all meet at a single point.

Start time going forward again and the Universe explodes with a **big bang**. This explanation is called the big bang theory.

Scientists believe that a long time ago the Universe was incredibly hot, tiny and dense.

Testing the theory

In 1948, a group of scientists predicted that an afterglow of the big bang event should still fill the whole Universe with microwaves. In 1965, two scientists in New Jersey noticed annoying background radiation in their radio-telescope data. When they reported this noise, astronomers recognised it as the cosmic microwave background radiation that had been predicted. The big bang theory had passed a major test.

Find out about

- ✓ an explanation called 'big bang'
- ✓ the age of the Universe

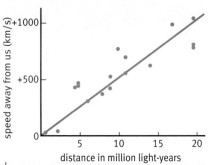

Edwin Hubble published a famous paper in 1929. It showed that distant galaxies are moving away from us.

Imagine yourself on the surface of a very big balloon, with galaxies on the surface. If the balloon is expanding, all the galaxies are moving away from you. All of them are moving further apart.

Summary box

- ✓ The big bang theory describes how the Universe formed.
- ✓ The Universe is about 14 thousand million years old.

Questions

1 What evidence do scientists have that the Universe is expanding?

2 Describe the big bang theory.

The age of the Universe

Scientists estimate that the Universe is 13 700 million years old, plus or minus 200 million years.

The diagram on the right compares this with the age of the oldest stars and the Solar System. They are younger than the Universe.

Scientists at work

Around the world, there are thousands of scientists studying theories of the Universe. Most of them work in universities, usually in groups. When a group develops a new idea, they write a paper for a scientific journal.

Before a scientific paper is published, other experts must first review it. They check it to make sure it has something useful, reliable and new to say. This process is called **peer review**.

Will the Universe expand for ever?

Scientists want to predict how the Universe will end. The available data is uncertain because it is difficult to measure the very large distances to the furthest galaxies, and their speeds.

Because the evidence is so uncertain, there are several competing theories of the ultimate fate of the Universe.

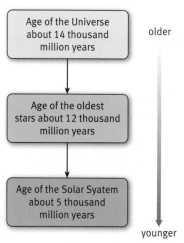

Age of the Universe about 14 thousand million years

Age of the oldest stars about 12 thousand million years

Age of the Solar Syatem about 5 thousand million years

older

younger

The Universe is older than everything in it. There would be a problem with the theory if it wasn't.

Scientists make computer models of the Universe. They work with vast amounts of data. This requires a supercomputer, such as the one at Durham University shown here. It can perform 500 billion calculations each second.

Questions

3 List three observations that support the big bang theory.

4 Give an approximate age for each of the following, and list them from oldest to youngest:
- the oldest stars
- the Universe
- the Solar System.

5 Explain why the discovery of the cosmic background radiation in 1965 was important to the scientists who had proposed the big bang theory.

Find out about

- ✓ James Hutton's explanation for the variety of rocks he found
- ✓ how old rocks are and how scientists date them

Around 300 years ago, people were finding fossils of seashells and other marine organisms in rocks at the tops of mountains. 'Why here?' they wondered.

James Hutton and the stories that rocks tell

Without some way of building new mountains, erosion would wear the continents flat.

Rivers carry sediment to the oceans, where it settles at the bottom as sand and silt.

Sediments form sedimentary rocks. In some places, layers of sedimentary rocks are tilted or folded.

Over very long periods of time very slow processes such as erosion and deposition of sediment take place. They add up to huge changes in the Earth's surface.

Heating inside the Earth changes rocks and lifts land up. Erosion makes new soil.

The Earth has a history. It was not created all at once.

James Hutton was a farmer. He watched heavy rains wash valuable soil off farmers' fields. He noticed that many rocks are made up of eroded material (now called sedimentary rocks). In his mind, he connected these two observations with the idea of a cycle – continents are both eroded and created.

Using the present to interpret the past

In 1785 Hutton presented his startling new theory of the Earth. He explained it at a meeting of the Royal Society of Edinburgh. Hutton described the rock cycle like this.

The millions of years over which the Earth has changed are called 'deep time'.

Dating rocks

Gradually, geologists learned to work out the history recorded in rocks. They used clues like these:

- Deeper is older – in layered rocks, the youngest rocks are usually on top of older ones.
- Fossils are time markers – many species lived at particular times and later became extinct.

But these clues only tell you which rocks are older than others. They don't tell you how old the rocks are.

Some rocks are radioactive. Scientists today estimate their age by measuring the radiation that these rocks give off. The Earth's oldest rocks were made about four million years ago; this means the Earth is older than four million years.

Older rocks are usually found under younger rocks. Different creatures lived at different times in the past. Their fossils can help geologists decide when rocks were formed.

The development of scientific ideas

This case study about James Hutton, contains examples of:

- data
- explanations
- the role of imagination.

Data

Fossils, rocks of different types, the way that rock types are layered, folded, or joined.

Explanations

Hutton's idea of a rock cycle, different ways of dating rocks.

Imagination

Most people in James Hutton's time believed in a young Earth but Hutton could imagine the millions of years needed for familiar processes to slowly change the landscape.

Questions

1 In what time order did the creatures shown in the picture of the cliff above live?

2 Which layer has the fallen rock come from?

Summary box

- ✓ **The oldest rocks are about four thousand million years old.**
- ✓ **Today we see erosion and deposition of sediments.**
- ✓ **These can explain changes in the Earth in the past.**

Find out about

- ✔ a scientific debate started by Alfred Wegener
- ✔ evidence that the continents are very slowly moving

250 million years ago

Wegener showed how all the continents could once have formed a single continent, called Pangaea.

Questions

1 In this case study, identify examples of
   a data
   b explanations.

2 What reasons did other scientists give for rejecting Wegener's ideas?

Summary box

- ✔ Alfred Wegner thought the continents were once joined together and were drifting apart.
- ✔ This theory was not believed at the time.

How are mountains formed?

In the 1800s, most geologists believed that the Earth began hot. They thought the Earth was like a drying apple. The picture shows how an apple shrinks and wrinkles as it dries. If the Earth had cooled and shrunk, its surface would have wrinkled too. The geologists claimed that chains of mountains are those wrinkles.

Moving continents?

Many people can spot the match between the shapes of South America and Africa. The two continents look like pieces of a jigsaw. Alfred Wegener thought this meant that the continents were moving. They had once been joined together. He looked for evidence, recorded in their rocks.

In 1915 Wegener wrote a famous book to present his idea of **continental drift**. In the book he explained the evidence that backed up his idea.

POLAR EXPLORER DIES

The frozen body of the German meteorologist and polar explorer Alfred Wegener was found on 12 May 1931. Wegener had been leading an expedition in Greenland and went missing on 1 November 1930. Unfortunately he is likely to be remembered for being too bold in his science.

Wegener claimed that continents move, by ploughing across the ocean floor. That, he said, explains why there are mountain chains at the edges of continents.

As evidence of continental drift, he found some interesting matches between, rocks and fossils on different continents. But most geologists reject such a grand and unlikely explanation for these observations. Wegener was regarded as an outsider by the community of geologists.

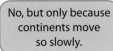
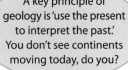

Find out about

- ✓ a big explanation for many Earth processes
- ✓ ways to limit the damage caused by volcanoes and earthquakes

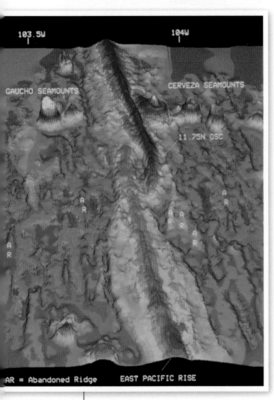

This computer-generated model shows part of the Pacific Ocean floor. (Water is not shown.)

Question

1 Why does seafloor spreading support Wegener's idea of continental drift?

Mapping the seafloor

During the 1950s the US Navy paid for a lot of ocean science research. The Navy wanted to know how to move its submarines near the ocean floor, where they could avoid detection.

Ocean research completely changed our understanding of how the Earth changes.

From stripes in rocks to seafloor spreading

Scientists started to make maps of the ocean floor. To their great surprise, they found a chain of mountains under most oceans. This is now called an **oceanic ridge**. In 1960 a scientist called Harry Hess suggested that the seafloor moves away from either side of an oceanic ridge. This process, called **seafloor spreading**, could make continents drift apart.

Beneath a ridge, solid material pushes up on the ocean floor. Some of the material melts to form magma. Hot magma erupts and cools to make new rock.

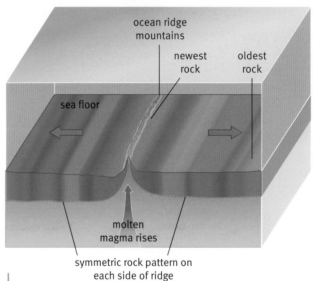

Seafloor spreading makes new rock.

- The new rock forms at the ridge and then slowly moves away.
- The rock has a pattern of stripes.
- The newest stripes are closest to the ridge and the oldest are furthest away. The pattern is symmetric on each side of the ridge.

Plate tectonics

By 1967, several Earth processes were linked together in one big explanation. It was called plate tectonics.

This is the plate tectonics explanation of the Earth's outer layer.

- The Earth's outer layer, is made up of the crust plus the rigid upper mantle.
- It is broken into about 12 giant slabs of rock, and many smaller ones. These are called **tectonic plates**.
- The lower mantle is hot and soft. It can flow slowly. Currents in the lower mantle carry the plates along.
- The ocean floor continually grows wider at an oceanic ridge by seafloor spreading. This is shown in the ocean ridge diagram.
- The ocean floor is destroyed where one plate moves beneath another at an ocean trench. You can see this in the ocean trench diagram.
- The result is that the rigid plates move slowly around the surface of the Earth. In some places, they move apart. In other places, they push together or slide past one another.

Global Positioning Satellites (GPS) can detect the movement of continents. The Atlantic is growing wider by about 2.5 cm a year. This is about the same rate that your fingernails grow.

Plate tectonics explanations

The movement of tectonic plates causes continents to drift. It also explains:

- mountain-building
- most earthquakes
- most volcanoes

Summary box
- ✔ There are ocean ridges under the oceans.
- ✔ The seafloor is spreading and this supports the idea of continental drift.

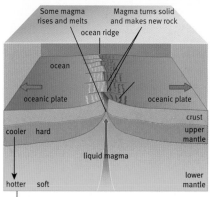

An ocean ridge forms.

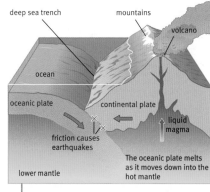

A deep ocean trench forms.

Questions

2 a Why is the Atlantic getting wider?

  b What does this suggest about the Atlantic millions of years ago?

3 Similar fossils are found in South America and Africa. Use plate tectonics to explain why.

Look at the map showing the tectonic plates. You can see that the sites of volcanoes and earthquakes lie along the edges of the plates.

Making mountains

Collisions between tectonic plates cause mountains to be formed.

- Where an ocean moves back down into the Earth, forming an ocean trench, volcanic peaks may form at the surface.
- Sometimes an ocean closes completely, and two continents collide in slow motion. The edges of the continents crumple together and pile up, making mountain chains. This is happening today in the Himalayas and Tibet.

Mount Everest is a young mountain. Mountain building is taking place now in this region.

The tectonic plates are moving. The blue arrows show the direction of movement. Earthquakes happen at the boundaries between tectonic plates.

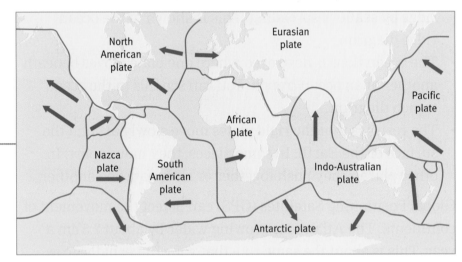

Earthquakes

In some places tectonic plates slide past each other, as at the San Andreas Fault in California.

The shunting of the Earth's plates causes forces to build up along breaks, called fault lines. Eventually the forces are so great that rocks locked together break, and allow plate movement. The ground shakes, making an **earthquake**.

Summary box
- ✓ The Earth's outer layer is made up of about 12 tectonic plates.
- ✓ Mountain building, earthquakes, and volcanoes occur at the edge of the plates.

Questions

4 Where do most earthquakes and volcanoes occur?

5 Mount Everest is on the edge of two tectonic plates.
   a Are these plates moving apart or colliding?
   b Explain how you decided your answer to part a.

Earthquakes and seismic waves

Energy of an earthquake

Earth scientists record more than 30 000 earthquakes a year. Living through a major earthquake is a terrifying experience. The ground shakes violently, buildings collapse, and whole hillsides form landslides. Huge amounts of energy are released. This energy spreads out from the source of the quake and can be detected far away.

Detecting seismic waves

We detect the vibrations of an earthquake using an instrument called a seismometer. The photograph below shows a seismometer for use in schools.

The vibrations travel out in all directions from the site of an earthquake. These waves are called **seismic waves**. Seismometers all over the world pick up seismic waves. Scientists collect the data to find out as much as possible about the earthquake.

The charts below are seismograms produced by seismometers after an earthquake. Two sets of vibrations have been detected, and labelled P and S.

- The P-waves arrive at the detector first (P = primary).
- The S-waves arrive second (S = secondary).

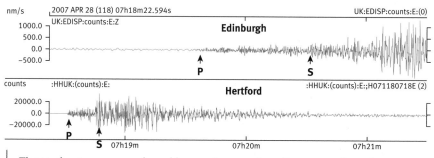

These charts were produced by a seismometer after an earthquake.

Find out about

- ✔ the seismic waves produced by earthquakes
- ✔ how waves travel
- ✔ how waves are measured

Earthquake damage in Port au Prince, Haiti, after the earthquake of 12 January 2010.

A seismometer used in schools – the horizontal and diagonal rods are hinged at the left-hand side, like a garden gate. They swing from side to side in an earthquake.

Question

1 Look at the charts showing the earthquake data.

   a Which place detected the earthquake first?

   b Did the earthquake happen nearer to Edinburgh or to Hertford?

   c Explain how you decided your answer to part b.

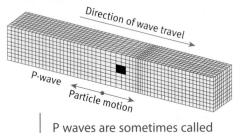

P waves are sometimes called 'push-and-pull' waves.

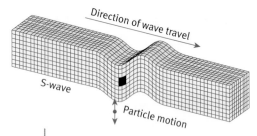

S waves are sometimes called 'sideways' waves.

What is a wave?

In science the word 'wave' has a special meaning.

- A wave is a travelling vibration that transfers energy from place to place.

Sound and light are examples of waves. The energy released in an earthquake is carried by seismic waves. Waves do not carry material, for example, in a water wave the water goes up and down but doesn't travel along.

Types of wave

There are two different types of wave. They are called **longitudinal** waves and **transverse** waves. The pictures below show how they can be sent along a slinky spring.

Longitudinal waves

Longitudinal waves travel as a series of compressions (squashed-up regions). The diagram in the margin shows how seismic P-waves travel like this through the Earth. Sound waves are also longitudinal waves.

Transverse waves

Transverse waves travel as the material moves sideways at a right-angle to the direction the wave travels. Water waves travel like this. The water moves up and down and the crests and troughs travel along.

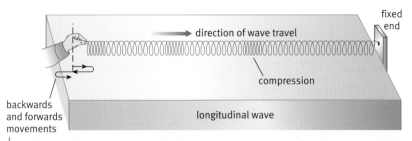

A longitudinal wave is made by compressing and releasing the spring.

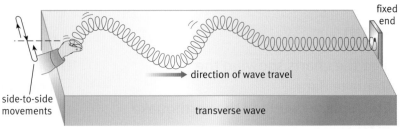

A transverse wave is made by moving the spring from side to side.

Summary box

- ✓ **A wave is a travelling vibration that transfers energy.**
- ✓ **Waves can be longitudinal or transverse.**
- ✓ **P-waves and sound waves are longitudinal.**
- ✓ **S-waves and water waves are transverse.**

Measuring waves

Two measurements that scientists use to describe waves are the **wavelength** of the wave and its **amplitude**.

Wavelength

The wavelength is the length of one complete wave. The diagram shows waves with different wavelengths.

To measure the wavelength of the longitudinal wave, measure the distance from the centre of one compression to the next.

To measure the wavelength of the transverse wave. measure the distance from the centre of one crest to the next (or from one trough to the next).

Amplitude

The amplitude is the height of a wave crest above the undisturbed level.

Imagine you are making transverse waves travel along a rope by moving your hand up and down. You can increase the amplitude by moving your hand further up and down. Your hand is the source of the waves. Larger vibrations of a source increase the amplitude of waves.

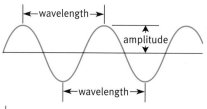

Important information when describing a wave.

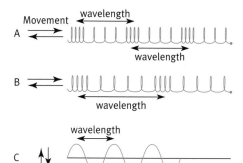

A and B are longitudinal waves. Wave A has a shorter wavelength than wave B. C is a transverse wave. Wave C has a shorter wavelength than wave A and wave B.

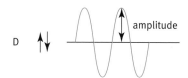

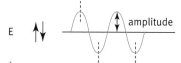

Wave D has a larger amplitude than wave E.

Questions

2 List:
   a three types of longitudinal wave
   b three types of transverse wave.

3 Use a ruler, and follow the instructions above, to:
   a measure the wavelengths of the waves A, B, and C.
   b measure the amplitude of the waves D and E.

4 Which will have a greater amplitude, waves from a strong earthquake or waves from a weak earthquake?

Summary box
✓ **The wavelength is the length of one complete wave.**
✓ **The amplitude is the height of a wave crest above the undisturbed level.**

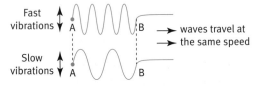

Fast vibrations

Slow vibrations

A   B   → waves travel at
                  → the same speed
A   B

When the source vibrates faster there are more waves per second, but the wave still travels away at the same speed.

The frequency and speed of a wave

Imagine you are making transverse waves travel along a spring by moving your hand from side to side. Your hand is the vibrating source of the waves. The diagrams show what happens if you move your hand faster. It produces more waves per second. You have increased the frequency of the waves.

The **frequency** of a wave is the number of waves that pass any point each second. It is the same as the number of vibrations per second of the source. Frequency is measured in hertz (Hz). 1 Hz means 1 wave per second.

There is something that you cannot do to the waves on the spring. No matter how you move your hand, you cannot increase their speed. To change the speed of the waves, you would need to use a different spring.

Wave speed is the speed at which each wave crest moves. It is measured in metres per second (m/s).

It is important to realise that frequency and wave speed are two completely different things. The frequency depends on the source – how many times it vibrates every second. Once the wave has left the source, its wave speed depends only on the medium or the material the wave is travelling through.

The distance travelled by a wave can be calculated using the equation:

$$\textbf{distance} = \textbf{speed} \times \textbf{time}$$

The wave equation

When you make waves travel along a spring moving your hand faster makes more waves per second. You have increased the frequency.

Questions

5 Water waves travel at 6 m/s. How far will they travel in
   a 4s?   b 1 minute?

6 P-waves travel through the Earth with a wave speed of about 6 km/s. How far will P-waves from an earthquake travel in 5 minutes (300 s)?

The waves still travel out from your hand at the same speed. They travel the same distance in one second, so there must be more of them squashed together in the same distance. They must be shorter. You have decreased the wavelength.

This shows that there is a link between the frequency of a wave, its wave speed, and its wavelength. In general:

wave speed = **frequency** × **wavelength**
metres per second (m/s)   hertz (Hz)   metres (m)

This link between the three wave quantities applies to all waves of every kind.

The blue waves have a higher frequency than the red waves and so their wavelength is shorter.

Worked example

The diagram shows a source that vibrates five times per second. It produces waves with a frequency of 5 Hz. They have a wavelength of 2 metres in the medium they are travelling through, so every wave moves forward by 10 metres (5 × 2 m) in one second. The wave speed is 10 m/s.

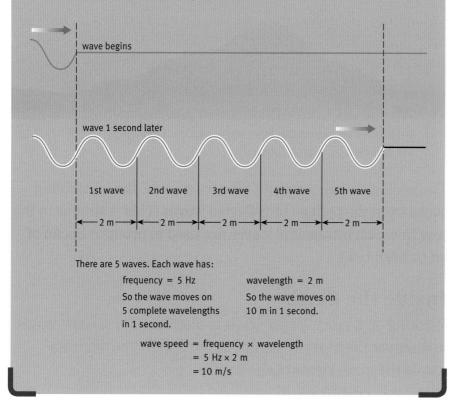

wave begins

wave 1 second later

1st wave   2nd wave   3rd wave   4th wave   5th wave

2 m   2 m   2 m   2 m   2 m

There are 5 waves. Each wave has:

frequency = 5 Hz

So the wave moves on
5 complete wavelengths
in 1 second.

wavelength = 2 m

So the wave moves on
10 m in 1 second.

wave speed = frequency × wavelength
= 5 Hz × 2 m
= 10 m/s

Summary box

✓ Wave speed = frequency × wavelength.
✓ Increasing frequency decreases wavelength.
✓ Decreasing frequency increases wavelength.

Questions

7 A seismic wave has a wavelength of 20 km and a frequency of 0.5 Hz. What is its speed?

8 The wave travels into a different rock where the wavelength is 10 km. What is the new speed of the wave?

9 Explain what is meant by saying that the wavelength is proportional to the speed.

Find out about

- ✔ **how seismic waves travel through the Earth**
- ✔ **how seismic waves reveal the Earth's internal structure**

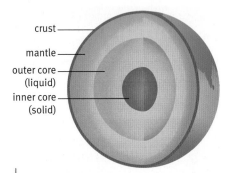

crust
mantle
outer core (liquid)
inner core (solid)

A cross-section through the Earth. This picture is the result of several decades of studies of seismic waves produced by earthquakes.

Questions

1 How can geologists find out what is inside the Earth?

2 Name the internal layers of the Earth, starting at the crust.

A geological scan

Seismic waves are a useful tool for geologists who want to look inside the Earth. They set off small explosions on the Earth's surface and detect the reflected seismic waves. The picture shows how this is used in oil exploration.

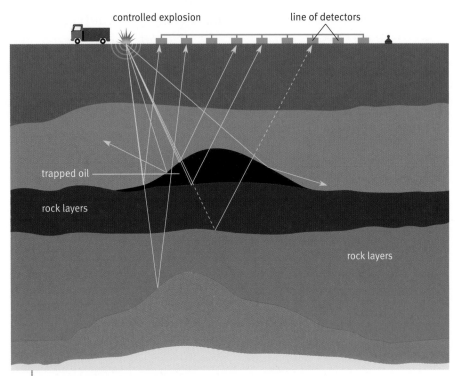

controlled explosion   line of detectors

trapped oil

rock layers

rock layers

Seismic waves spread out from the explosion and are detected by microphones.

The geologists can work out the structure of the underlying rocks from the pattern of reflected waves. This is similar to the way in which ultrasound waves are used to produce a scan of an unborn baby.

Inside the Earth

Working on a much larger scale, geologists used seismic waves to discover the inner structure of the Earth. The diagram shows the main layers of the Earth:

- the thin crust
- the mantle
- the **core**.

Finding out about the inner structure of the Earth

Scientists set up seismometers at different sites around the world. They detected earthquakes all over the Earth. They compared the charts from different sites and worked out where and when the quake had happened, as well as how strong it was.

Shadow zones

Scientists noticed that both P-waves and S-waves reached seismometers close to the earthquake centre, but only P-waves reached seismometers far off, on the other side of the Earth. There was a large 'shadow zone' where S-waves never reached.

- P-waves are longitudinal waves and can travel through solids and liquids (just like sound waves).
- S-waves are transverse waves; they can travel through solids but not through liquids.

In 1914, a German scientist called Beno Gutenberg realised that the Earth had a liquid core that was blocking the S-waves. He was able to work out the size of the core from the size of the shadow zone. It is about 7000 km thick, roughly half of the Earth's diameter.

When more sensitive seismometers were set up, scientists found out more about the Earth's interior. A Danish scientist, Inge Lehmann, looked at the pattern of P-waves. In 1936, she worked out that there must be a small, solid core inside the liquid core.

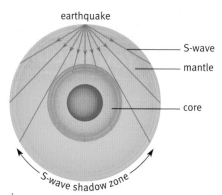

S-waves from an earthquake are blocked from reaching almost half of the Earth's surface.

Questions

3 Which type of seismic waves:
   a reach the opposite side of the Earth?
   b do not reach the opposite side of the Earth?

4 What is meant by the 'shadow zone'?

5 What did the S-wave shadow zone tell scientists about the Earth?

Summary box
- The Earth has a crust, a mantle, and a core.
- P-waves travel through solids and liquids.
- S-waves cannot travel through the liquid core.

Science
Explanations

To understand the world, scientists gather evidence through data and observations. These data and observations are related to the space beyond Earth – the Solar System, stars, and galaxies – and also to the structure of the Earth and the changes that take place in it.

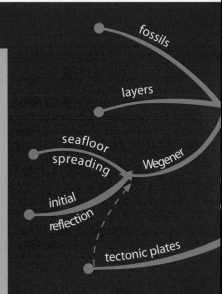

- that the Solar System consists of the Sun, eight planets and their moons, dwarf planets, asteroids, and comets
- that the Sun is one of many millions of stars in the Milky Way galaxy
- how the size of the diameters of the Earth, the Sun, and the Milky Way compare
- that light travels at very high speed and the huge distance it travels in one year (a light-year) is used to measure the enormous distances between stars and between galaxies
- that distant objects in the night sky are observed as younger than they are now because the light now reaching us left them a very long time ago
- that the fusion of hydrogen nuclei is the source of the Sun's energy
- that distant galaxies are moving away from us and that this is because the Universe began as a 'big bang' about 14 000 million years ago
- how the ages of the Universe, the Sun, and the Earth compare
- that the Earth is older than its oldest rocks, which are about 4000 million years old
- that Alfred Wegener's theory of continental drift can explain mountain building
- that seafloors spread by a few centimetres each year
- that earthquakes, volcanoes, and mountain building generally occur at the edges of tectonic plates
- that earthquakes produce wave motions on and inside the Earth
- that earthquake waves can be transverse or longitudinal
- that the Earth consists of the inner and outer core, mantle, and crust
- that waves are caused by vibrating sources and the number of waves produced each second is the frequency of the wave
- that waves have amplitude and wavelength, where the amplitude is the distance from the top of a crest (or the bottom of a trough) to the undisturbed position, and the wavelength is the length of one complete cycle
- that wave motion can be described by the equations
  distance = speed × time and wave speed = frequency × wavelength

THE EARTH IN THE UNIVERSE

- measuring distances
  - parallax
  - brightness
- light-year
- stars
  - expanding Universe
  - galaxies
    - Solar System
      - Sun
      - planets
      - moons
      - comets
      - asteroids
      - dwarf planets
- our place in the Universe
- the changing Earth
  - evidence in the rocks
  - core, mantle, and crust
- waves
  - longitudinal
  - transverse
  - frequency
  - amplitude
  - wavelength
- tectonic plates
- light
- slow and fast
- Earth and Universe
  - ages
  - sizes
- sense of scale
- mathematical skills
  - calculating with data
    - mean
    - range
  - using equations
    - speed = distance/time
    - wave speed = frequency × wavelength
    - wave properties
- developing explanations
  - data
  - imagination
  - explanation
  - predictions
  - accept
  - reject
- scientific community
  - testing new explanations
    - peer reviewed?
    - replicated or reproduced?
  - disagreement
    - different possible explanations
    - different personal experiences

Ideas about Science

In addition to developing an understanding of the structure of the Earth and the nature of the Solar System, stars, and galaxies, you should understand how scientists develop these ideas and how the work of individual scientists becomes accepted or rejected by the scientific community.

- New scientific data and explanations become more reliable after other scientists have critically evaluated them. This process is called peer review. Scientists communicate with other scientists through conferences, books, and journals.
- Scientists test new data and explanations by trying to repeat experiments and observations that others have reported.

From these you should be able to identify:
- the statements that are data
- statements that are all or part of an explanation
- data or observations that an explanation can account for
- data or observations that don't agree with an explanation.

Scientists don't always come to the same conclusion about what some data means. The debate about Wegener's idea of continental drift provides an example of this.

You should know:
- why Wegener's explanation was rejected at the time
- that some scientific questions have not been answered yet
- that distances to many stars and galaxies are not known exactly because they are so difficult to measure
- that the ultimate fate of the Universe is difficult to predict.

Review Questions

1 Besides the Sun, the Solar System contains planets, moons, comets, and asteroids. Explain the differences between these. You should explain how they move and put them in order of size.

2 Vesto Slipher was an astronomer.

In 1915, he measured the speed of a number of distant galaxies.

These are some of his results.

Galaxy	Speed (km/s)
A	1100
B	500
C	1100
D	600
E	300

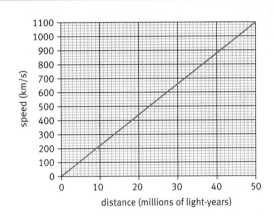

Recent work by astronomers shows that these galaxies are moving relative to us with speed given by the graph:

Use the graph to decide which galaxy in Vesto Slipher's table is 23 million light-years away from us.

3 The following statements describe the events leading to an earthquake. They are in the wrong order. Place them in the right order.

a Great pressure builds up where the plates cannot move easily.

b Two tectonic plates meet at a plate boundary at the San Andreas Fault.

c Slow movements of the magma make tectonic plates move.

d Friction at the edges prevents the plates from sliding easily.

e The sudden movement causes an earthquake.

f When the pressure becomes too great, the plates suddenly slip.

4 Copy and complete the following sentences about observing stars.

Choose words from this list.

detection	galaxies
light	planets
pollution	sound

We can only see stars because they give out

…………………………………… .

People in cities find it hard to see stars because of light ………………….. .

Astronomers have found that some nearby stars have ……………… in orbit around them.

B2 Keeping healthy

Why study keeping healthy?

Good health is something everyone wants. Stories about keeping healthy are all around you. News reports tell us what to eat, how much to drink, and about new viruses and 'superbugs'. New evidence is reported every day. So the message about how to stay healthy often changes. It's often hard to know which advice is best.

What you already know

- Microorganisms can cause infections.
- White blood cells in the body fight disease.
- Antibiotics can kill some microorganisms but not viruses.
- Immunisation protects against some diseases.
- An unhealthy lifestyle causes some diseases.
- Scientists work together to investigate and reduce the spread of infectious disease.

Find out about

- how your body fights infections
- where 'superbugs' come from
- how new vaccines and drugs are developed and tested
- what causes a heart attack
- finding the causes of heart disease
- how your body balances water.

The Science

Some diseases are caused by harmful microorganisms. If you are infected, your body has amazing ways of fighting back. Vaccines and drugs can help you survive many diseases. Doctors are always trying to develop new ones. But your lifestyle may also put you at risk of disease.

Ideas about Science

So, which health reports are reliable? Knowing about correlation, cause, and peer review will help you decide. How should you use vaccines and drugs? There are arguments about right and wrong (ethics) that you can consider.

Find out about

- ✓ **how some microorganisms make you ill**
- ✓ **how bacteria reproduce**
- ✓ **infections**

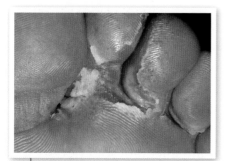

The fungus that causes athlete's foot grows on the skin.

Everyone has some health problems during their lives. Usually these are minor – like a cold. But some illnesses may be life-threatening, like heart disease or cancer.

There are lots of reasons for feeling ill. In the doctor's waiting room:

- the man with the painful knee has arthritis
- the man having his monthly check-up has had heart disease.

None of these conditions can be passed on to other people. But the other patients all have **infectious** diseases. Infections can be passed from one person to another.

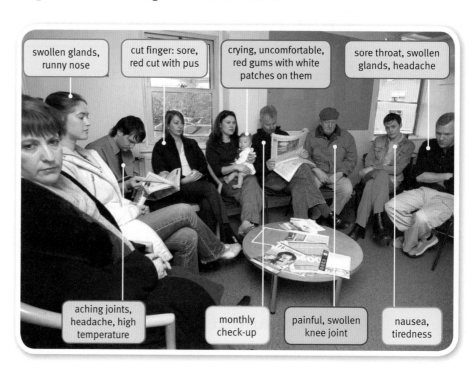

swollen glands, runny nose

cut finger: sore, red cut with pus

crying, uncomfortable, red gums with white patches on them

sore throat, swollen glands, headache

aching joints, headache, high temperature

monthly check-up

painful, swollen knee joint

nausea, tiredness

Questions

1 Name three types of microorganism that can cause disease.

2 Write down two different diseases caused by each type of microorganism you have named.

3 Explain two ways that microorganisms make you feel ill.

Passing it on

Infections are caused by some **microorganisms** (MOs) that invade the body. Microorganisms are **viruses**, **bacteria**, and **fungi**.

Why do you feel ill?

Disease microorganisms get inside your body and reproduce. This makes you feel ill. **Symptoms** can be caused by:

- damage done to your cells when the microorganisms reproduce
- poisons (toxins) made by the microorganisms.

Microorganisms

Microorganisms are very small. To see bacteria you need a microscope. Viruses are even smaller. They are measured in nanometres, and one nanometre is only one millionth of a millimetre.

	Virus	Bacterium	Fungus
Size	20–300 nm	1000–5000 nm	50 000+nm
Appearance	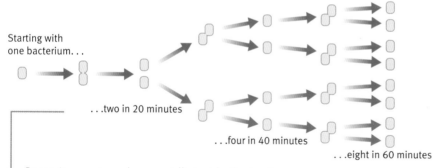		
Examples of diseases caused	flu, polio, common cold, AIDS, measles	tonsillitis, tuberculosis, plague, cystitis	athlete's foot, thrush, ringworm

Microbe attack!

Microorganisms are everywhere. But most of the time you stay fit and healthy. This is because:

- most microorganisms do not cause human diseases
- your body has barriers that keep most microorganisms out.

Jolene's finger

Jolene cut her finger when she was gardening. She didn't wash it quickly, so bacteria on her skin and in the soil invaded her body. Once inside they started to reproduce.

Starting with one bacterium. . .

. . .two in 20 minutes

. . .four in 40 minutes

. . .eight in 60 minutes

Bacteria can reproduce rapidly inside the body.

Each bacterium splits into two new ones. These grow for a short time before splitting again. To reproduce, bacteria need warmth, nutrients, and moisture. If conditions are right they can split every 20 minutes.

> It was just a small cut, so I ignored it. By the time I went to bed it was a bit sore and red. Now it's all swollen and shiny. It really hurts.

Questions

4 What are ideal conditions for bacteria to reproduce?

5 Three harmful bacteria get into a cut. How many might there be after three hours?

Summary box

- ✔ **Fungi, bacteria, and viruses are all microorganisms.**
- ✔ **Some invade your body and cause disease. The disease is infectious when it spreads to other people. When they reproduce and give off toxins, they make you feel ill; you have symptoms.**

Find out about

- ✔ **how white blood cells fight infection**
- ✔ **how you become immune to a disease**

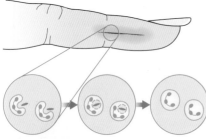

Jolene's body responds by sending more blood to the area.

White blood cells surround the bacteria and digest them.

The battle for Jolene's finger

Conditions inside Jolene's body are ideal for the bacteria. But they don't have everything their own way.

The redness and swelling in Jolene's finger is called inflammation. Extra blood is being sent to the wounded area, carrying with it the body's main defenders – the **white blood cells**. One type of white blood cell surrounds the bacteria and **digests** them.

The worn-out white blood cells, dead bacteria, and broken cells collect as pus. So redness and pus show that your body is fighting infection. As the bacteria are killed, the inflammation and pus get less until the tissue heals completely.

Your body's army – fighting infection

The parts of your body that fight infections are called your **immune system**. White blood cells are an important part of your immune system.

How antibodies work

All cells have markers on their outsides. These are called antigens. These are unique to that type of cell. A microorganism, invading the body, has foreign antigens. White blood cells make chemicals called **antibodies**. These stick to the foreign antigen markers. This helps to destroy the microorganism.

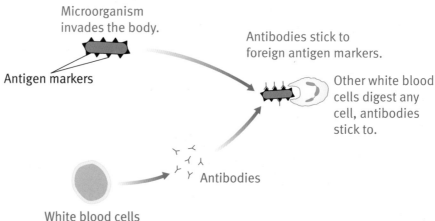

Microorganism invades the body.

Antigen markers

Antibodies stick to foreign antigen markers.

Other white blood cells digest any cell, antibodies stick to.

Antibodies

White blood cells

One type of white blood cell makes antibodies to label microorganisms. A different type digests the microorganisms.

Questions

1 Explain two ways that white blood cells protect the body from invading microorganisms. You could do this with a diagram.

2 Write down one sentence to describe the job of the immune system.

Why do I get ill?

The **antigens** on every microorganism are different. So your body has to make a different antibody for each new kind of microorganism. This takes a few days, so you get ill before your body has destroyed the invaders.

This doesn't really matter for diseases like a cold. But for more serious diseases this is a problem. The disease could kill a person before their body has time to destroy the microorganisms.

Antibiotics

In most cases the body will overcome invading bacteria. Keeping the cut clean and using antiseptic is usually enough treatment.

But Jolene's cut is quite deep, so her doctor gives her a course of **antibiotics**. These are chemicals that kill bacteria and fungi.

Different antibiotics affect different bacteria or fungi. Antibiotics are a type of **antimicrobial**. Antimicrobials are chemicals that can kill bacteria, fungi, and viruses.

Everybody needs antibodies – not antibiotics!

A bad cold is something we've all had. And there's not usually much sympathy – 'What's all the fuss about? It's just a cold!'

Natalie has been ill for a few days. Her doctor explains that he won't be giving her any antibiotics. Her cold is caused by a virus. Antibiotics cannot treat viruses. Natalie's own body is fighting the infection by itself.

Fighting the virus

Natalie's neck glands are swollen. Millions of new white blood cells are being made there. These white blood cells are fighting the virus in her body.

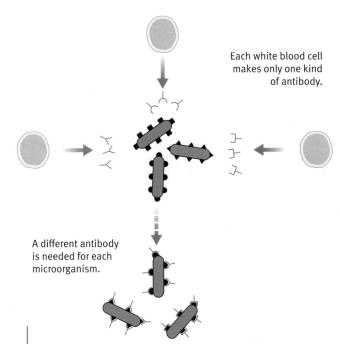

Each white blood cell makes only one kind of antibody.

A different antibody is needed for each microorganism.

Only the correctly shaped antibody can attach to each kind of microorganism.

Question

3 Why are antibiotics not given to patients infected with a virus?

Questions

4 Draw a flowchart to explain how you can become immune to chickenpox.

5 Write a few sentences to explain to Natalie why she will never be immune to catching colds.

Why do you get some diseases just once?

Once your body has made an antibody your body can react faster. Some of the white blood cells that make the antibody stay in your blood. These are called **memory cells**. If the same microorganism invades again, these white blood cells recognise it. They reproduce very quickly and start making the right antibody. This means that the body reacts much faster the second time you meet a particular microorganism. Your body destroys the invaders before they make you feel ill. So you are **immune** to that disease.

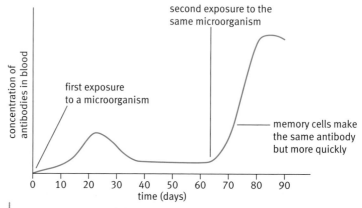

A person is infected twice by a disease microorganism. Their white blood cells make antibodies much faster the second time.

Not another one!

Natalie's cold soon got better. She had only been back at school for about three weeks before she caught another one. If you have an illness like chickenpox, you are very unlikely to catch it again. This is because you are immune. So why do we catch an average of three to five colds every year?

The problem is that there are hundreds of different cold viruses. So every cold you catch is caused by a different virus. To make things worse, viruses change. The markers on their surface change too. The antibody that worked last time will no longer match the marker. Your body needs to make a different antibody to fight the virus. This is why we suffer the symptoms of a cold all over again.

Find out about

- ✔ how vaccines work
- ✔ deciding if vaccines are safe to use

Age	Diseases protected against by childhood vaccinations
2, 3, and 4 months	DTB-Hib (diphtheria, tetanus, whooping cough, polio and Hib (pneumonia and meningitis)) Pneumococcal infection Meningitis C
13 months	MMR (measles, mumps, and rubella)
3–5 years	Diphtheria, tetanus, whooping cough and polio MMR
Girls aged 12–13 years	Cervical cancer
13–18 years	Diphtheria, tetanus, polio

Many childhood diseases are very rare in the UK because of vaccination programmes.

In the UK we are lucky to be able to get medicines for many diseases. But it would be even better not to catch a disease in the first place. **Vaccinations** aim to do just that.

How vaccines work

Vaccinations make use of the body's own defence system. They kick-start your white blood cells into making antibodies. So you become immune to a disease without having to catch it first.

Small amounts of disease microorganisms are put into your body. Dead or inactive forms are used so you don't get the disease itself. Sometimes just parts of the microorganisms are used.

White blood cells recognise the foreign microorganisms. They make the right antibodies to stick to the microorganisms.

The antibodies make the microorganisms clump together. Other white blood cells digest the clump.

Your body stores some of the white blood cells (memory cells). If you meet the real disease microorganism, the antibodies you need are made very quickly.

The microorganisms are destroyed before they can make you ill. (Not to scale)

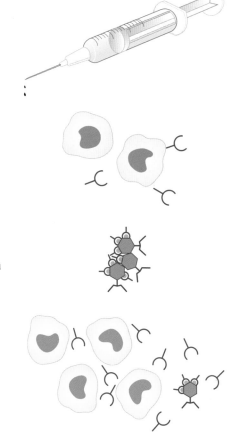

How vaccines work.

Questions

1 What is a vaccine made of?

2 Describe how a vaccine can stop you from catching an infectious disease.

Vaccinating children means that they are very unlikely to catch the disease.

Are vaccines safe?

Any medical treatment you have should do two things:

- improve your health
- be safe to use.

Vaccines can improve your health by protecting you from disease. They are tested to make sure that they are safe to use. But remember, no action is ever completely safe. People are genetically different, so they react differently to medical treatments, including vaccines.

Doctors decide that a treatment is safe to use when:

- the risk of serious harmful effects is very small
- the benefits outweigh any risk.

Why does the government encourage vaccinations?

Doctors encourage parents to have their children vaccinated at an early age. In the UK there are vaccination programmes for some diseases, such as measles. This means that few people suffer from these diseases. Parents have to balance the possible harm from the disease against the risk of side-effects from the vaccine.

- Almost no-one who has a vaccine notices any harmful effects.
- MMR vaccine has a mild effect (3 in every 10 000 children) or produces a serious allergic reaction (1 in every million children).
- Some children who catch measles are left severely disabled (1 in every 4000 cases).
- Measles can be fatal (1 in 100 000 cases).

For society as a whole, vaccination is the best option. But for each parent it is a difficult choice. They have to decide what is best for their child. People often perceive the risk of vaccination to be greater than the risk of measles. It is important that people have clear and unbiased information to help them make their decision.

Question

3 Explain why a vaccine can never be 'completely safe'.

Smallpox

Smallpox was a terrible disease. In the 1950s there were 50 million cases worldwide. This fell to 10–15 million cases by 1967 because of vaccination.

In 1967 the World Health Organisation began a campaign to wipe out smallpox. People across the world were vaccinated. The last natural case of smallpox was in 1977.

Vaccinations by law?

Governments make decisions about who should be offered vaccinations based on an asessment of risk and benefit. All children are offered the measles vaccine. There is enough measles vaccine for every child in the UK. Everyone could be vaccinated. Then there would be a much lower risk of any child catching the disease.

Very occasionally vaccination doesn't work. So a very few children would still get the disease. The law could say that everyone has to have a measles vaccination. But it doesn't. Society does not think it is right to force anyone to have this particular treatment. There is a difference between what *can* be done with science, and what people think *should* be done.

Vaccination and where you live

People in poorer countries are more likely to live in bad, overcrowded conditions. This means they catch diseases more easily and will suffer more. This is because they may:
- be weaker because of a poor diet or other diseases
- not be able to get medicines and other healthcare.

So people from poorer communities may decide to have vaccinations. People in better-off communities may not.

Smallpox killed every fourth victim. It left many survivors blind and scarred.

Some people are concerned about the safety of vaccines for their children. But for many, the decision is easy.

Summary box
✓ **Vaccination is when you get a vaccine. Vaccines are dead or inactive forms of a disease microorganism. So you don't get the disease. Your body still makes antibodies. The memory cells can make antibodies very quickly if you are infected with the real disease microorganism.**

Questions

4 Explain why you don't have to have a measles vaccination in the UK.

5 Give two reasons why people in different parts of the world may feel differently about having vaccinations.

Find out about

- ✔ **where 'superbugs' come from**
- ✔ **how you can help fight them**

Antimicrobial chemicals kill microorganisms (fungi, bacteria, viruses). Bleach is an antimicrobial chemical. It will kill fungi, bacteria, and viruses.

Antifungal chemicals kill fungi. Antibiotics from the doctor only kill bacteria. They do not kill viruses.

The first antibiotics

The Ancient Egyptians may have been the first people to use antibiotics. They used to put mouldy bread onto infected wounds. Scientists now know that the mould is a fungus. It makes penicillin. In the 1940s scientists started to grow the fungus. They wanted to make larger amounts of penicillin.

The bugs fight back

To begin with, penicillin was called a 'wonder drug'. Before the 1940s, bacterial infections killed millions of people every year. Now they could be cured by antibiotics. Antibiotics were also used to treat animals. They were even added to animal feed. This stopped farm animals from getting infections.

But within ten years, one type of bacterium was no longer killed by penicillin. It had become resistant. New antibiotics were discovered, but each time resistant bacteria soon developed. Now we have 'superbugs'. They are resistant to all known antibiotics, except one. How long that will last, we don't know. Fungi can also cause infections. Thrush is caused by a fungus. Fungi can also become resistant to commonly used antimicrobial chemicals.

Antibiotics are made naturally by bacteria and fungi. They destroy other microorganisms. The fungus growing on this bread makes penicillin.

Not finishing a course of antibiotics can result in antibiotic-resistant bacteria.

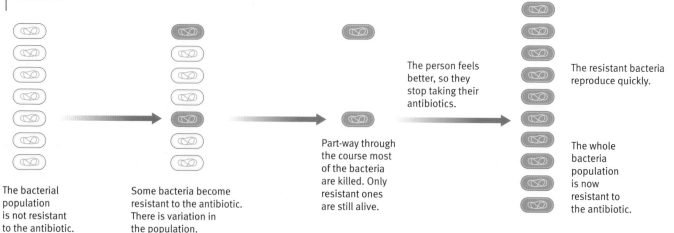

The bacterial population is not resistant to the antibiotic.

Some bacteria become resistant to the antibiotic. There is variation in the population.

Part-way through the course most of the bacteria are killed. Only resistant ones are still alive.

The person feels better, so they stop taking their antibiotics.

The resistant bacteria reproduce quickly.

The whole bacteria population is now resistant to the antibiotic.

Why are superbugs developing so quickly?

Two things increase the risk of **antibiotic-resistant** superbugs developing:

- people taking antibiotics they don't really need
- people not finishing their course of antibiotics.

If you are given antibiotics, you should take the whole course. It is then likely that all the harmful bacteria will be killed.

If you stop taking the antibiotics because you feel better, some microorganisms may survive. These will be the ones most resistant to the antibiotic. They will reproduce. A population of antibiotic-resistant bacteria soon grows.

How can we stop the superbugs?

Scientists cannot stop resistant bacteria and resistant fungi from developing. It is part of a natural process.

Scientists can develop new antibiotics and other antimicrobial chemicals. But there are other ways of tackling the problem:

- have better hygiene in hospitals to reduce the risk of infection
- only prescribe antibiotics when a person really needs them
- make sure people understand why it is important to finish all their antibiotics (unless side-effects develop).

New drugs in strange places?

Scientists are always looking for sources of new drugs. For example, crocodile blood might be the source of the next type of antibiotics.

A chemical found in crocodile blood stops bacteria reproducing. Crocodiles bite each other's legs off but they don't die of infections. A scientist wondered why this was and discovered the chemical.

Crocodile blood could be the source of important new antibacterial drugs.

Questions

1 What are antibiotic-resistant bacteria?

2 Describe two things that you can do to reduce the risk of antibiotic-resistant bacteria developing.

Summary box

✓ Bacteria and fungi can become resistant to antimicrobials. Then they are no longer killed. Bacteria may become **antibiotic resistant**.

✓ You can help prevent this by:

- only taking antibiotics when you really need them
- finishing the course.

Find out about

- ✓ **how new drugs are developed**
- ✓ **how they are tested**

From painkillers to vaccines, antibiotics to antihistamines, medicines are part of everyday life.

Sian is a cancer research scientist.

Most of us take medicines prescribed by our doctor. We don't ask too many questions. But what if you could ask the scientist who developed the medicine some questions?

Is it safe?

How much should I take?

Are there any side-effects?

How did you discover the drug?

Has it been tested properly?

Scientists are trying to develop new drugs. Developing a new drug takes years of research, and lots of money. A successful discovery can improve human health. Drug companies may also make large profits.

A scientist explains how a new drug is developed:

> First we study the disease. We have to understand how it makes people ill. We can then work out what we need to treat it. For example, we could be looking for a chemical to kill a microorganism.
>
> We search through many natural sources to find possible chemicals. Then we test our ideas with computer models of the molecules.
>
> When we find a chemical that could work, there are many more tests.
>
> Being able to make lots of the drug easily is also important. Only a few possible drugs get through all these stages.

Stage 1: human cells

Early tests are done on human cells grown in a laboratory. Scientists try out different concentrations of a possible new drug. They test it on different types of body cells with the disease. These tests check how well the chemical works against the disease – how effective it is. They also tell scientists how safe the drug is for the cells.

Drugs are tested on cells in the laboratory.

Stage 2: animal tests

The drug has passed tests on human cells in the laboratory. Scientists now carry out animal trials. These are to make sure that the drug works well in whole animals.

> If animal trials go well, we apply for a patent. It costs a lot of money to develop a new drug. If we have a patent, no other company can sell the medicine for 20 years. But clinical trials take many years. So we often only have about 10 years when we're the only people making the drug.

Stage 3: clinical trials

If the drug passes animal trials then scientists can test it on people. These tests are called **human trials** or **clinical trials**. Scientists carry out human trials on healthy volunteers to test for safety. They then carry out trials on people with the disease. These trials test that the drug is safe and shows how well it works – how effective it is.

Some people think that it is wrong to test drugs on animals. The British Medical Association (BMA) believes that experiments on animals are still necessary but we should use other methods whenever possible.

Questions

1 Copy and complete the table:

Stage	Testing	To find out
One	Drug is tested on human cells grown in the laboratory.	• how safe the drug is for human cells • how well it works against the disease.
Two		
Three		

2 Developing a new drug is usually very expensive. Suggest why.

Summary box

✓ **New drugs are found in chemicals from natural sources.**
✓ **The drugs have many tests using human cells, and animals. Finally (stage three), they are tested on people in human or clinical trials.**

Clinical trials – crunch time

Five years ago Anna had breast cancer. Luckily her treatment worked and she recovered. Now her doctor has asked Anna to take part in the trial of a new drug. Hopefully it will reduce the risk of the cancer coming back.

Anna talks to her doctor:
The problem is I won't know if I'm getting any treatment or not. Could I be risking my health? I know the trial could help people in the future – but what about me? Can you tell me if I will be given the real drug or not?

Before the trial Anna would sign a patient consent form. She signs it to say that all of her questions have been answered. She can also leave the trial at any time. Anyone taking part in a drug trial must give their 'informed consent'.

What treatment would Anna get?

People who agree to take part in this trial will be put randomly into one of two groups. Having **random** groups is very important. It makes sure the results of the study are reliable.

One group of people in the trial will be given the new drug, another group will not. This is the **control** group. The results from both groups will be compared.

What treatment will the control group have?

In most clinical trials the control group are given the treatment that is currently being used. Scientists compare the results from both groups. This shows whether the new treatment is an improvement.

Placebos

In Anna's trial, the drug being tested is a new treatment. The control group will be given a **placebo**. This looks exactly like the real treatment but has no drug in it. Using a placebo in a clinical trial is very rare.

Question

3 Explain why drug trials must be random.

Human trials – ethical questions

If Anna takes the placebo her risk of cancer returning would not increase. Taking the new drug may bring other risks. But her doctor will be looking out for any harmful effects. The new drug may increase her chance of staying well.

It may seem unfair that the control group could miss out on any benefits of the new drug. But remember that not all drugs pass clinical trials. Proper testing is needed to find out if a new drug has real benefits. Tests also give doctors data about the risk of unwanted harmful effects.

- If the trial shows that the risks are too great it will be stopped.
- If the trial shows that the drug has benefits it will be offered to the control group straight away.

Trials without a control group

In rare cases a new drug is given to all the patients in a trial. This happens when there is no other treatment. Patients are so ill that doctors are sure they will not recover from the illness. It is possible that the new drug could extend their lifespan or be a cure. This outweighs the risk of the drug harming them. No-one is given a placebo. It would be wrong not to offer the hope of the new drug to all the patients. Penicillin is one example where this happened.

Questions

4 Describe a situation in which it would be wrong to use placebos in a trial.

5 What do you think Anna should do? Explain why you think this.

Summary box

✓ **In human trials people are put into one of two groups. One group has the new treatment. The control group do not have the new treatment. They have the current treatment or a placebo. A placebo looks like the new drug treatment but has no drug in it.**

Find out about

- ✔ **your heart**
- ✔ **heart attacks**
- ✔ **looking after your heart**
- ✔ **measuring your heart**

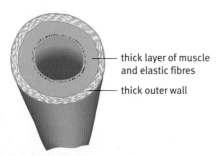

— thick layer of muscle and elastic fibres

— thick outer wall

Arteries take blood from the heart to your body. The thick outer walls can withstand the high pressure created by the pumping heart.

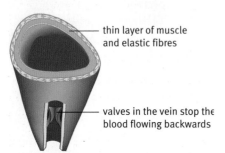

— thin layer of muscle and elastic fibres

— valves in the vein stop the blood flowing backwards

Veins bring blood back to the heart. The thin layer of muscle and elastic fibres allows the vein to be squashed when you move. This pushes the blood back to the heart.

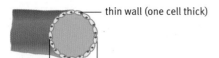

— thin wall (one cell thick)

5–20 μm diameter

Capillaries take blood to and from tissues. The very thin walls allow oxygen and food to diffuse into cells and waste from cells.

Oliver is 45 years old. He suffered a serious heart attack. He was very lucky to survive. Now he wants to try and make sure it doesn't happen again.

What your heart does

Your heart is a bag of muscle in your body. When you are sitting down it beats about 70 beats every minute. It has four chambers. The upper two receive blood. The lower two have thick muscular walls to pump the blood.

The right lower chamber pumps blood to your lungs. The left lower chamber pumps blood to the rest of your body. The heart is described as a double pump.

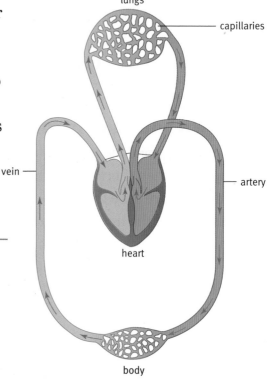

lungs

capillaries

vein

artery

heart

body

Blood flow around the body.

Keeping your heart working

The heart needs energy to keep going. Blood brings oxygen and food to cells. Cells use these materials for a supply of energy. Heart muscle cells must have their own blood supply.

Questions

1 Explain why your heart is known as a 'double pump'.

2 Explain why arteries have thick muscular walls.

3 Explain why heart cells need a good blood supply.

What is a heart attack?

Sometimes fat can build up in the coronary arteries. A blood clot can form on the lump of fat. This could block an artery. Some heart muscle is starved of oxygen. The cells start to die. This is a heart attack.

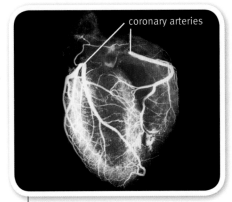
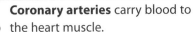

Coronary arteries carry blood to the heart muscle.

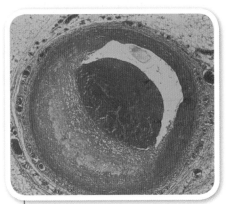

Fat build-up in a coronary artery.

I went cold and clammy, covered in sweat. And the pain – it was in my chest, down my arm, up my neck, and into my jaw. I woke up in intensive care. I was lucky – only a small part of my heart was damaged.

How serious is the problem of heart disease?

Heart disease is any illness of the heart, for example a blocked coronary artery and a heart attack.

In the UK 230 000 people a year have a heart attack. Heart disease is more common in the UK than in countries with less industry. This is because people in the UK do less exercise. Most people travel in cars and have machines to do many jobs. A typical UK diet is high in fat.

What causes heart disease?

Heart attacks are not normally caused by an infection. Your **genes** and your **lifestyle** affect whether you suffer a heart attack. There isn't one cause of heart attacks. There are many different **risk factors**. Heart disease and some cancers, like lung cancer, are known as **lifestyle diseases**.

Questions

4 How can too much fat in a person's diet lead to a heart attack?

5 Heart disease is more common in the UK than in non-industrialised countries. Suggest why.

Summary box

- ✔ **Your heart pumps blood to your lungs and your body.**
- ✔ **Arteries take blood away from the heart.**
- ✔ **Veins return blood to the heart.**
- ✔ **Capillaries take blood to and from tissue.**
- ✔ **A heart attack happens when a coronary artery is blocked and blood cannot get to part of the heart.**
- ✔ **Risk factors for heart disease can be due to your genes and your lifestyle.**

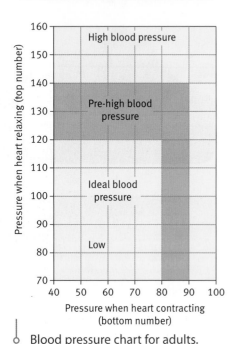

Blood pressure chart for adults.

Summary box

✓ **You can change lifestyle factors to reduce your risk of heart disease.**

✓ **Recording your blood pressure or your pulse rate measures the health of your heart.**

Is Oliver at risk of another heart attack?

Oliver's family has a history of coronary heart disease. He is overweight, smokes, and often eats high-fat, high-salt food. This diet has given Oliver high blood pressure and high cholesterol levels. Taking drugs like cannabis and Ecstasy also increase his heart rate and blood pressure. These factors increase his risk of a heart attack. A stressful job would also increase the risk. They are all **lifestyle factors**.

But Oliver can do something about these things. Oliver's doctor has given him advice about reducing his risk. See the 'Healthy Heart leaflet' that he was given.

Oliver will now have regular check-ups. His doctor will measure his **blood pressure** and **pulse rate**.

Monitoring the heart

Pulse rate measures how hard your heart is working. Your pulse is taken on the inside of your wrist. You can measure the number of beats per minute (bpm).

Blood pressure measurements record the pressure of the blood on the walls of the artery. It is recorded as two numbers, for example 120/80. The top number is the pressure when the heart is contracting. The bottom number is when the heart is relaxing. There is a range of 'normal' blood pressure. People differ in height, weight, lifestyle, and gender. All these factors influence what will be normal for that person.

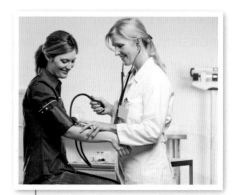

The doctor measures the blood pressure of a patient. High blood pressure can cause heart disease.

Questions

6 List four lifestyle factors that increase a person's risk of heart disease.

7 Suggest some ways that Oliver could get exercise into his daily life without going to the gym.

Causes of disease – how do we know?

G

It is easier for doctors to find the cause of infectious diseases. The microorganism is in the patient's body. It is harder to find the causes of lifestyle diseases, like heart disease or cancer.

Health warning in 1971.

Health warning in 2003.

Find out about

- how scientists identify risk factors for lifestyle diseases
- the evidence needed to prove a causal link

Smoking and lung cancer

In 1971, evidence showed a link – a **correlation** – between smoking and lung cancer. Health warnings were put on cigarette packets. In 2003 the message was made much stronger. How did doctors prove that smoking *caused* lung cancer?

An early clue

Richard Doll and Austin Bradford Hill were two scientists. In 1950 they compared people in hospital with lung cancer to people in hospital for other reasons. There were smokers in both groups. But there were more smokers in the lung cancer group.

This data showed a correlation between smoking and lung cancer. Doll and Hill suggested that smoking caused lung cancer. But a correlation doesn't always mean that one thing causes another.

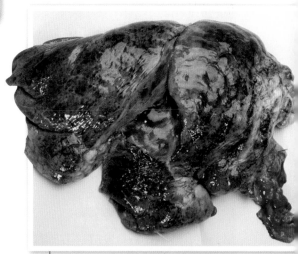

Lung tissue blackened by tar from cigarette smoke.

Cigarettes smoked per day	Number of cases of cancer per 100 000 men
0 – 10	55
11 – 20	210
21 – 30	460
31 – 40	775

The data shows how the number of cigarettes smoked affects the number of cases of lung cancer in men.

Questions

1 Write down one example of correlation.

2 Draw a graph to show how the number of cigarettes smoked affects the number of cases of lung cancer in men.

Questions

3 Explain what happens during 'peer review'.

4 Explain why scientists think it is important that a scientific claim can be repeated by other scientists.

Summary box

✓ **A correlation** between two things is when one factor changes another one does too. One may not cause the other to change. If it does, we call it a **causal link**.

✓ Scientists use **epidemiological** studies to find out what the risk factors are for lifestyle diseases. They use large samples of people. These match apart from the factor being tested.

✓ **Genetic studies** find out how much the risk of getting a disease is down to your genes.

Before 1920 lung cancer was very rare. As smoking became more popular with men, the number of lung cancer cases rose. This happened later for women, because very few women smoked until after World War II.

How reliable was the claim?

Doll and Hill published their results in a medical journal. This is called 'peer review'. Other scientists look at the data and how it was gathered. They look for faults. If they can't find them, then the claim is more reliable.

The claim is even more reliable if other scientists can produce data that suggests the same conclusions.

A major study

In 1951 Doll and Hill followed the health of more than 40000 British doctors for over 50 years. The results were published in 2004. They showed that:

- smokers die on average 10 years younger than non-smokers
- stopping smoking at any age reduces this risk.

The last piece of the puzzle – an explanation

Lung cancer rates in the USA rose sharply after 1920. The same pattern was seen in the UK.

But cigarette companies did not agree that smoking caused lung cancer. They said other factors could cause the increase in lung cancer, for example, more air pollution from motor vehicles.

In 1998 scientists discovered *how* chemicals in cigarette smoke damage cells in the lung, causing cancer. This confirmed that smoking *causes* cancer.

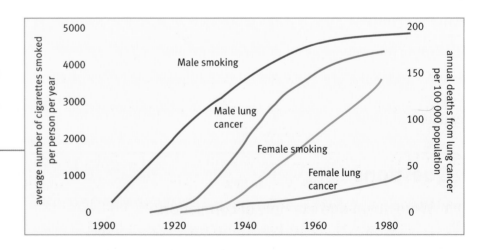

What makes a good study?

Studies of diseases, using large numbers of people, are called **epidemiological studies**. They often look for the different risk factors for a disease, for example, heart disease.

These studies are often in the news. You may want to use this information to make a decision about your own health. So it's important to know if the study has been done well and how it's reported.

How many people were involved in the study?

A good study usually looks at a large sample of people. This means that the results are less likely to be affected by chance.

In the USA a long-term study looked at over 13 000 people. This study found all the known major risk factors for heart disease.

How well matched are the people in the study?

Health studies sometimes compare two groups of people. For example, a study might compare people who exercise with people who do not. It is important to **match** the people in the two groups as closely as possible. Other factors apart from the one being tested, such as age and sex, should be similar.

How big is the risk?

Imagine a headline like "Risk of disease doubles." It is important to know the size of the risk. If one person in a million will be affected, a doubling makes it only two in a million. The risk is still small.

Genetic studies of heart disease

The Wellcome Trust carried out a **genetic study**. They wanted to know which genes added to the risk of heart disease. The research team studied the genes of 2000 people with heart disease and 3000 healthy controls.

In 2007 they reported that six common alleles are linked with heart disease. A person who carries a 'risk' allele is more likely to develop heart disease. But they can still reduce their risk. They can adopt a healthy lifestyle, monitor their blood pressure and cholesterol levels, and take medication.

Scientists look at the health of lots of people. This can show them risk factors for different diseases.

Questions

5 Name one factor that increases a person's risk of heart disease.

6 Suggest two things you should look for when deciding whether a study was well planned.

Find out about

- ✓ **homeostasis**
- ✓ **why it is important**
- ✓ **control systems**

Running has made this athlete hot. His body is sweating more to cool back down. This is an example of homeostasis.

Inside your cells thousands of chemical reactions are happening every second. These reactions are keeping you alive. But for your cells to work properly they need certain conditions. Keeping conditions inside your body the same is called **homeostasis**.

Homeostasis is not easy – lots of things have to happen for your body to 'stay the same'. Look at just a few of the changes happening every second.

Your body works hard to:

- keep the correct levels of water and salt
- control the amounts of nutrients
- get rid of toxic waste products, for example carbon dioxide and urea.

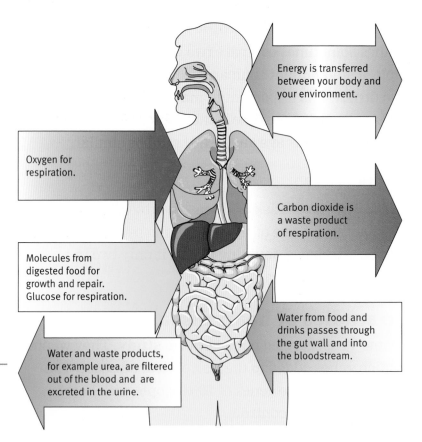

Energy is transferred between your body and your environment.

Oxygen for respiration.

Carbon dioxide is a waste product of respiration.

Molecules from digested food for growth and repair. Glucose for respiration.

Water from food and drinks passes through the gut wall and into the bloodstream.

Water and waste products, for example urea, are filtered out of the blood and are excreted in the urine.

Some of the inputs and outputs that are going on all the time in your body.

Control systems

Control systems keep a steady state in your body. They work in a similar way to artificial control systems.

All control systems have:
- **receptors**, which detect the stimuli (the change)
- **processing centres**, which receive the information and coordinates a response
- **effectors**, which produce an automatic response.

How does an incubator work?

Premature babies cannot control their temperature. So they are put in incubators. The incubator is an artificial control system.

An incubator has a temperature sensor, a thermostat with a switch, and a heater. If the temperature in an incubator falls too low, the heater is switched on. The temperature goes up. When the temperature is high enough, the heater is switched off.

What about your body?

Some of the temperature control in your body is automatic too. For example, you do not consciously decide to shiver when you are cold. Water control is also automatic. You do not decide to feel thirsty or to make less urine.

Your body has its own control systems. For example, when you are cold, receptors in your skin send signals along nerves to your brain. Your brain is the processing centre. It sends signals to effectors. In the case of cold, one type of effector is muscle. Muscles make you shiver. In other control systems, nerves or hormones take messages between receptors, the brain, and effectors.

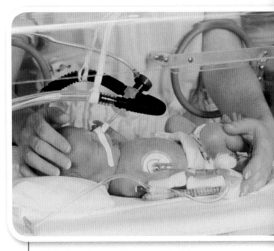

This incubator is an artificial control system. It is keeping this baby's temperature steady.

Summary box
- ✓ **Homeostasis is the body keeping conditions inside the same.**
- ✓ **Control systems have receptors, a processing centre and effectors.**

Questions

1 Explain what homeostasis means.

2 In an incubator, name:
   a a receptor
   b a processing centre
   c an effector.

3 In your body, name:
   a a receptor
   b a processing centre
   c an effector.

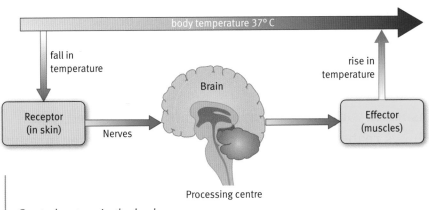

Control system in the body.

Water homeostasis

Make sure you drink enough water at school.

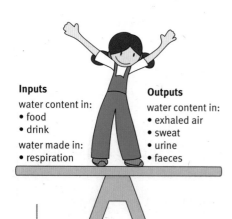

Inputs

water content in:
• food
• drink

water made in:
• respiration

Outputs

water content in:
• exhaled air
• sweat
• urine
• faeces

Water intake and water loss must balance for your body to work well.

Why water is important

Water homeostasis is keeping a steady water level in your body. This is very important. You need to drink enough to stay healthy. Scientists carried out experiments on students to see how much they should drink. They showed that being able to drink water in the classroom:

• increased students' concentration time
• improved test results.

Your body balances your water inputs and water outputs. The diagram below shows how you gain and lose water.

What do your kidneys do?

Your **kidneys** control the water balance in your body. They do this by changing the amount of urine that you make. When you are hot, you lose a lot of water in sweat. So your kidneys make a smaller volume of urine. Your urine will be more concentrated that day.

Your kidneys have two jobs:
• water homeostasis
• **excretion**.

Excretion is getting rid of toxic waste products. Chemical reactions in your cells produce these. These two jobs are linked. You use water to flush out waste products. Getting the water level in cells right is very important. It maintains the correct concentrations of chemicals for cell activity.

More about water balance

Remember that the concentration and volume of your urine varies. On cold days you probably make lots of pale-coloured urine. On hot days you make a smaller volume of darker, more concentrated urine.

All the parts of blood are in a watery liquid called blood plasma. If your blood plasma becomes concentrated, your kidneys reabsorb more water. You excrete less water in your urine. If your blood plasma has too much water, your kidneys reabsorb less water. You excrete more water in your urine.

The concentration of your blood can become higher than normal because of:

- sweating due to exercise or higher external temperature
- not drinking enough water
- eating salty food.

In these cases, your kidneys will reabsorb more water. You will make less urine.

Drugs and urine

Some drugs affect the amount of urine a person makes. **Alcohol** causes a greater volume of dilute urine to be produced and can make people very dehydrated.

Dehydration can cause dizziness, headaches, and tiredness. You may have problems with your kidneys, liver, joints, and muscles. Severe dehydration can cause low blood pressure, seizures, increased heart rate, and affect consciousness.

The drug **Ecstasy** has the opposite effect. It reduces the volume of urine a person makes. It may also affect the body's temperature control. Overheating may cause dehydration or lead to the person drinking too much water. The amount of water in the body can become dangerously high. This can also cause seizures. Ecstasy also increases blood pressure and heart rate. This increases the risk of a heart attack.

Dry air in aeroplanes can cause dehydration. Drinking alcohol can make the dehydration worse.

Questions

1 Copy and complete the table below to show what happens when the concentration of the blood plasma changes.

	Concentration of blood plasma falls	Concentration of blood plasma rises
Kidney reabsorb		
Urine volume		
Urine concentration		increases

2 Explain the effect Ecstasy has on water balance.

Summary box

- ✓ **Your kidneys balance the water level in your body.**
- ✓ **Your kidneys make more or less urine when the concentration of the blood plama changes.**
- ✓ **You excrete waste in your urine.**
- ✓ **Alcohol causes you to reabsorb less water. So you can become dehydrated.**
- ✓ **Ecstasy causes you to reabsorb more water. So water levels can become too high.**

Science Explanations

Keeping healthy involves maintaining a healthy lifestyle, avoiding infection, using medication when necessary, and our bodies maintaining a constant internal environment.

You should know:

- how microorganisms multiply rapidly in the human body, damaging cells and releasing toxins to produce disease symptoms
- how white blood cells produce antibodies, engulf, and digest microorganisms to destroy them
- how specific antibodies recognise different microorganisms
- how memory cells make specific antibodies rapidly if the body is re-infected, destroying the microorganisms; they provide the body with immunity
- how a safe form of a microorganism, called a vaccine, causes the body to produce antibodies
- that drugs and vaccines can never be completely safe because people are different genetically and react differently
- that antimicrobials are used to kill bacteria, fungi, and viruses; for example, antibiotics are effective against bacteria but not viruses
- how new drugs are tested on animals, human cells, and healthy volunteers, then ill people for safety and effectiveness
- why using placebos in human trials raises ethical issues
- that the circulatory system consists of the heart (a double pump with its own blood supply), arteries, veins, and capillaries
- how fatty deposits in blood vessels can trigger heart disease
- how genetic and lifestyle factors, such as diet, exercise, stress, smoking, and misuse of drugs, can cause heart disease
- how to measure a person's pulse rate
- that high blood pressure may indicate heart disease
- how nervous and hormonal systems help maintain homeostasis
- how body systems detect stimuli with receptors, coordinate responses with a processing centre, and produce a response with effectors
- how kidneys regulate water balance by producing dilute or concentrated urine
- how drugs, such as Ecstasy, and alcohol affect the volume of urine produced.

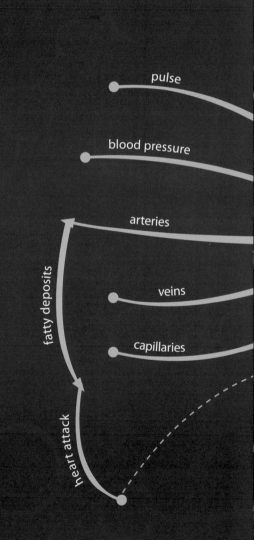

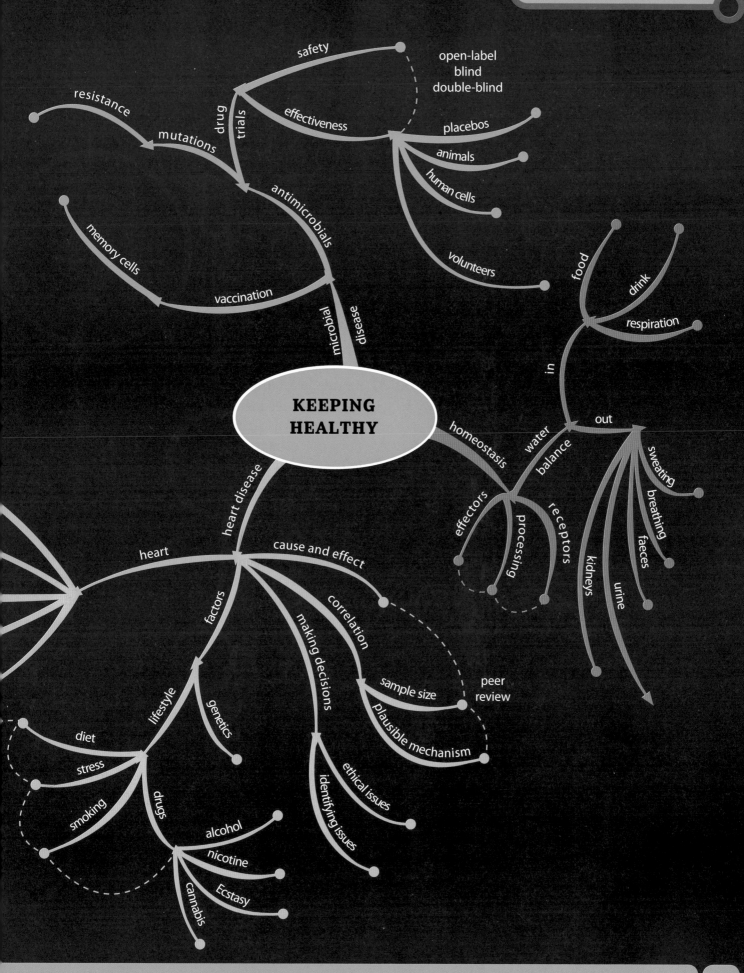

KEEPING HEALTHY

safety

open-label
blind
double-blind

trials

drug

effectiveness

placebos

animals

human cells

volunteers

resistance

mutations

antimicrobials

memory cells

vaccination

microbial

disease

food

drink

respiration

in

homeostasis

water

out

balance

sweating

effectors

processing

receptors

breathing

faeces

kidneys

urine

heart disease

heart

cause and effect

correlation

factors

making decisions

sample size

peer review

plausible mechanism

lifestyle

genetics

diet

stress

smoking

drugs

alcohol

nicotine

Ecstasy

cannabis

ethical issues

identifying issues

Ideas about Science

This module provides opportunities to develop your understanding of cause–effect explanations, how scientists share their ideas, and how decisions about scientific issues are made, including ideas about risk.

If an outcome increases or decreases as an input variable increases there is a correlation between the two. You should be able to:

- suggest and explain an example of a correlation from everyday life, such as an increase in the number of cigarettes smoked increases the risk of developing heart disease
- identify a correlation when given data such as text, a graph, or a table
- understand that a correlation does not prove a cause and that the outcome might be caused by some other factor, for example, icecream sales increase as hayfever increases, but icecream does not cause hayfever.

Scientists investigate claims that a factor increases the probability of an outcome, such as the link between smoking and heart disease by closely matching different groups of the population or choosing them randomly. You should be able to critically evaluate such studies by commenting on sample size and how well the samples are selected or matched.

Even when evidence exists that a factor is correlated to an outcome, scientists look for a causal mechanism. For example, smoking increases the effect of heart disease because of the effects of nicotine on the body. Nicotine is the mechanism.

Scientists report their claims to scientific conferences or scientific journals. This is so that other scientists can peer review the evidence and claims. This gives the claim credibility, especially when the findings have been replicated by another scientist.

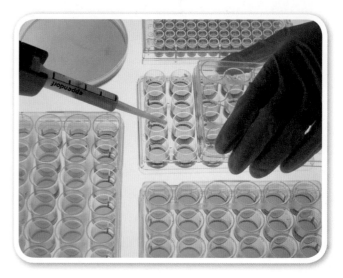

Some questions cannot be answered by science, for example, those involving values. You will need to be able to distinguish questions that can be answered by using a scientific approach from those that cannot, such as should vaccinations be compulsory?

When discussing these questions the benefits and the size of the perceived and measured risk must be considered.

Some forms of scientific work have ethical implications that some people will agree with and others will not. When an ethical issue is involved, you need to be able to:

- state clearly what the issue is
- summarise the different views that people might hold.

When discussing ethical issues, you will need to identify examples of common arguments based on the ideas that:

- the right decision is the one that leads to the best outcome for the majority of the people involved
- certain actions are right or wrong whatever the consequences; wrong actions can never be justified.

Review Questions

1 Microorganisms sometimes invade our bodies. We can protect ourselves by having a vaccination. This contains dead organisms. The statements below describe how vaccination helps to protect us from disease-causing microorganisms.

Place them in the correct order.

a Antibodies destroy disease-causing microorganisms.

b The body rapidly makes antibodies to the disease.

c The body slowly makes antibodies to the disease.

d The disease-causing microorganisms enter the body.

e We receive a vaccination against the disease.

2 New drugs are tested for effectiveness and safety. Explain the stages in the testing process.

3 Doctors have to make decisions about when to use placebos. Explain what placebos are and why they are used.

4 Kidneys regulate the amount of water present in the human body.

a i List the factors that affect water balance.

ii Explain how the kidneys balance water levels.

b What are the effects of:

i alcohol on the functioning of the kidney?

ii Ecstasy on the functioning of the kidney?

5 Eating a diet containing a lot of fatty food can increase the risk of heart disease.
Different people have different views about this.

Jane
I read that eating fatty foods will cause heart disease. But I believe scientists who say it will just increase my risk of developing heart disease.

Ranjit
My grandad ate fatty food all his life. He died of influenza at 83. Scientists look at lots of data before they conclude that a high-fat diet increases the risk of heart disease.

Peter
We only know that fatty foods can cause heart disease because many scientists have collected data. If there was only one study they would be less sure.

Stella
I am a food scientist. My findings are always checked by other scientists before they are published.

To answer these questions, you may use each person once, more than once, or not at all.

a Which person says that not having the results replicated by another scientist is a reason for questioning a scientific claim?

b Which person is suggesting that individual cases do not provide convincing evidence for or against a correlation?

c Which person is describing the process of peer review?

d Which **two** people are suggesting that factors might increase the chance of an outcome but not always lead to it?

C2 Material choices

Why study materials and their uses?

All the things we buy are made of 'stuff'. That stuff must come from somewhere. Before about 1900, virtually everything we used was made of materials that came from plants, animals, or rocks. Since then, people have discovered ways to make completely new materials. Materials are chosen for specific jobs because of their properties.

What you already know

- Chemicals can be elements, compounds, or mixtures.

- A mixture contains two or more elements or compounds that are mixed but are not chemically combined.

- Different chemicals and materials have different properties.

- Molecules are made of atoms.

- In a chemical reaction, atoms separate and recombine to form different chemicals.

Find out about

- the testing and measurement that helps people to make good choices when buying products

- the variety of polymers and plastics, and how they are used to meet our needs

- how nanotechnology is helping scientists to design new materials with a wide range of properties.

The Science

Scientists use their knowledge of molecules to explain why different materials behave in different ways. This means they can design new materials to meet a wide range of needs.

Ideas about Science

Scientists test products to check that they can do the job, are good value, and safe. You can use data from these tests when you buy a product. So you need to be able to judge whether or not the results can be trusted.

Products are made from a wide range of materials.

Choosing materials

We make items from a huge range of materials. We use:

- **ceramics** for mugs, plates, tiles, bricks, sinks, and toilets
- **metals** for an enormous number of products including aircraft, cars, pipes, wires, jewellery, and sports equipment
- **polymers** for making bags and clothes, window frames, and computers.

All these materials are chemicals. Some of the metals are pure chemicals, not mixed with anything else; most of the materials we use are **mixtures** of chemicals.

When a designer is deciding how to make a product they can choose which material to use according to which properties they require the finished item to have.

What is a material?

Sometimes words can have more than one meaning. The word 'material' can mean cloth or fabric, but to a scientist it means any sort of stuff you can use to make things from.

What are polymers?

All polymers have one thing in common. Their molecules are very long chains of atoms. This is true for **natural** polymers such as cotton, leather, and wool and for **synthetic** polymers such as polythene, nylon, and neoprene.

The newest fashion
CHOCOLATE SHOES

Glossy shoes with a perfect fit. No rubbing, no corns, making your feet comfy, tasty, and attractive. Just dip you feet in luxurious molten chocolate to form a close-fitting shoe in one of three gorgeous colours: milk, dark, or white.

Summary box
- ✓ Materials have different properties and are used for different things.
- ✓ Some materials are natural. Others are synthetic, made by people.
- ✓ Polymers are long-chain molecules.

Don't make shoes from chocolate

Of course chocolate shoes are a joke. Chocolate is not a good material for making shoes. Here are some reasons:
- chocolate would crack
- it would melt in warm weather
- dogs would follow you and lick your feet
- it would wear away too quickly
- it would leave a mess on the carpet.

Properties of materials for shoe-making

Any material chosen to make our shoes needs to be **flexible**. Chocolate is not. A material for making shoes also needs to be:
- hard wearing because you will walk on it
- waterproof
- a solid at room temperature
- elastic so it keeps its shape
- tough so that it won't crack when it bends.

Most of the materials used to make shoes are polymers.

Questions

2 Leather is a natural polymer. Suggest which properties of leather make it a good material for smart shoes. Use the list of 'Properties of materials for shoe-making' to help you.

3 Steel is a metal. Steel is sometimes used to make toecaps for work boots, but it is not used to make the whole boot. Suggest some properties that steel does *not* have that would be useful in a boot. Use the list to help you.

Find out about

- ✓ **how natural and synthetic polymers meet our needs**
- ✓ **examples of polymers and their uses**
- ✓ **how and why natural polymers are being replaced with synthetic ones**

All sorts of polymers meet people's most basic needs. These needs include:

- shelter, warmth, and transport
- food, water, and healthcare
- human contact and leisure.

Natural polymers

Before synthetic polymers were discovered, these needs were met using natural polymers as well as materials like metals, glass, and ceramics.

The pictures below show some materials that are natural polymers.

Cotton has been used for clothing and household textiles for many years. Cotton comes from the cotton plant.

Silk is used for high-quality clothing. It comes from silkworms.

Wool is used in clothing and textile products. It comes from animals such as sheep.

Doctors and other health workers wear gloves made of natural **rubber** (latex) for protection and to prevent infection. Latex comes from the rubber tree.

Fur was one of the first materials used for clothing. Today some people think it is cruel and should not be used.

Wood is used for building and for furniture. It is also used to make paper.

From natural to synthetic

The pictures below and on the following page show some synthetic polymers. These are polymers that are made by people. Many items that used to be made from natural polymers are now made from synthetic ones. Each new polymer has different properties, which may be better than those available in nature.

- Natural fibres for clothing are replaced with synthetic fibres, which may be easier to wash, hold their shape better, or be available in a wider range of colours.
- Fur and leather may be replaced with synthetic polymers, which avoids using animal products.
- Wood is often replaced with synthetic polymers, which are much lighter and do not rot or require painting.
- Paper bags are often replaced with ones made from synthetic polymers, which are lighter and also waterproof.

Questions

1 List three natural polymers that come from plants.

2 List three natural polymers that come from animals.

3 What does 'synthetic' mean?

Polythene bags help people to protect, store, and carry food.

This patient in Sri Lanka is fitting a new leg made of polypropylene.

The world's first inflatable church made from PVC.

PET is used to make soft-drinks bottles and food containers.

Polyester is used to make hulls and sails.

This painting was done with acrylic, which is a synthetic polymer.

Manchester City's stadium roof is made from polycarbonate 'glass'.

Summary box

- ✓ **Natural polymers were used before synthetic ones were made. They are still in use today.**
- ✓ **Synthetic polymers are made by people.**
- ✓ **Synthetic polymers are sometimes used instead of natural polymers, because of their better properties.**

Kevlar helmets have saved many soldiers' lives.

A wet suit made from neoprene offers warmth and protection.

Questions

4 List five synthetic polymers and write down one item or product made from each. Use the images on these pages to help you.

5 a List three objects that were once made from natural polymers but are now made from synthetic polymers.

  b For each object in your list from part a, write down one property that the synthetic polymer has that the natural one does not.

6 Name an object that was once made from metal but is now made of synthetic polymers and explain why.

7 Name an object that was once made from ceramics but is now made from synthetic polymers and explain why.

Getting the right material

When making a product it is important to choose the right material. People designing and making things decide which materials to use based on their **properties** and cost. In many products, the materials include polymers.

Rollerblades are made of synthetic polymers. These are modern materials with special properties.

For example, the soles of shoes have to be flexible, hard wearing, and strong. A synthetic rubber is a good choice.

The case of a computer needs to be stiff, strong, and tough. People want a case that resists scratches and stays looking good. So the polymer has to be hard.

Material words

When scientists describe the properties of materials, they use special words, such as strong, weak, stiff, and flexible.

A suspension bridge must be strong. The cables are made of steel, a material that is strong in tension. The columns are made of concrete, a material that is strong in compression.

Question

1 Look at the picture of rollerbladers. Their clothing and the different parts of the rollerblades are made from different materials. List two items that are:
   a flexible b stiff c strong d hard

This machine measures the strength of sewing threads by measuring the force needed to break them. Samples from every batch that leaves the factory are tested to make sure the threads are always the same.

A material is **strong** if it takes a large force to break it. Some materials are strong when stretched. They are strong in **tension**. Others crack under tension but they are strong when they are squashed or under **compression**.

Stiff is the opposite of flexible. It is difficult to stretch or bend a stiff material. High stiffness is very important in many of the materials that are used to make aeroplanes, bridges, and engines.

Hard and **soft** are also opposites. The softer a material, the easier it is to scratch it. A harder material will always scratch a softer one.

For many uses it is important to know how heavy a material is for its volume. Materials such as steel and concrete have a high **density**. Other materials are very light for their volume and have a low density. Examples are foam rubber and expanded polystyrene.

Measuring the properties

Technical words help to describe materials. There are times when more than a description is needed. Accurate measurements of properties are necessary when it is important to compare materials and test their quality.

For example, a pole used for pole vaulting must be flexible, but not too flexible or it will not support the weight of the person using it. The landing pit must be soft but not too soft so that the pole vaulter lands safely. In situations like these the properties of the materials must be measured to make sure that they are just right.

Questions

2 Steel and nylon are strong when they are stretched. Are they strong under tension or compression?

3 Concrete is strong when it is squashed. Is it strong under tension or compression?

Quality control

It is particularly important to take accurate measurements when someone's safety depends on it.

Abseiling ropes must not break when they are being used, so the ropes are tested to make sure that they are strong and safe.

Most ropes are produced in batches. A machine is used to test a sample of rope from each batch and find out the force that is needed to break it. Standard procedures are followed carefully to make sure the measurements are accurate. **Accuracy** is how close a measurement is to the true value.

Repeatable data

Each time a test is carried out the same method is used. This means that if someone tested the same rope twice they would expect to get the same result – the measurement is **repeatable**.

In reality there may be small differences in the results each time because of errors from the person carrying out the test, or from the machine. The best estimate of the true value of the force needed to break a rope is found by repeating the measurements on at least three samples. The mean and range are then recorded.

It is important to control all the factors that are not being tested that may affect the results, for example, temperature. If the rope was tested at a different temperature this might affect the strength of the rope and you would not be able to compare your results easily with other tests.

Abseiling ropes must be strong in tension. Climbers want to be sure that their ropes have been tested.

Questions

4 Give one factor that is controlled when abseiling ropes are tested.

5 Explain why is it important to repeat measurements.

6 Samples of abseiling rope were tested for their strength in tension and the following results were collected:
27, 546 N   27, 356 N   27, 598 N   27, 467 N
Calculate the mean and the range for this set of measurements.

Summary box

✔ **Materials can be flexible, hard, tough, stiff, and strong.**
✔ **Materials and products are tested to find out their properties.**
✔ **Standard procedures are followed to make sure measurements are accurate and repeatable.**

Find out about

- materials under the microscope
- molecules and atoms in materials
- models of molecules

Silk.

A woollen jumper is very different from a silk shirt. The shirt is more formal and less stretchy than the jumper. They are both made from natural polymers but they are very different. Their properties depend on what they are made of, from the large scale to smaller than you can see:

- the visible weave of a fabric
- the shape and texture of the **fibres**, which can be seen with a microscope
- the molecules that make up the polymer, which cannot be seen even with a microscope
- the atoms that make up the molecules.

The visible weave

The fabric of a woven shirt is tightly woven but it is possible to see the criss-cross pattern of threads. The fabric is hard to stretch because the strong threads are held together so tightly.

The weave and the stitches are visible to the naked eye. However, the properties of a fabric also depend on smaller structures.

FABRIC
Magnification: × 20.
Visible: to naked eye.
Width of circle:
4 millimetres.

FIBRES
Magnification: × 1000.
Visible: down a microscope.
Width of circle:
80 micrometres.

MOLECULES
Magnification: × 50 million.
Visible: not even in a
microscope. Width of circle:
1.5 **nanometres**.

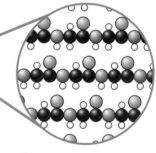

Levels of structure and detail. A millimetre is a thousandth of a metre. A micrometre is a thousandth of a millimetre. A nanometre is a thousandth of a micrometre.

Question

1 Put the following in order of size:
fibre   fabric   atom   thread   molecule

The invisible world of molecules

Microscopes can be used to look at fibres but even this does not explain all the different properties. Scientists explain the differences between silk, wool, and other fibres by finding out about their molecules. Molecules are very small indeed, so small that it needs a giant leap of the imagination to think about them.

Molecules are made of atoms. Scientists measure the sizes of atoms and molecules in nanometres. There are 1 000 000 000 nanometres in a metre. Some molecules, such as the small molecules in air, are even smaller than one nanometre but many are bigger.

The molecules in fibres are big on the nanometre scale. They are very long – 1000 nanometres or more. The shape and size of the **long-chain molecules** in a fibre make the material what it is. Polymers have special properties because the molecules in them are so long.

Model molecules

Even the largest molecules and atoms are invisible. So in the nanoworld of molecules, scientists build models to help them imagine what they look like. A different colour is used for each element.

ethanol

water

propane

Models of molecules. A different colour is used for each element. Carbon is black, hydrogen is white, and oxygen is red.

Questions

2 Look at the pictures of models of molecules above. How many different chemical elements are there in
   a ethanol?
   b water?
   c propane?

3 A hydrocarbon is a molecule that is made up of hydrogen and carbon atoms only. Which of the molecules in question 2 is a hydrocarbon?

4 Look at the diagram on page 142.
   a How many chemical elements are there in silk?
   b Is silk a hydrocarbon?

Summary box
✔ **Molecules are too small to be seen with a microscope.**
✔ **Molecules are made of atoms.**
✔ **Scientists make models of molecules.**

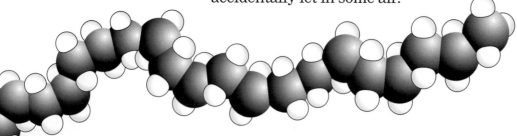

The discovery of polythene

The first synthetic polymer was discovered by accident.

Eric Fawcett and Reginald Gibson were working for a chemical company. Their job was to investigate the reactions of gases at very high pressures. They put some ethene gas into a container and squashed it to 2000 times its normal pressure. They accidentally let in some air.

Two days later, they found a white, waxy solid inside the container. This was a surprise. They decided that the gas must have reacted with itself to form a solid. They realised that, in some way, the small molecules of ethene had joined with each other to make bigger molecules.

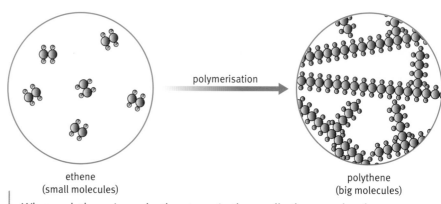

ethene
(small molecules)

polymerisation

polythene
(big molecules)

When polythene is made, the atoms in the small ethene molecules are rearranged to form big polythene molecules.

Questions

1 Are the following molecules hydrocarbons?
  a ethene   b polythene

2 Which is a polymer – ethene or polythene?

Fawcett and Gibson worked out that the new molecules were like repeating chains. The chains were made from repeating links of ethene molecules.

Later they understood that oxygen in the air leaking into the container was a catalyst. The oxygen speeded up what would otherwise have been a very, very slow reaction to join the ethene molecules together.

What are polymers?

Polymers all have one thing in common: their molecules are long chains of repeating links. Each link in the chain is a smaller molecule. These small molecules are called **monomers**.

The monomers each connect to the next one to form the chain. This is true for natural polymers such as cotton, silk, and wool and for synthetic polymers such as polythene and nylon.

The common name for the polymer discovered by Fawcett and Gibson is polythene. This is short for the chemical name poly(ethene). The word poly means 'many'; a poly-ethene molecule is made from many ethene molecules joined together.

Polymer by design

Not all polymers were discovered by accident. Nylon was designed as an alternative to silk because silk was very expensive.

This bottle is made from polythene.

Summary box

✓ Some polymers were discovered by accident – others were designed.
✓ Polymers are made of long chains of smaller molecules joined together.

Questions

3 Copy and complete the sentences below using these words:
big, small, chain, monomers

Polythene is a long _____ molecule made of lots of _____ molecules of ethene. The ethene molecules are called _____. The _____ molecule is a polymer.

4 Name one polymer discovered by accident.

5 Name one polymer that was designed.

6 What is a polymer?

7 What is a monomer?

Find out about

✓ **long and short polymer chains**

Candle wax is weak and brittle. The molecules contain only a few atoms.

Polythene is much stronger and tougher than candle wax. The molecules contain thousands of atoms.

Summary box

✓ **Materials made up of molecules with longer chains are usually stronger than materials made up of molecules with shorter chains.**

Long and short molecules

The properties of a polymer depend on the length of its molecules. The molecules in candle wax are very similar to those in polythene. However, wax is weaker because the wax molecules are much shorter. They contain only a few atoms but polythene molecules contain many thousands of atoms.

Two different bonds

Molecules are made of atoms. The bonds between *atoms* in molecules are strong. So it is very hard to pull a molecule apart. The molecules do not break when materials are pulled apart.

But the forces between *molecules* are very weak. It is much easier to separate molecules from one another. They can slide past each other.

Breaking and melting wax and polythene

Stretch or bend a candle and it cracks. This is because separating the small molecules is not difficult.

Breaking a lump of polythene is much more difficult. Its long molecules are all jumbled up and tangled. It is harder to make them slide over each other. The long molecules make polythene stronger than wax.

Polythene has a higher melting point than wax. This is because the forces between long polythene molecules are slightly stronger than the forces between short wax molecules. More energy is needed to separate the polythene molecules from each other so it melts at a higher temperature.

Questions

1 Which is stronger – wax or poythene? Explain why in terms of the size of the molecules and the strength of the forces between them.

2 Why is a milk carton made of polythene instead of wax?

Designer stuff

Hardening rubber

Natural rubber is a very flexible polymer. But it wears away easily. This makes it good at rubbing away pencil marks but not for much else.

In 1840, an American inventor called Charles Goodyear was experimenting with mixing rubber and sulfur. Goodyear found a way to make rubber into a stronger and harder material that didn't wear away as easily. It made rubber an excellent material for car tyres and Goodyear started a successful business. He called his process **vulcanisation**.

Cross-links

Goodyear did not know why the rubber hardened – only that it did. Now that we understand more about molecules, we know what's going on.

The sulfur makes **cross-links** between the long rubber molecules. The molecules are locked together and cannot slip over each other. More energy is needed to separate the polymer chains from each other, so the rubber is less flexible, stronger, and harder. It also gives the rubber a higher melting point.

Find out about

- ✓ **using science to change polymer properties**
- ✓ **cross-links to make polymers harder**
- ✓ **plasticisers to make polymers softer**

Vulcanising natural rubber produces gloves that are strong enough not to tear.

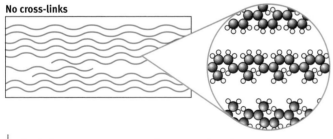

No cross-links

Each line represents a polymer molecule. Without cross-linking, the long chains can move easily and slide past each other.

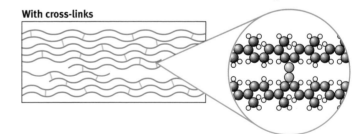

With cross-links

These chains are cross-linked. This stops the rubber molecules sliding past each other.

Questions

1 Name one property of natural rubber.

2 Give two properties of cross-linked rubber that are different from natural rubber.

3 Explain the differences in the properties of natural rubber and cross-linked rubber. Use ideas about molecules in your answer.

Plasticisers

PVC is a polymer. It is often used for making window frames and guttering. These need to be **durable** and hard.

PVC is also a good polymer for making clothing. For this purpose it needs to be softer and more flexible.

To make PVC softer, a **plasticiser** is added. This is usually an oily liquid with small molecules. The small molecules sit between the polymer chains.

The polymer chains are now further apart. This weakens the forces between them, so they slide over each other more easily. Less energy is needed to separate the chains from each other. This means the polymer is softer, more flexible, and has a lower melting point

This PVC has no plasticisers. It is called uPVC, which means unplasticised PVC.

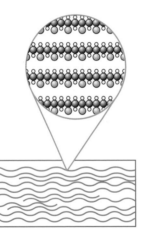

The red lines represent PVC molecules. These PVC molecules are long chains that lie close together.

This PVC has been plasticised to make it soft.

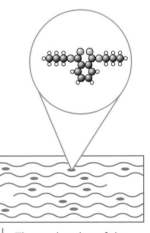

The molecules of the plasticiser hold the PVC chains apart. This weakens their attraction and makes it easier for them to slide past each other.

Questions

4 Write down two properties of PVC, which does not contain plasticisers, that make it good for making window frames.

5 Write down two properties of plasticised PVC that make it good for clothing.

6 Explain the differences in the properties of the two types of PVC. Use ideas about molecules in your answer.

Cling film

Cling film was first made from plasticised PVC. Unfortunately, the small plasticiser molecules were able to move through the polymer and into the food – especially fatty foods such as cheese. Some people were worried that the plasticiser might be bad for their health.

The evidence that plasticisers are harmful to health is controversial and strongly challenged by the plastics industry.

There is stronger evidence that using plastic food wrap regularly can cut down on food poisoning, which is a serious and growing risk to health.

Some cling film is now made using PVC with plasticisers that are much less likely to move from the polymer to food. Cling film can also be made from polythene. This is just as flexible but does not cling so well.

Cling film is used to wrap food. Some cling films contain plasticisers.

Questions

7 a List some of the benefits of using cling film.
  b List some of the risks of using cling film.
  c Do you think that the benefits outweigh the risks of using cling film? Explain your answer.

8 Write down two ways in which the properties of a polymer can be changed.

Summary box

- ✓ The properties of polymers can be changed by cross-linking and using plasticisers.
- ✓ Cross-links hold the polymer chains together. This makes the polymer harder and stronger.
- ✓ Plasticisers let the polymer chains move past each other. This makes the polymer softer and more flexible.

Find out about

✔ **using science to design new polymer products**

Gore-tex is waterproof and windproof but it allows the moisture from sweat to pass through.

Summary box

✔ **Gore-tex, Kevlar, and Velcro are all polymer products designed to have specific properties.**

Gore-tex

Sometimes layers of different polymers with different properties are sandwiched together. One example is the waterproof fabric Gore-tex, named after its inventor Bob Gore. He was working with a polymer called PTFE. This is the plastic coating for non-stick pans.

Gore discovered that if a sheet of PTFE is stretched, it forms very small holes and becomes porous. A single water molecule can pass through the small holes. A whole water droplet is too large to get through. Gore thought that vapour evaporating from someone's skin would pass through the polymer sheet, but that raindrops would not.

Gore-tex has a layer of PTFE sandwiched between two layers of cloth. The wearer stays dry and comfortable no matter how energetic they are or what the weather is like. Sweat can always pass out through the fabric, but no water can get in.

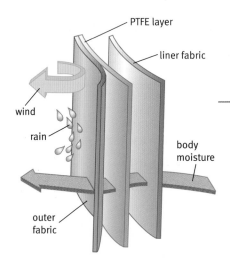

Gore-Tex membrane: there are billions of tiny holes in the film of PTFE. The holes are much smaller than a raindrop but much larger than a water molecule.

Questions

1 What was the polymer PTFE originally used for?
2 What happens to PTFE when it is stretched?
3 Put these in order of size, starting with the smallest: water droplet, water molecule, hole in PTFE film
4 Explain how Gore-tex is waterproof but still lets water vapour pass through it.

Kevlar

Nearly all the early synthetic polymers were discovered by accident. But once chemists started to understand how to make polymers they could design them to have certain properties.

DuPont is a company that wanted to make a very strong but light-weight polymer with a high **melting point**. The chemists designed and made a polymer with very long molecules, linked together in sheets. It is called Kevlar and is 5 times stronger than steel. It is used in bullet-proof vests.

Velcro

The two surfaces of Velcro stick together with a strong bond but can be peeled apart. One surface is covered in hooks, the other in loops.

The inventor of Velcro, George de Mestral, was copying seed pods that he found stuck to his socks when he was out walking. The pods were covered with tiny hooks that attached themselves round threads in the socks.

De Mestral used nylon to make Velcro. He worked out how to weave the polymer thread in just the right way to produce hooks and loops.

Stephanie Kwolek, chemist at DuPont. She is wearing gloves made of Kevlar. She discovered how to turn the polymer into fibres.

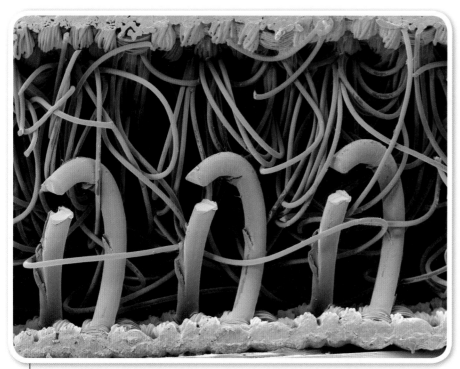

Nylon hooks and loops in Velcro material. Magnification × 30.

Questions

5 State two uses for Velcro. For each one, suggest what may have been used before Velcro was invented.

6 Soldiers' armour and bullet-proof vests used to be made from metal. Now they are made from Kevlar. Suggest two ways in which Kevlar is a better material for this purpose.

Plant for processing chemicals from oil.

A fractionating tower, where crude oil is separated into fractions.

Question

1 Crude oil is made of hydrocarbons.
   a What is a hydrocarbon?
   b How do the hydrocarbons in crude oil vary?

Crude oil

Polymers are made from small molecules called monomers joined together in long chains. In most synthetic polymers, the small molecules originally come from **crude oil**.

Crude oil is a thick, sticky, dark-coloured liquid that formed over millions of years from the remains of tiny plants and animals called plankton. It is pumped out of the Earth's crust from wells under the ground or sea.

Crude oil is not very useful as it is.

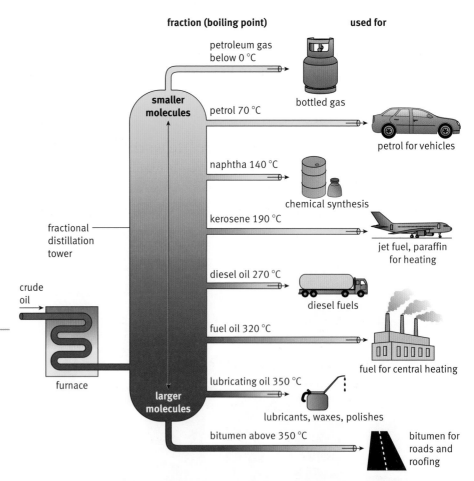

Crude oil is a mixture of lots of different **hydrocarbon** compounds. Hydrocarbons are molecules containing hydrogen and carbon only. Because it is a mixture, crude oil is not very useful as it is, so the mixture is separated by fractional distillation.

Fractions

Fractional distillation separates crude oil into groups of molecules of similar size, called **fractions**.

In the diagram on page 152, the crude oil is being heated in a furnace. The crude oil then goes into the fractionating tower, which is hottest at the bottom and coolest at the top.

The hydrocarbon molecules are separated by their boiling points. The smallest molecules have the lowest boiling points. This is because the forces between the small molecules are weak, and only a little energy is needed for them to break out of the liquid and form a gas. These molecules go right to the top of the tower. The biggest molecules have stronger forces between them and have higher boiling points. They stay at the bottom of the tower.

Each fraction produced is still a mixture of molecules, but they are of similar size and boiling point.

Uses

Each fraction has different uses related to its properties. Most of the fractions are used to provide energy for transport, homes, and industry. About 4% of crude oil is used in **chemical synthesis** to make new materials such as polymers, while about 1% of crude oil is used as lubricants.

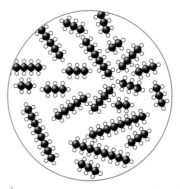

Crude oil is a mixture of hundreds of different hydrocarbons.

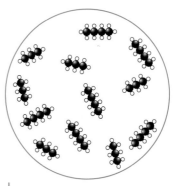

These molecules go right to the top of the fractionating column. This fraction contains some of the shortest hydrocarbons. There are weak forces between the molecules, giving them a low boiling point.

Questions

2 a Which part of a fractionating tower is hottest, the bottom or the top?

   b Small molecules travel to the top of the tower because they have a low boiling point. Explain why they have a low boiling point.

3 Look at the diagram on p152. How many fractions are used for:

   a transport?

   b lubrication?

   c making new chemicals?

Summary box

✔ **Crude oil is a mixture of different sized hydrocarbons.**

✔ **Hydrocarbons contain hydrogen and carbon atoms only.**

✔ **Fractional distillation separates crude oil into fractions – groups of molecules of similar size and boiling point.**

✔ **Most crude oil is used as a fuel.**

Find out about

- ✔ **the size of a nanometre**
- ✔ **explaining the properties of nanoparticles**
- ✔ **making new materials containing nanoparticles**

Some bus companies use an additive in diesel fuel that contains nanoparticles. This reduces the amount of fuel used and the emissions from the vehicle, making the buses more efficient.

Not just small – very small

The photographs on this page show some recent scientific and technological advances. Each of them uses **nanotechnology**.

Nanotechnology is the use and control of structures that are very small. The particles used in nanotechnology are called **nanoparticles.** They are measured in nanometres (nm) and are about 1 to 100 nm in size.

Each nanometre (nm) is a billionth of a metre or 0.000 000 001 m. A nanometre is about:

- the width of a few molecules
- the distance your fingernails grow in a second
- 1/80 000 the thickness of the average human hair.

It is difficult to understand just how tiny a nanometre is.

The diagram on the right shows a nanoparticle. It is 10 nm across, which is about 0.0001 mm. You could fit about 10 000 of them across 1 mm on your ruler. Let's think about it another way.

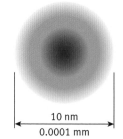

10 nm
0.0001 mm

Imagine if a nanoparticle about 10 nm across was scaled up to the size of a football.

- An atom would become about the size of a 10p coin.
- A red blood cell would be the size of a football pitch.
- A cat would be about the same size as the Earth.

Questions

1 What unit is used to measure particles in nanotechnology?

2 Write a description of what a nanometre is for a student in Year 7.

Some sunscreens contain nanoparticles.

Size of surface

For nanoparticles, the ratio of the **surface area** to the volume is very large.

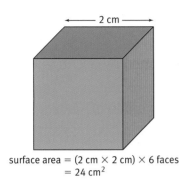

surface area = (2 cm × 2 cm) × 6 faces
= 24 cm²

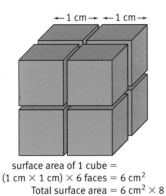

surface area of 1 cube =
(1 cm × 1 cm) × 6 faces = 6 cm²
Total surface area = 6 cm² × 8
= 48 cm²

Total surface area is larger for smaller particles

The atoms on the surface tend to be more reactive than those in the centre. This means materials containing nanoparticles are often highly reactive or have unusual properties.

Nanotechnology in medicine

Silver is best known for use in jewellery because it is shiny and unreactive. For a long time, it has been known that silver also has antibacterial properties.

In 1999, a new bandage for serious injuries was invented. It is called Acticoat and contains silver nanoparticles. It is particularly important that the bacteria in a serious wound are killed before they can cause infections. The tiny nanoparticles of silver in an Acticoat bandage dissolve very quickly once they are moistened (for example by blood from the wound) and the silver can get to work straight away.

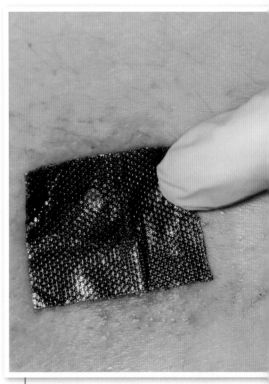

Acticoat is a type of bandage that contains silver nanoparticles with antibacterial properties.

Question

3 Silver has many different uses.
 a Which properties of silver make it good for making jewellery?
 b Why is silver used in wound dressings?
 c How are the particles of silver in Acticoat different from the silver particles in jewellery?
 d Why will nanoparticles of silver be more effective in a wound dressing than ordinary silver?

Summary box

✔ **A nanometre is one-billionth the size of a metre.**
✔ **Nanoparticles have a very large surface area, which can give them unusual properties.**
✔ **Silver nanoparticles are used in wound dressings to kill bacteria.**

Find out about

- ✓ **nanotechnology in nature**
- ✓ **uses of nanotechnology**
- ✓ **risks of using nanotechnology**

Nanotechnology in nature

Nanotechnology sounds very strange and new – but there are nanoparticles in nature.

They include:

- tiny salt particles in the atmosphere, formed by ocean waves in windy conditions
- the enamel in your teeth, which is partly made of nanoparticles.

Humans have been making nanoparticles for years by accident, without knowing it. Some fires, particularly those burning solid fuels, produce nanoparticles (along with other waste).

Uses of nanotechnology

There are products already available that use nanotechnology. These include healthcare products, sports gear, and clothing.

Sunscreen

Many sunscreens contain particles that are white solids. In older products, the particles are relatively large and leave the skin looking white. More modern products use nanoparticles instead, which can be rubbed in and look more natural.

Tennis balls and rackets

Nanotechnology was first used in a professional tennis match in 2002. The nanotechnology balls have an extra layer inside them made of nanoparticles mixed with rubber. This helps to slow down the rate at which air escapes from the balls, keeping them inflated for longer.

Nanoparticles of salt are formed above the sea.

Older sunscreens could be seen on the skin.

Nanotechnology is improving the performance of sports equipment.

Nanoparticles are also added to carbon fibre used to make tennis rackets. The resulting materials are lighter and stronger than the old ones.

Clothing

Scientists have developed clothes that contain the same nanoparticles as those used in sunscreen. Clothes with these particles offer better UV protection.

Stain-resistant clothes have also been produced. These have tiny nanoscale hairs that help repel water and other chemicals.

Socks have been made that contain nanoparticles of silver. This gives the socks antibacterial properties to help prevent feet from smelling.

Different properties, different risks

Nanoparticles have different properties compared to larger particles of the same material. This may mean that they have different effects on plants, animals, and the environment. It may also mean that they are more toxic to people.

Exactly how all the various nanoscale substances differ from larger particles of the same material is not fully understood. At present, there are only a few separate health and safety studies for nanoparticles. Some groups and organisations think that there should be more.

Coatings containing nanoscale particles can repel water and other chemicals that might stain.

Questions

1 Using Sections J and K, give an example of each of the following products that may have been improved by using nanoparticles:
   a a sports product
   b a healthcare product
   c an item of clothing.

2 For each of your answers to question 1 explain how nanoparticles have improved the product.

3 Copy and complete the sentences using these words
   toxic   small   environment   same   properties

   Nanoparticles are very _____. They often have different _____ compared to the _____ material in its more usual or bulk form. They can have different effects on the _____ and can be _____ to people and animals.

Summary box

- ✓ Nanoparticles are found in nature.
- ✓ Nanotechnology is now used in a wide variety of products. These include sunscreen and sports equipment.
- ✓ Nanoparticles can have a different effect on the environment compared to larger particles of the same material because they have different properties.

Science Explanations

Scientists use their knowledge of molecules to develop new materials with useful properties. A wide range of different synthetic polymers can be made from hydrocarbons obtained from crude oil.

You should know:

- that one way of comparing materials is to measure their properties, such as melting point, strength, stiffness, hardness, and density
- why it helps to have an accurate knowledge of the properties of materials when choosing a material for a particular purpose
- that polymers such as plastics, rubbers, and fibres are made up of long-chain molecules
- why modern materials made of synthetic polymers have often replaced materials used in the past such as wood, iron, and glass
- that crude oil is one of the raw materials from the Earth's crust and that it is used to make synthetic polymers
- that crude oil consists mainly of hydrocarbons, which are chain molecules of varying lengths
- that hydrocarbons are made from carbon and hydrogen atoms only
- why the boiling point of a hydrocarbon depends on its chain length
- that the petrochemical industry makes useful products by refining crude oil
- that fractional distillation separates the hydrocarbons in crude oil into fractions according to their chain length
- that some of the small molecules from refining crude oil are used to make new chemicals
- that polymerisation is a chemical reaction that joins up small monomer molecules into long chains
- how the properties of polymers depend on the way in which the long molecules are arranged and held together
- how it is possible to modify polymer properties in various ways such as increasing the length of the chains, cross-linking the molecules, and adding plasticisers
- that nanotechnology is the use and control of structures that are very small
- that nanoparticles can occur naturally, by accident, and by design
- why nanoparticles of a material show different properties from larger particles of the same material
- how nanoparticles can be used to modify the properties of materials.

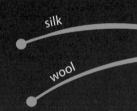

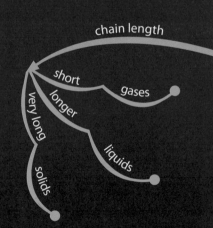

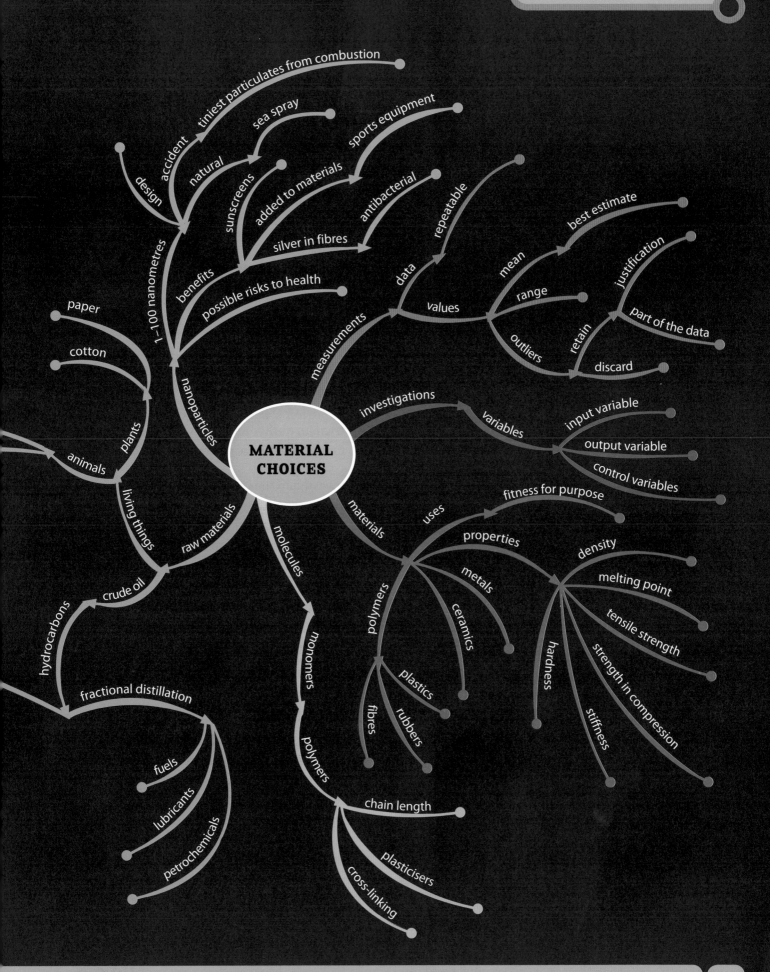

MATERIAL CHOICES

design
accident — tiniest particulates from combustion
natural
sea spray
sunscreens
added to materials
sports equipment
silver in fibres
antibacterial
benefits
possible risks to health
1–100 nanometres
nanoparticles

paper
cotton
plants
animals
living things
raw materials
crude oil
hydrocarbons
fractional distillation
fuels
lubricants
petrochemicals

measurements
data
repeatable
values
mean
range
outliers
retain
discard
best estimate
justification
part of the data

investigations
variables
input variable
output variable
control variables

molecules
monomers
polymers
chain length
plasticisers
cross-linking

materials
uses
fitness for purpose
properties
metals
ceramics
polymers
plastics
fibres
rubbers

density
melting point
tensile strength
strength in compression
hardness
stiffness

Ideas about Science

Scientists measure the properties of materials to decide what jobs they can be used for. Scientists use data rather than opinion to justify the choice of a material for a purpose.

Scientists can never be sure that a measurement tells them the true value of the quantity being measured. Data is more reliable if it can be repeated. When making several measurements of the same quantity, the results are likely to vary. This may be because:

- you have to measure several individual examples, such as several samples of the same material
- the quantity you are measuring is varying, for example, different batches of a polymer made at different times
- the limitations of the measuring equipment or because of the way you use the equipment.

Usually the best estimate of the true value of a quantity is the mean (or average) of several repeat measurements. The spread of values in a set of repeat measurements, the lowest to the highest, gives a rough estimate of the range within which the true value probably lies. You should:

- be able to calculate the mean from a set of repeat measurements

- know that a measurement may be an outlier if it lies well outside the range of the other values in a set of repeat measurements
- treat an outlier as data unless there is a reason for doubting its accuracy.

To investigate the relationship between a factor and an outcome, it is important to control all the other factors that you think might affect the outcome. In a plan for an investigation into the properties of a material, you should be able to:

- identify the effect of a factor on an outcome
- explain why it is necessary to control all the factors that might affect the outcome other than the one being investigated
- recognise that the control of other factors is a positive design feature or that it is a design flaw if they are not controlled.

Some applications of science, such as using nanoparticles, can have unintended and unwanted impacts on the quality of life or the environment. Benefits need to be weighed against costs. You should know that:

- some nanoparticles may have harmful effects on health and that there is concern that products containing nanoparticles are being introduced before these effects have been fully investigated.

Review Questions

1 a A farmer opens a fishing lake in an old quarry. He needs to choose the best rope for the lifebelts. He collects the secondary data shown in the table. Use the data to suggest the best material for the lifebelt ropes. Give reasons for your choice.

	Polypropene (synthetic polymer)	Nylon (synthetic polymer)	Manila (natural fibre)
Minimum breaking strength (kN)	10.8	14.4	5.4
Does it absorb water?	no	yes	yes
Does it float on water?	yes	no	no
Does it rot?	no	no	yes

b A company tested the minimum breaking strength of 10-mm-diameter nylon rope. The test results are in the table.

Test number	1	2	3	4	5
Minimum breaking strength (kN)	14.1	13.9	14.4	14.8	14.8

   i Suggest why the company repeated the test five times.

   ii Work out the best estimate of the true value of the strength of the rope.

   iii Estimate the range within which the true value probably lies.

2 a The table gives data about three hydrocarbons.

   i Which hydrocarbon has the biggest molecules and which has the smallest?

   ii Which hydrocarbon has the highest boiling point and which has the lowest?

   iii Describe the trend in boiling points as the molecule size increases.

Number of carbon atoms in one molecule	Hydrocarbon name	Boiling point (°C)
1	methane	−162
6	hexane	69
16	hexadecane	287

b Sally uses a thermometer to measure the temperature at which heptane boils. She repeats the test five times. Suggest why the results of her five tests are all different.

3 a When cross-links are made between long rubber molecules the properties of the rubber change. For each property below write down whether cross-linking makes the property increase or decrease.

   i flexibility

   ii hardness

   iii melting point

b Identify two property changes that occur when a plasticiser is added to a polymer.

4 a Titanium dioxide nanoparticles are used in some sunblock creams. The nanoparticles are so small that they do not reflect visible light. This means that they look transparent. Nanoparticles do block harmful UV light.

   i Within what range is the diameter of a nanoparticle?

   ii Suggest one advantage of using nanoparticles in sunblock creams.

   iii Give one reason why some people are concerned about the safety of using sunblock creams that contain nanoparticles.

b Give examples of two more uses of nanoparticles.

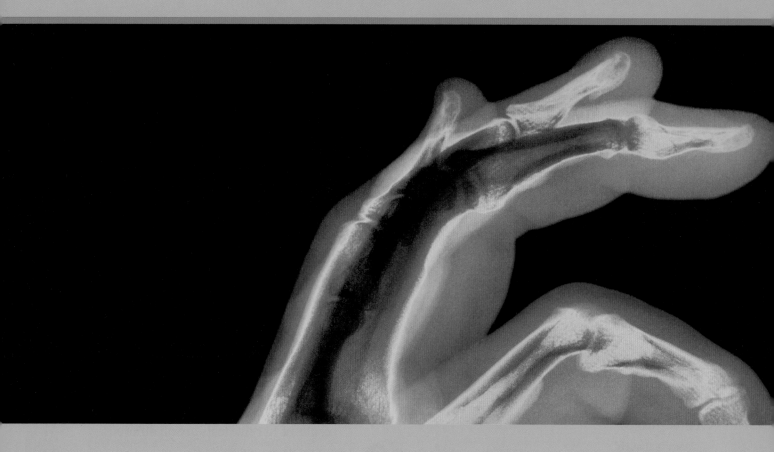

P2 Radiation and life

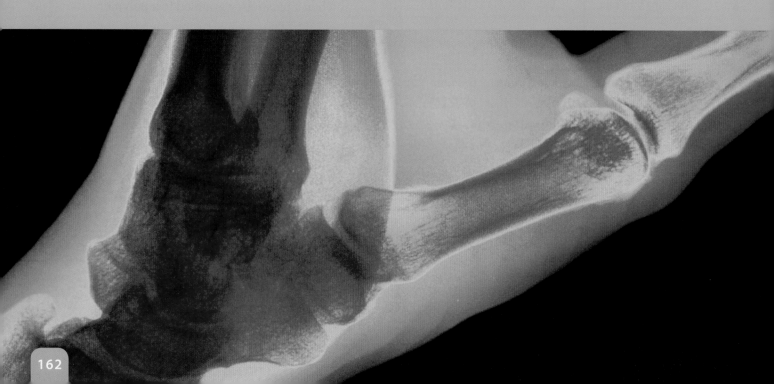

Why study radiation and life?

Human eyes see one type of radiation – visible light. But there are many other types of 'invisible' radiation. Radiation can be harmful. You hear a lot about the health risks of different radiations. For example, from natural sources such as sunlight, and from devices such as mobile phones. Radiation is involved in climate change, and this is the biggest risk of all.

What you already know

- Light travels in straight lines.
- Light travels very fast.
- When light strikes an object, some may be reflected, some absorbed, and some passes straight through.
- White light can be split into the colours of the spectrum.

Find out about

- how radiation travels and is absorbed
- the evidence of global warming, and its effects
- how information is stored and transmitted digitally
- microwave radiation from mobile phones
- weighing up risks and benefits.

The Science

There are several types of radiation that belong to one 'family', called the electromagnetic spectrum. We use electromagnetic radiation for sending information, such as TV programmes, and mobile phones. Science can explain what happens when radiation is absorbed by our bodies and how radiation warms the atmosphere.

Ideas about Science

To make sense of media stories about radiation, you need to understand how to evaluate reports from health studies and statements about risk.

Find out about

- ✓ benefits and risks of exposure to sunlight
- ✓ the electromagnetic spectrum

Fair skin is good at making vitamin D. But fair skin gives less protection against skin cancer. One bad sunburn in childhood doubles the risk of serious skin cancer in later life.

Question

1 Look at the diagram of the electromagnetic spectrum.
   a Which type of radiation has the lowest frequency?
   b Which colour of visible light has the highest frequency?

The Sun and skin cancer

The **ultraviolet radiation (UV),** in sunlight can cause skin cancer. Skin cancer can kill.

What is UV radiation?

Ultraviolet radiation is one type of electromagnetic radiation. Electromagnetic radiation can be spread out to form the **electromagnetic spectrum**. The visible light spectrum, from red to violet, is one small part of this spectrum. UV is just beyond the violet end of the visible spectrum.

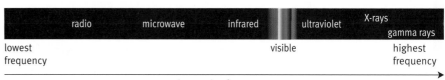

The electromagnetic spectrum is a family of electromagnetic radiation. They all travel at the same very high speed, 300 000 km/s, through space.

We can think of electromagnetic radiation travelling as waves. Radio waves are the waves with the lowest frequencies. Gamma rays and X-rays have the highest frequencies.

Sunlight and vitamin D

We need sunlight to fall on our skin because human skin uses sunlight to make vitamin D. Vitamin D:
- strengthens bones and muscles
- boosts the immune system, which protects you from infections
- may prevent cancer.

Melanin is a brown pigment in skin. It protects skin from UV radiation. People whose ancestors lived in sunnier parts of the world may have protective brown skin. In the sunnier parts of the world it is an advantage to have dark skin to protect you against UV radiation. In parts that are not very sunny it is an advantage to have fair skin so that you can make vitamin D.

Balancing risks and benefits

People like sunshine. But is sunlight good for you? There is no simple answer.

There are risks from exposure to UV in sunlight. There are also risks from avoiding sunlight.

Protecting your health involves reducing risks, whenever possible, and balancing risks against benefits.

Many people sunbathe. They reckon the benefits outweigh the risks.

Skin cancer warnings ignored

Too much exposure to the Sun is dangerous. A Cancer Research UK survey found a worrying gap between how much people know about skin cancer and how little they protect themselves from the Sun.

Among 16–24-year-olds, 75% believed that exposure to the sun might cause skin cancer. But only 25% apply high-factor sunscreen as protection. And only 33% cover up or seek shade from the Sun.

Correlation or cause?

A cataract is clouding of the eye lens. A study of 2600 people found that people who were exposed to high levels of sunlight were up to four times more likely to get a cataract. Exposure to sunlight is possibly a **factor** in causing cataracts. Eye cataracts are an **outcome**. There is a **correlation** between exposure to sunlight and eye cataracts. But doctors do not say that exposure to sunlight **produces** cataracts. It may not be the **cause**. There are other risk factors involved, such as age and diet.

Summary box

- ✔ UV radiation is part of the electromagnetic spectrum of radiation.
- ✔ UV radiation on the skin
  - makes vitamin D
  - may cause skin cancer.
- ✔ There may be a correlation between a factor and an outcome. This may or may not mean the factor causes the outcome.

Questions

2 a A person with dark skin moves to live in a region where there are few sunny days. Why should they try to spend a lot of time out of doors?

  b A person with fair skin goes on holiday in a very sunny region. Why should they avoid spending time out of doors when the Sun is at its hottest?

Find out about

- ✔ **sources of light, and the paths light follows**
- ✔ **how the ozone layer protects life on Earth**

Coloured materials added to glass can absorb some colours of light and transmit others.

Questions

1 Can glass reflect light? Explain how you know.

2 Materials can transmit, reflect, or absorb light. Which one of these is glass best at? How can this property of glass be changed?

3 Use the words *source*, *reflect*, and *detector* to explain how you can see to read at night, using a torch.

A beautiful world

All radiation has a source that emits it. Then it has a journey. It spreads out, or 'radiates'.

Many materials reflect light as it travels on its journey from its source to your eyes. The objects around you would be invisible if they did not reflect light.

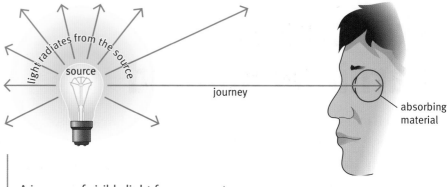

A journey of visible light from source to eye.

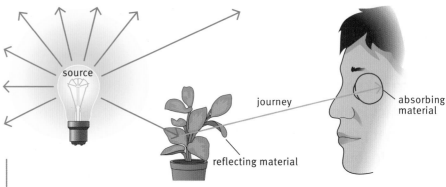

A journey of visible light, from source to reflector to eye.

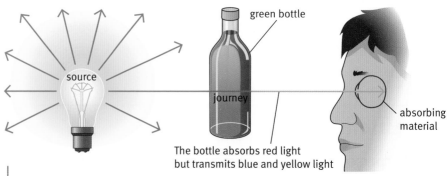

A journey from source to detector, but with absorption of light on the way.

The atmosphere aborbs some radiation

The diagram below shows that the atmosphere goes up many kilometres. The atmosphere is a mixture of gases and it is not the same all the way up. At about 30 km up there is a layer of oxygen in the form of ozone.

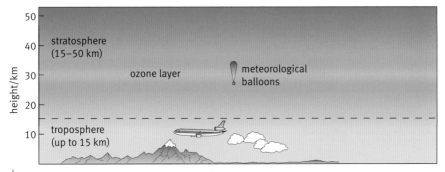

The ozone layer is good at absorbing harmful UV radiation.

Radiation from the Sun must be transmitted through the atmosphere to reach us. Some infrared radiation, visible light, and a small amount of UV radiation reach the Earth's surface from the Sun. Fortunately for us, most of the UV radiation is stopped by the ozone layer. Life on Earth depends on the ozone absorbing the harmful UV radiation.

Ozone holes

Humans have created a problem. Some synthetic (man-made) chemicals, such as **CFCs**, have been escaping into the atmosphere. They turn ozone back into ordinary oxygen. So more UV radiation reaches the Earth's surface. This happens most over the North and South Poles. It leaves only a very thin layer of ozone called the 'hole in the ozone layer'.

CFCs were used in aerosol cans. This has been stopped worldwide. Old fridges now go to special recycling centres so that CFCs can be safely removed from them.

Questions

4 What types of radiation from the Sun reach the Earth's surface?

5 a What type of radiation is absorbed by the ozone layer?
   b Why is this important for life on Earth?

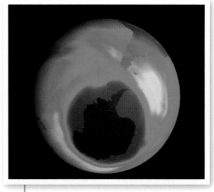

This image shows the thickness of the ozone layer above the Earth. The darker the color, the thinner the layer. There seems to be a 'hole' in the protective layer.

Old fridges waiting to have CFCs removed.

Summary box

✔ **Radiation is emitted from a source and travels to a detector.**
✔ **Radiation can be absorbed, reflected, or transmitted.**
✔ **The ozone layer in the atmosphere absorbs most of the UV radiation from the Sun.**

Find out about

- ✔ **what happens when electromagnetic radiation is absorbed**
- ✔ **why some kinds of radiation are more dangerous than others**

When materials absorb electromagnetic radiation they gain energy. Exactly what happens depends on the type of radiation.

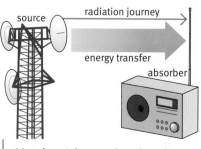

Metal aerials can absorb radio and microwave radiation.

Radiation can cause a varying electric current in a metal wire

Patterns of microwave and radio radiation can make patterns of electric current in radio aerials.

A fire transfers energy to the world around it. It warms its surroundings.

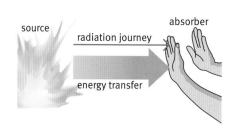

Radiation can have a heating effect

Radiation absorbed by a material may increase the vibration of its particles (atoms and molecules). The material gets warmer.

A leaf takes energy from the Sun's radiation so that photosynthesis can happen.

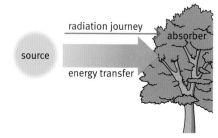

Radiation can cause chemical changes

If the radiation carries enough energy, the molecules that absorb it become more likely to react chemically. This is what happens, for example, in photosynthesis, and in the retinas of your eyes.

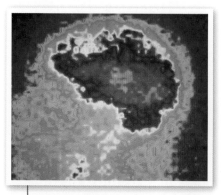

This medical image was made by a gamma camera. Each dot on the image was made by a single ionisation event.

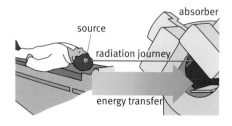

Ionisation can damage living cells

If the radiation carries a large amount of energy, it can remove an electron from an atom or molecule, creating a charged particle called an **ion**. This process is called **ionisation**.

Radiation arrives in energy packets

You can think of radiation carrying energy in small packets called photons.

The energy from a beam of electromagnetic radiation depends on:

- the number of photons arriving
- and the energy that each photon delivers.

Photons of ionising radiation

Radiation with the highest frequencies has the photons with the highest energies. **Gamma ray** photons carry most energy. Gamma rays, X-rays, and some UV are **ionising radiation**.

Lying in the sunshine. Infrared and visible radiations have a warming effect; UV radiation can cause a chemical change that could start skin cancer.

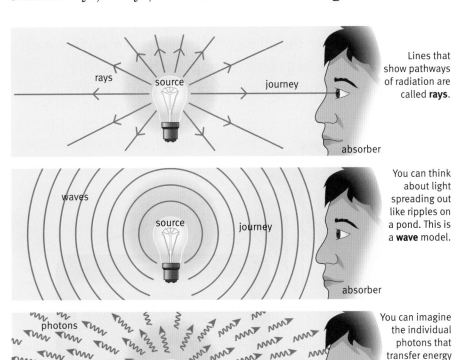

Lines that show pathways of radiation are called **rays**.

You can think about light spreading out like ripples on a pond. This is a **wave** model.

You can imagine the individual photons that transfer energy from the source to the observer. This is the photon model.

Radiation transfers energy. There are different ways of thinking about how it travels between source and absorber.

Photons of non-ionising radiation

Radio photons carry the least energy. Visible, infrared, microwave, and radio are all **non-ionising radiation** because a photon does not have enough energy to ionise an atom or molecule. The main effect is warming.

Summary box

- ✓ **Radiation can be thought of as waves or photons.**
- ✓ **Gamma ray photons have the most energy. Radio photons have the least energy.**
- ✓ **Gamma rays, X-rays, and UV are ionising radiation.**

Question

1 a Draw an electromagnetic spectrum. Label the different types of radiation.

   b Add labels 'lowest photon energy' and 'highest photon energy'.

   c Label the ionising radiation.

Find out about

- ✓ **reducing the risk from ionising radiation**
- ✓ **how ionising radiation can affect body cells**

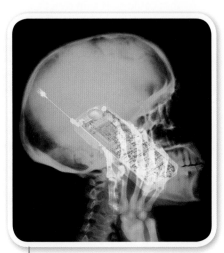

Both the health benefits and the risks of X-rays are well known.

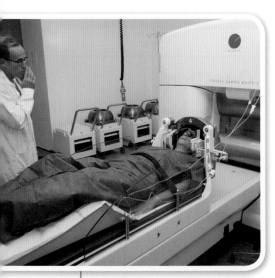

This patient is having cancer treatment. Gamma radiation from the machine above him is directed towards a cancer in his body.

Using X-rays

X-rays have saved many lives. To make an X-ray image:

- X-rays are made in an X-ray tube
- a beam of X-rays is shone through the patient
- the beam is detected on the other side using an X-ray camera.

Not all of the beam passes through the patient. Bones absorb the X-rays, and so bones show up as 'shadows' on the final image. When some of the beam is absorbed we say that the **intensity** of the beam is reduced.

The higher the intensity of a beam of electromagnetic radiation, the higher the energy that arrives at a surface each second. Intensity tells us how 'strong' the beam is. The intensity is less if you are further away from the source.

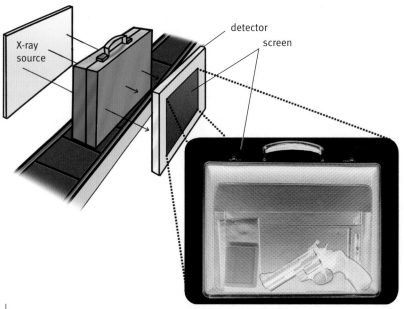

X-ray machines are used in airport security checks. Like bone, metal objects absorb X-rays strongly and produce a shadow picture.

Using gamma rays

Gamma radiation is similar to X-rays but it comes from **radioactive materials**. These are substances that emit radiation all the time – you can't switch them off.

Gamma radiation is used, like X-rays, for imaging a patient's internal organs. It is also used to destroy cancer cells.

UV radiation has enough energy to change atoms and molecules. Its photons can cause skin cancer. This is why it is advisable to cover up with clothes and sun-screen to reduce the risk on a sunny day.

Discovery of a correlation

Alice Stewart (see photo) and George Kneale carried out a survey on a large number of women and their children. They discovered a correlation between X-ray exposure of mothers during pregnancy and cancers in their children.

This study made doctors more cautious about using X-rays, but the risks associated with X-rays for small children and pregnant women usually outweigh any benefit.

Reducing the risk

When a patient has an X-ray, the X-ray exposure is the minimum that still produces a good image. People who work with ionising radiation must also be protected from its effects.

There are several ways to reduce exposure to ionising radiation:

- **time:** the shorter the time of exposure, the less radiation is absorbed, so the smaller the chance of damage to cells
- **distance:** intensity decreases as radiation spreads out from the source
- **shielding:** use materials such as lead and concrete, which absorb radiation strongly
- **sensitivity:** use a detector that is more sensitive so that less radiation is needed to produce an image.

Obituaries

Alice Stewart

Alice Stewart was a British doctor. She collected and analysed information from women whose children had died of cancer between 1953 and 1955. Soon the answer was clear. On average, one medical X-ray for a pregnant woman was enough to double the risk of early cancer for her child.

Questions

1 a Name the three types of electromagnetic radiation that are also ionising radiations.
  b Which of these has the least energetic photons?

2 Why do doctors still use X-rays, despite the link between X-rays in pregnancy and childhood cancer?

Summary box

✓ **Ionising radiation can:**
  - **kill cells**
  - **damage DNA**
  - **cause cancer.**
✓ **X-rays are used when the benefits, such as finding a broken bone, outweighs the risk of damage that might cause cancer.**

Find out about

- ✔ **the heating effect of microwaves**
- ✔ **how microwave ovens work safely**
- ✔ **radiation from mobile phones**

Microwave radiation is gradually absorbed as it passes into a potato. It may not reach the middle of a very large potato. The plate does not absorb energy from the microwave radiation.

Transmit, absorb, reflect … Inside a microwave oven, the glass plate transmits the radiation. The metal walls reflect it. The water in the potato absorbs it.

Summary box

- ✔ **Some materials absorb microwaves. Their molecules vibrate and they heat up.**
- ✔ **Some materials transmit or reflect microwaves.**

Any material that absorbs non-ionising radiation gets hot.

Microwave ovens

A microwave oven uses **microwave radiation** to transfer energy to absorbing materials. Molecules of water, fat and sugar are good absorbers of microwave radiation. The microwaves make these molecules vibrate strongly. Once the food has absorbed the energy, the radiation does not exist any more.

A potato contains water, so it absorbs microwave radiation. The intensity of the radiation decreases as it passes into the potato. The particles of glass or crockery do not absorb energy from the radiation. It does not increase their vibrations, so bowls and mugs are not heated directly. They are heated by the hot food or drink inside them.

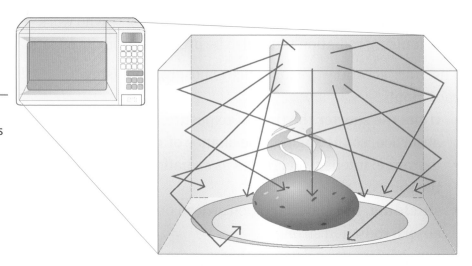

Safety features

People contain water and fat, two absorbers of microwave radiation. So microwaves could cook you. The oven door has a metal grid to reflect the radiation back inside the oven. A hidden switch prevents the oven from operating with its door open.

How well cooked?

Any material that absorbs microwaves gets hot.

You control the heating effect in a microwave oven by adjusting:
- the power setting (to control the radiation intensity)
- the cooking time.

Cooked brain?

Mobile phones use microwave radiation to send signals to and from the phone mast. When you make a call, some of this radiation reaches your brain and warms it. But ever so slightly. Your brain can be warmed more when you do physical exercise.

There is no evidence that this exposure is harmful. However, some people use a hands-free kit so that the phone is further from their head. This makes the radiation reaching the head less intense.

We're all radiators

Hot objects glow brightly. They emit visible light. In fact, cool objects emit electromagnetic radiation too. This is invisible **infrared** radiation.

The hotter an object is the higher the frequency of the radiation it emits. Very hot objects, such as the hottest stars, emit radiation whose **principal** or main frequency is in the UV region of the electromagnetic spectrum.

A phone sends a weaker signal when you are close to the phone mast. That's to save the battery, but it also means that less radiation penetrates your head.

Questions

1. What radiation has the next highest energy to microwave radiation in the electromagnetic spectrum?
2. Why is it important that the walls and door of a microwave oven reflect the microwave radiation?
3. Why might your exposure to microwave radiation from your phone be less if you lived close to a mast?
4. Why doesn't microwave radiation cause ionisation?

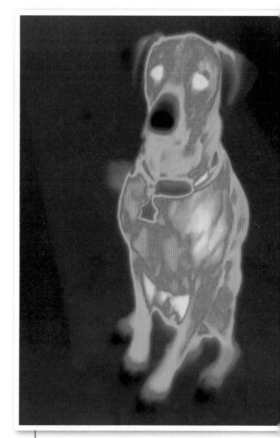

A special camera can detect the infrared radiation given out by people and other animals.

Find out about

- ✔ how the Earth is warmed by the Sun
- ✔ how the atmosphere keeps the Earth warm

Question

1 Personal experience does not provide reliable evidence of climate change. Why not?

Are summers now hotter and winters milder than they once were? This is a question about **climate**, or average weather in a place over many years. You cannot answer it from personal experience, because you can only be in one place at a time. And memory can be unreliable. Instead, you need to collect and analyse lots of data.

A comfortable temperature for life

The Earth's average temperature is about 15 °C, which is very comfortable for life. Why does it have this temperature?

Firstly, we are in orbit around the Sun. The Earth's surface absorbs radiation from the Sun, and this warms the Earth. At the same time, the Earth emits radiation back into space.

- During the day, our part of the Earth is facing the Sun. The Sun's radiation is absorbed by the Earth. It warms us up and the temperature rises.
- At night, we are facing away from the Sun. Energy radiates away into space and the Earth gets colder.

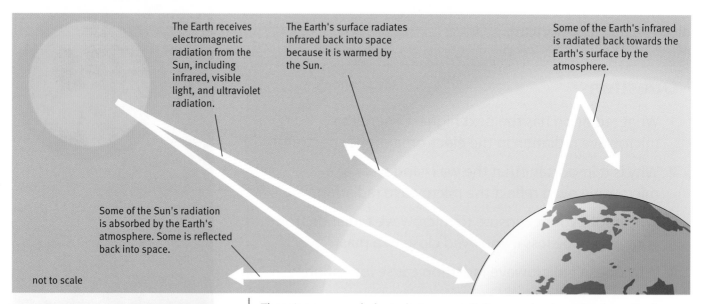

The Earth receives electromagnetic radiation from the Sun, including infrared, visible light, and ultraviolet radiation.

The Earth's surface radiates infrared back into space because it is warmed by the Sun.

Some of the Earth's infrared is radiated back towards the Earth's surface by the atmosphere.

Some of the Sun's radiation is absorbed by the Earth's atmosphere. Some is reflected back into space.

not to scale

There is an energy balance between radiation coming in and going out of the atmosphere. The atmosphere lets in infrared radiation from the Sun, but stops the infrared emitted by the Earth from escaping.

Summary box

- ✔ Climate is the average weather over many years.

The greenhouse effect

The Earth's average surface temperature would be –18 °C if it had no atmosphere. That's how cold it is on the Moon. This warming effect is called the **greenhouse effect**.

Life on Earth depends on the greenhouse effect. Without it, the Earth's water would be frozen. Living things need water in its liquid form.

Greenhouse gas

If the atmosphere consisted entirely of the commonest gases (nitrogen and oxygen), there would be no greenhouse effect. Carbon dioxide, methane, and water vapour absorb some of the Earth's infrared radiation. They are called **greenhouse gases**.

Past temperatures

Weather stations have kept temperature records for over a century. The graph shows the results.

There is a clear pattern. The Earth's average temperature has been rising since 1800. This conclusion is supported by evidence from growth rings in trees, from ocean sediments, and from air trapped in ancient ice.

Most climate scientists think that carbon dioxide in the atmosphere is causing the rise in temperatures because:

- temperature and CO_2 levels have risen at the same time
- evidence from the distant past suggests that temperature and CO_2 levels go up and down together
- scientists know how CO_2 in the atmosphere warms the Earth.

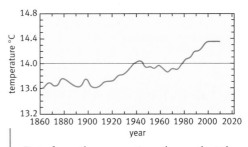

Data from thermometers shows that the Earth's surface temperature has risen over the past 150 years.

Questions

2 Which of the following gases found in the Earth's atmosphere are not greenhouse gases: nitrogen, methane, oxygen, carbon dioxide, water vapour?

3 All of the statements about CO_2 and the Earth's average temperature describe correlations. Which statement is also about cause and effect?

Summary box

✔ **Radiation emitted by the Earth is absorbed or reflected back by carbon dioxide in the atmosphere. This keeps the Earth warm. It is called the greenhouse effect.**

The carbon cycle

Carbon dioxide is a greenhouse gas that plays a key role in global warming. Industrial societies produce much more CO_2 than they did in the past.

The Earth's crust, oceans, atmosphere, and living organisms all contain carbon. Carbon atoms are used over and over again in natural processes. The **carbon cycle** describes the stores of carbon and the processes that move carbon.

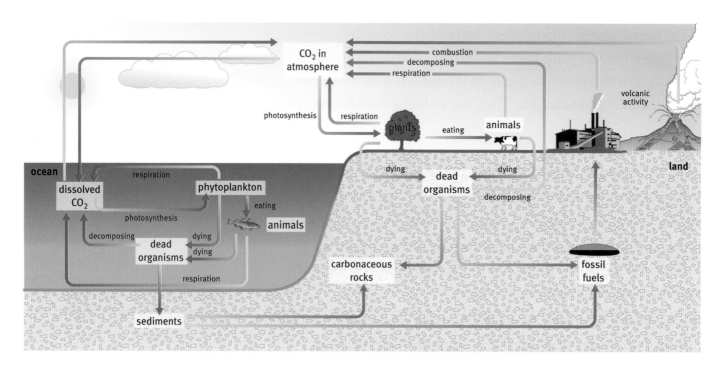

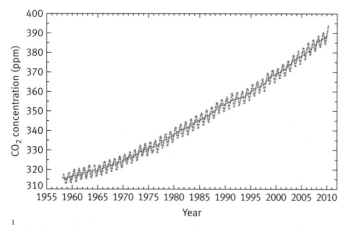

Carbon dioxide concentrations have been recorded in Hawaii since 1958. They rise and fall each year, but overall there has been an increase of about 1.5 parts per million per year since 1980.

Carbon dioxide in the atmosphere

Hundreds of millions of years ago, the amount of CO_2 in the atmosphere was much higher than it is today. Green plants made use of that CO_2 and released oxygen. This made life possible for animals. Eventually, lots of carbon was locked up underground in the form of fossil fuels, as well as rocks such as limestone and chalk.

For thousands of years CO_2 levels were stable. Plants absorbed CO_2 during photosynthesis and then animals returned it to the atmosphere during respiration. The industrial revolution changed all that as fossils were burned in large quantities.

Human activities release carbon

People want to live comfortably. In some parts of the world, many feel they have a right to processed foods, unlimited clean water and electricity, manufactured goods, cars and bigger homes. All of these things require energy.

But whenever fossil fuels (coal, oil, and gas) are burned, they increase the amount of carbon dioxide in the atmosphere. Cutting down or burning forests also releases CO_2. This is called **deforestation**. It also reduces the amount of CO_2 removed by photosynthesis.

The amount of CO_2 that humans produce is huge – thousands of millions of tonnes each year.

Motor vehicles are a major source of greenhouse gas emissions.

Every day this power station uses several train loads of coal and sends thousands of tonnes of carbon dioxide into the atmosphere.

Air transport is a big user of fossil fuels.

People in the UK use more energy for keeping buildings warm than for anything else.

Questions

4 Study the diagram of the carbon cycle opposite.
  a List six processes that release CO_2 into the atmosphere.
  b List two processes that remove CO_2 from the atmosphere.
  c Which of the above processes has changed so that the amount of CO_2 in the atmosphere is increasing?

5 Look at the graph of CO_2 levels opposite. Explain its shape. Why does it go up and down every year? Why is the long-term trend upwards?

6 Forest land can be cleared for farming by burning trees. List two reasons why tree burning increases the amount of carbon dioxide in the atmosphere.

Summary box
✓ **The increase in CO_2 in the atmosphere is due to human activities like burning fossil fuels and deforestation.**

Find out about

✓ **possible effects of climate changes**

An 'ice core' like this stores a record of the Earth's changing atmosphere over hundreds of thousands of years.

Questions

1 How do climate scientists know what the atmosphere was like in the past?

2 What do computer models show is happening to the climate?

Nature's records

The polar ice caps are frozen records of the past. Each year a new layer of ice is formed by the snow. In parts of the Antarctic, ice made from annual layers of snow is four kilometres thick. That ice contains tiny bubbles of air, a record of the atmosphere over 800 000 years. It shows that climate has always changed. There have been ice ages and warm periods.

But temperatures have never increased so fast as during the last 50 years.

Climate modelling

The atmosphere and oceans control climates. Climate scientists use computer models to predict the effects of increasing CO_2 levels. The models show that the climate is changing. We are living in a time of global warming.

Alarming predictions

What these models show is alarming.

- Human activities now contribute more to climate change than natural factors.
- Future emissions of CO_2 are likely to raise global temperatures by between 2 and 6 °C during your lifetime.
- If CO_2 concentration rises much further, there may be nothing we can do to stop climate change.
- Just to stop climate change increasing further, carbon emissions need to be reduced by at least 70% all over the world.
- In the UK, winters will become wetter and summers drier.

Climate change is a slow process. It may take 20 to 30 years for climates to react to the extra CO_2 already in the atmosphere. This means we know global temperatures are going to rise by 2 °C. For the next 300 years or so, ice will continue to melt, and sea levels continue to rise. This will happen even if humans today stopped producing any CO_2 at all.

Effects of global warming

These maps show how the area of the Arctic ice sheet decreased between 1980 and 2007.

Humans need climates that stay fairly constant.

Extreme weather: There are likely to be more extreme weather events like violent storms and heat-waves. This is because there is more energy in the warmer atmosphere.

Rising sea levels: Water in the oceans will expand as it gets hotter, so sea level will rise. Continental ice sheets, such as in Antarctica, may melt, adding to the volume of the oceans. Low-lying land will be flooded, causing a problem for people who live on river deltas, or on low-lying islands. There will be fewer places to live and grow food.

Drought and desertification: Reduced rainfall may make it impossible to grow food crops in some areas. Tropical areas may become drier. Deserts, like the Sahara, may get bigger.

Health: Malaria will spread if mosquitoes can breed in more places.

All of these could add up to huge risks to humans from climate change.

In a warmer climate there will be more hurricanes...

...more drought...

...and more floods.

Summary box

✓ **Global warming could result in:**
- **fewer places to grow food crops**
- **extreme weather**
- **flooding.**

Climate change sceptics

Thousands of climate scientists have contributed to our understanding of how human activities are affecting the climate. They publish their results in scientific journals and test each other's ideas.

Some scientists and many other non-specialists have challenged parts of this work. These people are sometimes called 'climate sceptics'.

New evidence usually supports the climate scientists' ideas.

Questions

3 List three changes that may result from global warming.

4 Sea levels are rising. Give two reasons why they are likely to continue rising in the future.

5 What **two** effects of global warming may make it difficult to grow some food crops in particular regions?

6 Read the magazine extract. Do you think people should rely on technical solutions? Give reasons for your answer.

Science to the rescue

Several solutions have been proposed that might get around the difficulties of reducing carbon emissions.

- Spread iron granules on the southern oceans. This would help the growth of plankton, which take dissolved CO_2 from the ocean. The oceans would remove more CO_2 from the atmosphere.

- Capture the CO_2 produced at power stations. Then compress it into a liquid and pump it into disused oil reservoirs beneath the sea-bed.

- Cement production counts for 5% of the greenhouse gases produced in Europe and America and more than 10% in China. A new type of 'eco-cement' absorbs CO_2 while setting and goes on absorbing CO_2 for years afterwards.

These are currently being tried and evaluated.

Extract from a popular science magazine.

What is 'information'?

Images, sounds, text and numbers are all forms of information.

A mobile phone can store:

- images, for example, photographs
- sounds, for example, music and voice messages
- text, for example, SMS messages
- numbers, for example, telephone numbers.

The phone can receive and transmit information because it is part of a telephone network. It can also store and process information, for example, the user can amend a text message or play a game.

The phone is not full of pictures, sounds, and text. It stores the information as a code. It does this electronically. This makes it easy to process the information, display it on the screen, or send it to another user.

Communicating using waves

Electromagnetic waves travel from a source to a detector, so we can use them to send information from one place to another. We must choose the most suitable waves.

Radio waves and microwaves travel for long distances through the air. They are only weakly absorbed by the atmosphere. Mobile phones use microwaves. Radio waves are used to broadcast radio and TV programmes. Microwaves can travel to orbiting satellites and back, so they are used for satellite communications.

Visible light travels through the atmosphere in good conditions, but on a foggy day it doesn't travel far at all. Infrared doesn't travel far through the atmosphere because it is absorbed. But we can transmit information along optical fibres using visible light or infrared radiation. The fibres are made of very pure glass. Using optical fibres we can transmit information a long way with little absorption. Cable television systems and the high-speed internet phone lines use optical fibres.

Find out about

✓ using electromagnetic waves to transmit information
✓ analogue and digital signals

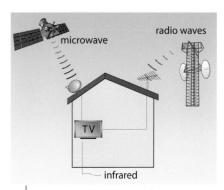

A TV programme can be received from satellite, cable, or broadcast. Different electromagnetic waves carry the information.

Questions

1 Why is infrared radiation NOT used for communicating with satellites?

2 What type of electromagnetic waves are used for broadcasting TV programmes?

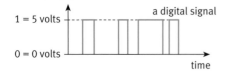

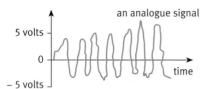

A digital signal has two values. An analogue signal continuously varies.

Carrying information

Information is sent from place to place using a **carrier wave**. The radio waves, visible light, or infrared can form the carrier wave. It must be changed to include the information. A wave or voltage carrying information is called a signal:

carrier wave + signal = transmitted wave

You can send information at night using a flashing torch. The light from the torch is the carrier wave; the on-off flashes are the coded information. This is very similar to what happens in an optical fibre. A series of on-off pulses of light travel through the fibre and are received at the other end.

A digital signal

A digital signal is an on-off signal. It has just two values. For the torch the two values are 'on' and 'off'. 'On' can be represented as 1, or a pulse. 'Off' can be represented as 0 or no pulse. The graph shows an electronic digital signal in which the two values are 0 volts and 5 volts.

An analogue signal

An analogue signal is one that is continuously changing. For example, sound can be turned into an analogue signal. When you speak into a microphone your sound waves are converted into a changing voltage. The graph shows how the voltage might change over a fraction of a second. The electrical signal has the same shape as the original sound wave.

Question

3 Name the type of signal that has:
a only two possible values
b a continuously varying value.

Summary box

✔ **Radio waves and microwaves can transmit information through the atmosphere.**

✔ **Visible light and infrared can transmit information for long distances along optical fibres.**

✔ **An analogue signal is continuously varying.**

✔ **A digital signal has only two values.**

Coding information

All types of information can be converted into digital signals. If the signal is a varying voltage then electronic circuits are used to give digital codes to the analogue values. The digital signal can then be transmitted, processed, and stored.

Photographs and other images can be coded by dividing them up into tiny dots (pixels). Each **pixel** is given a code for its colour and brightness.

Radiation carries information

Are you receiving me?

If you send a message to a friend by flashing torchlight, they must be able to decode it. Similarly, a mobile phone must be able to decode the digital signals it receives.

Inside the phone is a microprocessor that can do this. It converts the digital signal back to the original analogue signal. It takes the binary codes and converts them into a varying voltage. This is sent to the earphone and you hear the sound.

This transmitter tower sends and receives microwave signals to mobile phones. The digital signal carries code for text, sound, and images.

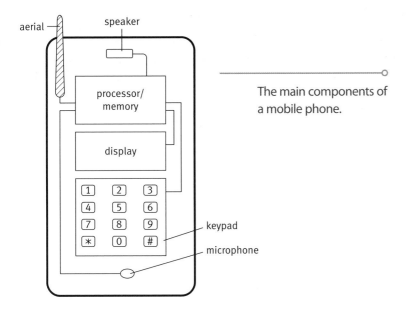

The main components of a mobile phone.

Question

4 Name four different types of information that can be converted to a digital form for transmission to a mobile phone.

More information

Information is easy to store digitally. The memory of a hand-held mp3 player can store a hundred gigabytes of information. That is several weeks' worth of music, or thousands of photographs.

The amount of information needed to store an image or sound is measured in bytes (B). It takes about 1 megabyte (1 MB) to store one minute's worth of music. 1 megabyte = 1 million bytes.

The more information that is stored about an image or sound, the better quality it is. The pictures below show the same photograph, printed from a small file with a few kilobytes of information and from a file with 10 MB of information.

Each pixel in the digital image has a number that gives information about the colour of that part of the picture. The bigger the choice of colours, the greater the range of numbers needed.

Mobile phones contain precious metals including gold, which can be recovered during recycling. Many people upgrade regularly as the technology improves.

Summary box

- ✓ The amount of information needed to store an image or sound is measured in bytes (B).

Questions

5 Two photographs are printed the same size. Which one will have the better quality?
   a 100 kb   b 10 MB

6 Which contains more information, a 100 kB image file or a 1 MB sound file?

7 Explain why a 10 MB image file will produce a better picture than a 1 MB file of the same image.

Noise

All signals get weaker as they travel along. **Noise** ('interference') also gets added in. Noise is unwanted changes to the signal. It is sometimes called interference. A noisy analogue signal carrying music might sound blurry, scratchy and distorted. But with digital signals, these effects can be corrected.

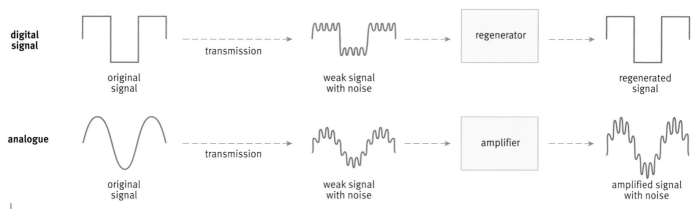

After transmission, a signal is weaker and noisier than the original.
A digital signal can be 'cleaned up' by a regenerator.

Advantages of digital transmission

For transmitting information such as sounds and pictures, digital signals have several advantages over analogue ones.

- Digital signals can be processed by microprocessors, for example, computers and phones.
- Digital information can be stored in memories that are very small, for example, in computers, phones, and mp3 players.
- Digital signals can carry more information every second than analogue ones.
- Digital signals can be delivered with no loss of quality because the noise cannot be removed. Analogue signals lose quality, which cannot be restored.

Questions

8 Which type of signal – analogue or digital – can be recovered most easily?

9 Give three advantages of digital signals over analogue signals.

Summary box
- ✓ Noise is unwanted changes to the original signal.
- ✓ A digital signal that is affected by noise can be recovered more easily than an analogue signal.

Find out about

- ✔ **radiation from mobile phones and masts**
- ✔ **how to judge whether a health study is reliable**

Mobile phones are useful and they are fun. But are they dangerous?

Neil makes a phone call. His mobile phone sends out signals that are detected by a nearby mast.

Neil's head will absorb some of the energy of the microwave radiation because the aerial is close to his ear. The amount of energy absorbed depends on:

- the intensity of the radiation
- the length of time Neil uses the phone.

Neil's head is slightly heated by the radiation it absorbs. This depends on the number of photons absorbed and the energy each delivers.

The intensity of the radiation, coming from Neil's mobile phone spreads out in all directions. It rapidly gets weaker the further away it travels from the phone.

Is there a risk?

People have concerns about radiation from phone masts. If you stood right next to the mast, the heating effect of the radiation absorbed by your body could be quite noticeable.

Fortunately, the diagram shows you cannot get that close. If you stand directly under a mast, its radiation is much weaker than the radiation from your phone.

Health studies

Over 50 million people in the UK use mobile phones. Few worry about any unknown risks. People like the benefits that a mobile phone brings. Research has so far failed to show that there are any harmful effects.

To look for any harmful effects, scientists compare a sample of mobile phone users with a sample of non-users. Does one group show a higher rate of cancer, for example?

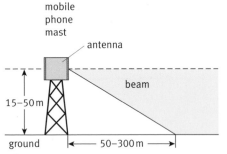

The microwave beam from a mobile phone mast doesn't reach the ground under the mast.

Summary box

- ✔ **There is microwave radiation from mobile phones and mobile phone masts.**
- ✔ **Research has so far failed to show harmful effects of mobile phone radiation on health.**

Are the results reliable?

The news often has reports of studies that compare samples from two groups, to see if a particular factor or treatment makes a difference. To judge whether studies like this give **reliable** results, this table list two things worth checking.

What to check ...	... and why
How were the two samples selected?	A study to find whether mobile phone use caused cancer would need to compare samples of mobile phone users and non-users.
Are any differences in outcomes really due to the factor claimed?	The samples should match as many *other* factors as possible, for example, each sample should have similar numbers of people in each age group. This is because the development of brain tumours might be age-related.
Are the numbers in each sample large enough?	With small samples, the results can be more easily affected by chance. With larger samples this is less likely, so you get a truer picture of the whole population.

How great is the risk?

Health outcomes are often reported as relative risks. For example, 'people exposed to high levels of sunlight were four times as likely to develop eye cataracts'.

- If your risk was one in a million, it rises to four in a million – not a worry!
- If your risk was 5 in 100, it rises to 20 in 100 – worth avoiding!

Also, some people might be more at risk than others, for reasons of family history or lifestyle.

Question

1 a Look at the first row of the table. What factor and what outcome are being studied?

b It is important to match the two samples. Give an example to show what sample matching means.

Summary box

✓ In health studies scientists compare sample groups.
✓ The factor being investigated should be the only difference between the groups.

Science Explanations

An understanding of the electromagnetic spectrum and the different types and sources of radiation is very important so that we can use them safely.

You should know:

- how to think about any form of radiation in terms of its source, its journey path, and what happens when it is absorbed, transmitted or reflected
- that a beam of electromagnetic radiation delivers energy in 'packets' called photons
- the parts of the electromagnetic spectrum, in order of their photon energies
- what different parts of the electromagnetic spectrum can be used for
- two factors that affect the energy deposited by a beam of electromagnetic radiation
- how the intensity of an electromagnetic beam changes with distance
- that gamma rays, X-rays, and high-energy ultraviolet rays have the highest photon energies and are ionising
- why ionising radiation is hazardous to living things
- how people can be protected from ionising radiation
- how microwaves heat materials, including living cells
- about the features of microwave ovens that protect users
- that sunlight provides the energy for photosynthesis and warms the Earth's surface
- how photosynthesis affects which molecules are in the atmosphere
- what the greenhouse effect is (and be able to identify greenhouse gases)
- how to use the carbon cycle to explain how the processes of photosynthesis and respiration have kept the carbon dioxide concentration constant for thousands of years
- how the atmosphere's ozone layer protects living organisms from ultraviolet radiation
- about global warming and its possible effects on agriculture, weather and sea levels
- that radio waves and microwaves carry information for radio and TV through the atmosphere and through space
- that infrared and visible light waves carry information along optical fibres
- that a sound wave can be added to an electromagnetic wave, and that this signal can be carried, and then decoded to produce a copy of the original sound
- that this coding can be done as an analogue signal, which varies continuously, or a digital signal, which is a series of pulses
- the advantages of digital signals in reducing noise, ease of storage, and manipulation of the stored signals.

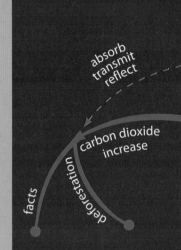

absorb
transmit
reflect

carbon dioxide increase

facts

deforestation

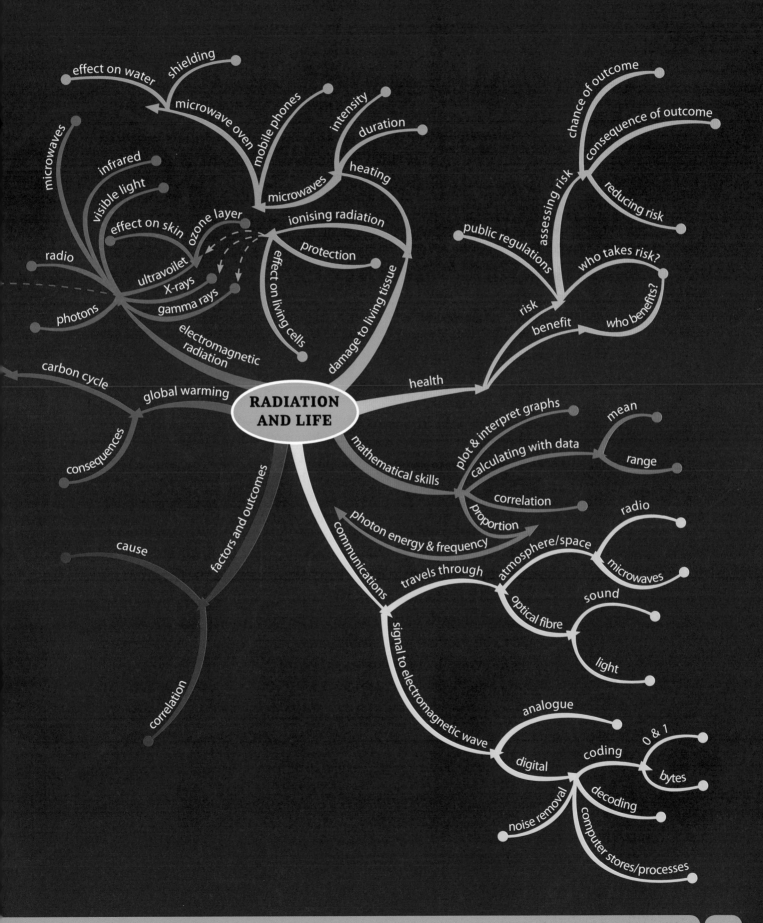

Ideas about Science

Besides developing an understanding of the electromagnetic spectrum, it is important to recognise the difference between correlation and cause and to assess the risks and benefits associated with the electromagnetic spectrum.

Factors and outcomes may be linked in different ways, and it is important to be able to tell the difference between a correlation, where a change in one factor is linked to a change in the other, and a cause, where there is a reason why the factor is responsible for the outcome.

In the context of the electromagnetic spectrum, you should be able to:

- suggest and explain everyday examples of correlation
- identify a correlation from data, a graph, or a description
- suggest factors that might increase the chance of a particular outcome, but not always lead to it.

Everything we do carries some risk, and new technologies often introduce new risks. It is important to assess the chance of a particular outcome happening, and the consequences if it did. Something that benefits us will often also have risks, so the benefits must be weighed against the risks.

You should be able to:

- identify risks arising from scientific or technological advances
- suggest ways of reducing a given risk
- interpret and assess risk presented in different ways
- discuss risk, taking into account both the chance of it occurring and the consequence if it did
- identify both the risks and benefits in a situation to the different people involved
- suggest why people are willing (or reluctant) to take certain risks
- discuss how risk should be regulated by governments and other public bodies.

Review Questions

 1 **a** Copy and complete the diagram of the electromagnetic spectrum.
Use words from this list:

microwaves   **gamma rays**   **ultraviolet**

radio waves		infrared	visible light		X-rays	

b Where in the electromagnetic spectrum do the photons have the most energy?

c Which **one** of the following is **not** ionising radiation?

     gamma rays   **microwaves**   **ultraviolet**   **X-rays**

2 The graph shows how the percentage of carbon dioxide in the atmosphere has changed over the past 300 years.

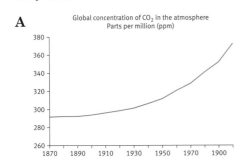

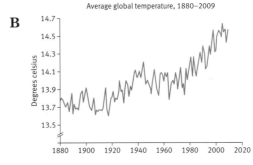

a Describe the trend in graph A.

b Describe the trend in graph B.

c Suggest a reason for what the graph shows.

d Use the two graphs to explain the meaning of correlation.

 3

A

C

B

D

Choose the letters of the correct diagrams to answer these questions.

a Which signal has picked up noise?

b Which signal shows the noisy signal after it is cleaned up?

c Which signal is an analogue signal?

B3 Life on Earth

Why study life on Earth?

There are over 30 million species of living things on Earth today. Where did they all come from? Why is there so much variety? Is that variety important? Can we learn to look after life on Earth better for future generations? These are the big questions we ask science to answer. Scientists think life began on Earth 3500 million years ago. The first simple organisms have developed and changed, and many species have become extinct.

What you already know

- Genetic information is passed on from both parents.

- Plants make biomass by photosynthesis.

- Environmental factors affect where organisms live.

- A habitat should provide all the essentials for life and reproduction.

- Organisms show adaptations to environmental conditions.

- Food webs show feeding relationships.

Find out about

- how different species depend on each other

- how life on Earth is evolving

- how scientists developed an explanation for evolution

- why it matters whether some species become extinct.

The Science

Fossils and DNA provide evidence for how life on Earth evolves. Simple organisms change slowly to form new species. All life forms depend on their environment and on other species to survive. Ultimately all life depends on energy from the Sun.

Ideas about Science

Evolution was a new idea 200 years ago, but is now accepted. Developing new explanations takes evidence and imagination. Even then, new evidence changes explanations.

The variety of species on Earth is a valuable resource. Scientists can help us find ways to use natural resources sustainably.

Find out about

- ✓ **differences in living things**
- ✓ **what a species is**
- ✓ **adaptations of organisms**

You can usually see the differences between different kinds of living things on Earth. But there are also a lot of similarities. For example, almost all living things use DNA to pass on information from one generation to the next.

Human skin cells and cells in these butterfly wings use the same chemical reaction to make pigment.

Classification – working out where we belong

Scientists use the similarities and differences between living things to put them into groups. It's called **classification**. The biggest group that humans belong to is the kingdom *Animalia* (the Animal Kingdom). The smallest is *Homo sapiens*, or human beings. *Homo sapiens* is our **species** name.

Classification names are in Latin. Everyone can use the same name for something. It doesn't matter what languages two people speak, they can always use the same Latin name.

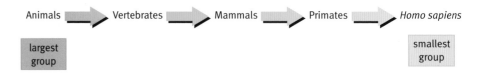

Animals → Vertebrates → Mammals → Primates → *Homo sapiens*

largest group

smallest group

Human beings belong to these groups. You are most closely related to other members of *Homo sapiens*. But you belong to these other groups as well. As groups get smaller they contain fewer organisms with more features in common. Vertebrates are all the animals that have skeletons with backbones. Mammals all have limbs with five digits. Primates have shoulder joints that can move in all directions and have eyes in bone sockets.

Summary box

- ✓ **Species** are groups of very similar organisms.
- ✓ Members of the same species can breed together. Their offspring can also breed. They are **fertile**. Different species can sometimes breed, but their offspring can't. They are **infertile**.
- ✓ **Adaptations** are features that help species to survive.

horse

What makes a species?

A species is a group of organisms so similar that:

*   they can breed together
*   their offspring can also breed (they are **fertile**).

Horses and donkeys are good examples to explain species. They can breed together and produce offspring called mules. But mules are **infertile**. Horses and donkeys look similar, but they are different species.

Variation in a species

Members of a species are different. You only need to look around your classroom to see that this is true. Both your genes and the environment cause this variation.

donkey

The art of survival

All of the 30 million or so species presently alive on Earth are successful survivors. They have features that help them survive in their environments and increase their chance of reproducing. These features are called **adaptations**.

Cactus plants live in hot, dry conditions. Their adaptations help them to survive:
*   Swollen stems store water.
*   Deep roots reach water in soil.

Fish have adaptations to live in water:
*   Gills absorb oxygen from the water.
*   A streamlined shape helps them to move through the water more easily.

mule

Questions

1   What species do you belong to?

2   Explain why horses and donkeys are different species.

3   Why are adaptations important?

Horses, donkeys, and mules look very similar.

Find out about

- ✓ **why some species become extinct**
- ✓ **how organisms are interdependent**

Fossil from burgess shale. This creature lived 505 million years ago. It is now extinct. Scientists think it may be the ancestor of crabs and centipedes.

Red squirrels used to live all over the UK. Now the larger American grey squirrels have taken over most of their habitats.

Summary box

- ✓ **A habitat is where species live.**
- ✓ **When every member of a species dies it is extinct.**
- ✓ **Species may become extinct if conditions change.**

Over the past few million years, many species of plants and animals have lived on Earth. Most of these species have died out. When all the members of a species die out it is **extinct**.

When many species die out at the same time, it is called **mass extinction**. There have been at least five mass extinctions on Earth. Fossils have told us this. Fossils are the dead bodies of living things. They have been preserved in rocks. Now we seem to be at the beginning of another mass extinction.

Around the world over 12 000 species of plants and animals are at risk of extinction. They are endangered.

Where an animal or plant lives is called its **habitat**. Any quick changes in their habitat can put them at risk of extinction.

Changes in the environment

All living things need factors like water and the right temperature to survive. Rising temperatures are changing many habitats. This global warming is putting many species at risk.

New species

New species moving into the habitat can put another species at risk of extinction.

- Animals and plants compete with each other for the things they need. Two different species that need exactly the same things cannot live together. One wins the **competition** for resources like food and shelter, if it is an animal. Plants compete for resources like light and water.
- The new species could be a **predator** of the species already living there.
- If the new species causes **disease**, it could wipe out the species already living there.

Going hungry

Plants and animals need other species in their habitat. For example, in this food chain spiders eat caterpillars.

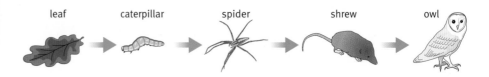

leaf   caterpillar   spider   shrew   owl

So if the caterpillars all died, the spiders could be at risk. That could also endanger the shrew and the owl.

The food web

Most animals eat more than one thing. Many different food chains contain the same animals. They can be joined together into a **food web**.

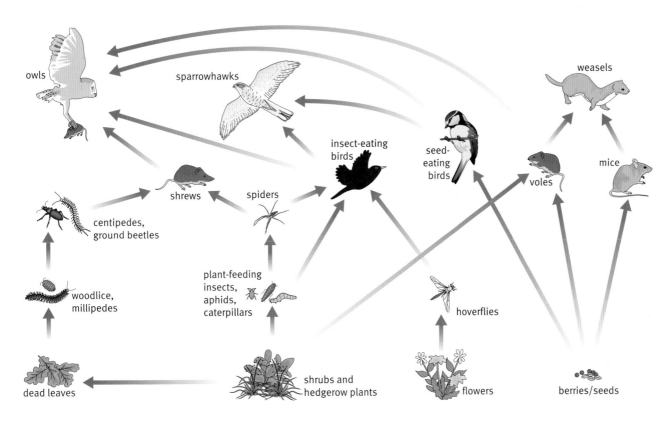

A new animal can come into a food web. It can affect plants, animals, and microorganisms already living there.

Questions

1 Explain what is meant by extinct.

2 Name two things that:
   a plant species may compete for
   b animal species may compete for.

3 Look at the food web on this page.
   a Name two different animals competing for the same food source.
   b A disease kills all the flowering plants. What happens to the number of hoverflies?

Summary box

- ✓ **Species may be in competition for the same resource**, for example, food.
- ✓ **One animal species may eat another. It is a predator.**
- ✓ **Living things with disease may not survive.**
- ✓ **Food webs show how organisms in a habitat depend on each other for food.**

Find out about

- ✓ **how organisms depend on the Sun's energy**
- ✓ **how energy and nutrients pass through food webs**

The plant is harnessing light energy to drive food production.

Woodlice feed on dead organic matter like rotting wood.

Question

1 Explain how you depend on the Sun's energy.

Nearly all organisms are ultimately dependent on energy from the Sun. The Sun provides energy to keep the Earth's atmosphere warm and drive the production of food chemicals.

Food chains like the one on page 197 all follow the same pattern. They start with plants, the **producers**.

Plants capture energy from sunlight. They use the energy to build up glucose and other compounds. Carbon dioxide and water are the raw materials. This is the process of **photosynthesis**.

Energy from sunlight is stored in these new compounds. They make up the plants' cells. The compounds can be broken down to release energy. The energy stored is passed to other organisms as the plants are eaten or **decompose**.

A lot of light reaches plant leaves. Plants trap only about 1–3% of the light energy in new plant material. This might sound small, but the Sun's energy output is enormous. So this 1–3% is still enough energy to power life on Earth.

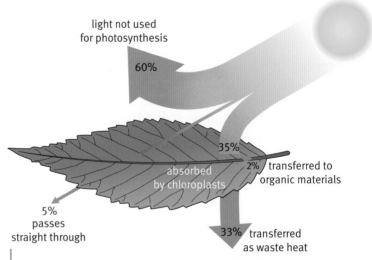

light not used for photosynthesis

60%

35% absorbed by chloroplasts

2% transferred to organic materials

5% passes straight through

33% transferred as waste heat

Most of the light energy reaching a leaf is reflected from the surface. Some is transferred as waste heat or passes straight through the leaf. The chloroplasts absorb only a small percentage for photosynthesis.

Energy transfer

Animals have to eat. They cannot make their own food so they need to take in organic molecules. They are called **consumers**. They break down food molecules in **respiration**.

Some of the energy released by respiration is used for growth. The food molecules then become part of the structure of new cells.

Animals also use energy released by respiration for other life processes, for example keeping warm.

Only about 10% of the energy at each stage of a food chain gets passed on to the next level. The rest:

- is used for life processes in the organism, such as movement
- escapes into the environment as heat energy
- is excreted as waste and passes to decomposers
- cannot be eaten and passes to decomposers.

This means that the number of organisms usually gets smaller at each level of an ecosystem. The food chain is limited to only a few levels. Usually there are only the producers, primary consumers, secondary consumers, and tertiary consumers.

Energy also flows into organisms that feed on dead organisms and waste material in the ecosystem.

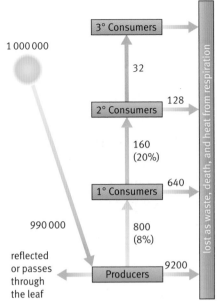

Energy flow through an ecosystem.

Bacteria and fungi are decomposers. This photograph shows fungus growing on a dead weevil.

Questions

2 Look at the food web on page 197. Identify two:
  a producers
  b primary consumers
  c secondary consumers
  d tertiary consumers.

3 Explain why the energy in a producer will not all be transferred to the primary consumer in the same food chain.

Summary box

✔ **Nearly all organisms depend on energy from the Sun.**

✔ **Plants convert carbon dioxide and water into glucose. This reaction uses energy from the Sun and is called photosynthesis.**

✔ **Plants and animals release energy from food by respiration.**

✔ **Plants make food chemicals, so they are producers.**

✔ **Animals eat plants, so they are consumers.**

✔ **Energy passes between organisms in a food chain.**

✔ **Some energy is lost at each stage, for example, it is used for movement.**

Find out about

- ✓ **how carbon and nitrogen are recycled through the environment**
- ✓ **how we can measure environmental change using living and non-living indicators**

Summary box

- ✓ **The carbon cycle shows how carbon is recycled through the environment.**
- ✓ **Combustion, decomposition, and respiration add carbon dioxide to the atmosphere.**
- ✓ **Photosynthesis uses light energy to produce glucose and oxygen from carbon dioxide and water. This removes carbon dioxide from the atmosphere.**
- ✓ **Respiration is when glucose and oxygen react to release energy and form carbon dioxide and water.**
- ✓ **Decomposition is the breakdown of dead bodies and waste.**

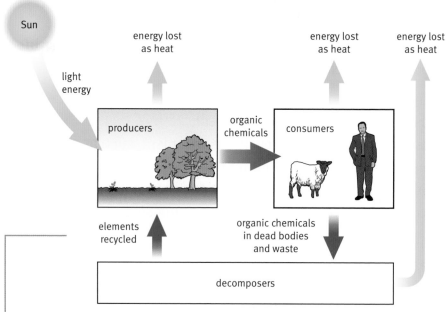

The transfer of energy and elements through an ecosystem.

Carbon and nitrogen are passed on to other organisms along food chains. In this way they move through the ecosystem like energy. But there is a big difference.

Carbon and nitrogen are recycled in an ecosystem.

Recycling carbon

There is only a certain amount of carbon on Earth. Much of the carbon is in molecules that make up the bodies of living things. A lot is also in the atmosphere and oceans as carbon dioxide, and in molecules of **fossil fuels** (gas, oil and coal).

Carbon dioxide is taken out of the atmosphere by **photosynthesis**. The carbon is used to produce glucose molecules. The glucose is broken down during **respiration**. This releases carbon dioxide back into the atmosphere.

When an animal or plant dies its organic compounds are broken down by microorganisms. This is called **decomposition**. The carbon atoms become part of a new organism in the system.

Combustion, or burning, of wood and fossil fuels adds carbon dioxide to the atmosphere.

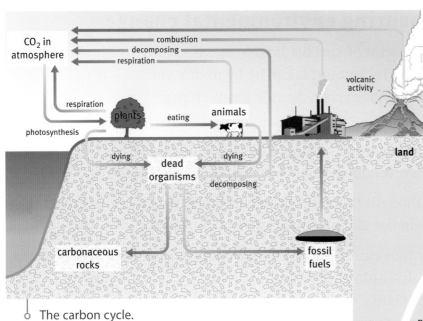

The carbon cycle.

Recycling nitrogen

Like carbon, nitrogen is recycled through the environment. It passes through the air, soil, and living organisms.

Nitrates in the soil are made using nitrogen from the air. This is called nitrogen fixation.

Plants take up nitrates from the soil. Plants use them to make proteins. Primary consumers (herbivore animals) eat plants. The nitrogen compounds pass along food chains.

When animals and plants die they decay. This releases nitrates back into the soil. They are available for plants to absorb once again. Urine and faeces contain nitrogen. When this waste is excreted, the nitrogen is recycled.

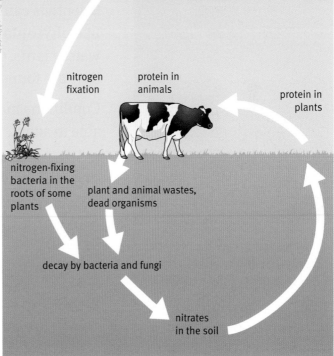

The nitrogen cycle.

Questions

1 Look at the diagram on page 200 of the transfer of energy and elements through an ecosystem. Explain how energy is transferred from:
   a the grass to the sheep
   b the tree to the decomposers.

2 List ways in which carbon dioxide is:
   a added to the atmosphere
   b taken out of the atmosphere.

Measuring environmental change

The amount of carbon dioxide released into the air should balance the amount taken up by photosynthesis. If not, atmospheric carbon dioxide levels change.

Most scientists agree that the average level of carbon dioxide in the atmosphere is rising. In 2010 the atmosphere is 0.04% carbon dioxide. It is expected to be 0.05% by the end of the century.

It is thought that the rise in carbon dioxide levels is linked to rises in the global temperature of the Earth.

Scientists can measure climate change by looking at organisms, like **phytoplankton** species. Phytoplankton are microscopic water plants. Changes in temperature in the ocean affect where they are found and their numbers.

Conditions may change too quickly. Many species may not be able to adapt. Then they may become extinct.

Phytoplanktons are microscopic plants that drift in water. There are lots of species of phytoplankton.

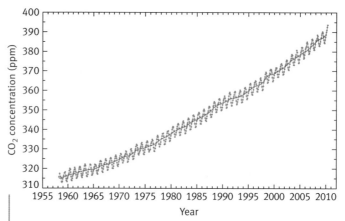

Carbon dioxide concentrations rise and fall each year. But there has been an increase of about 1.5 ppm per year since 1980.

Questions

3 How are humans causing the amount of carbon dioxide in the atmosphere to rise?

4 *Ceratium trichoceros* is a species of phytoplankton. Before 1970 it was only found off the south coast of England. It is now found in the waters off Scotland.

What environmental change may have affected where this phytoplankton live?

5 A gardener notices that the feathery-type lichens have disappeared from her garden. What change in the environment may have occurred?

Measuring water quality

Farmers often add nitrogen to their fields in the form of chemical fertiliser. This helps make the soil more fertile and increases plant growth. But this can also affect the environment badly.

Chemical fertiliser is very soluble in water. Water rich in nitrate can drain from fields into streams, rivers, and lakes. A high level of nitrate in water can affect the organisms that live there. It can cause the rapid growth of microscopic organisms called plankton. This results in massive algal blooms.

The algae use up oxygen in the water. The amount of oxygen dissolved in the water becomes low. Animals like **mayfly larvae** need high levels of oxygen. They cannot survive. Mayfly larvae will not be found in water that contains high levels of nitrates.

Measuring nitrate levels and living indicators shows if the environment is changing.

Monitoring air quality

Nitrogen compounds can also pollute the air. Air quality can be monitored by studying the types of lichens surviving in a particular area.

Some **lichens** are very sensitive to nitrogen compounds. They will only grow in places with no air pollution. Sensitive species are usually more feathery types. They die out when air pollution rises.

Summary box
- ✓ **Rising carbon dioxide levels have been linked to rising global temperatures.**
- ✓ **Changes in water quality can be measured by recording nitrate levels and species surviving in the water.**
- ✓ **Mayfly larvae cannot survive in water that has high levels of nitrate.**
- ✓ **Some lichens are very sensitive to air pollution. Both these species indicate environmental change.**

Monitoring invertebrates like these mayfly larvae allow changes in water quality to be measured.

The golden shield lichen can live in areas with high air pollution.

The heather rags lichen is very sensitive to nitrogen pollution in the air. It is rarely found close to roads in big cities.

Explaining similarities

Scientists agree that life on Earth began about 3500 million years ago. Life started from a few simple living things. This explains why living things are similar.

These simple living things changed over time. The enormous variety of different species of living things on Earth today came from there. The changes also produced many species that are now extinct. This process of change is called **evolution**. It is still happening today.

Fossil evidence for evolution

Fossils are very important as evidence for evolution. Almost all fossils found are of extinct species. This is more than 99% of all species that have ever lived on Earth.

How reliable is fossil evidence?

Fossils only develop in certain conditions. Only a very few living things end up as fossils. So there are gaps in the fossil record.

Scientists have collected millions of fossils. This evidence has helped to build up a picture of evolution, showing how one species evolves from another.

Find out about

✓ **how fossils and DNA provide evidence for evolution**

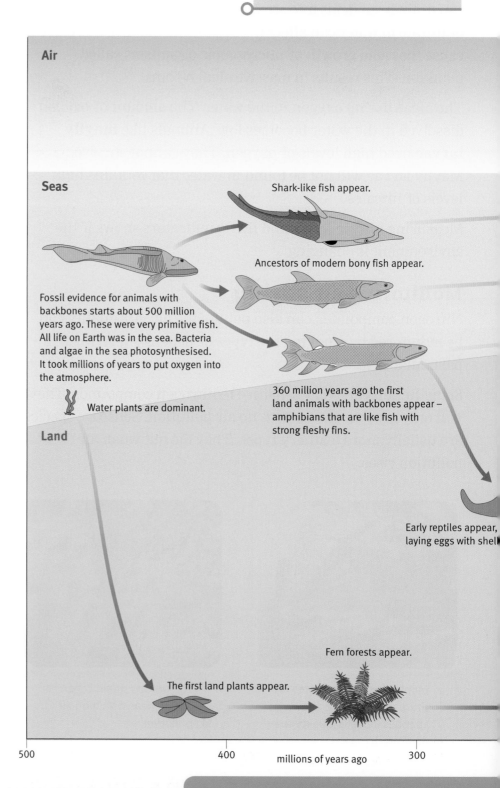

Air

Seas

Shark-like fish appear.

Ancestors of modern bony fish appear.

Fossil evidence for animals with backbones starts about 500 million years ago. These were very primitive fish. All life on Earth was in the sea. Bacteria and algae in the sea photosynthesised. It took millions of years to put oxygen into the atmosphere.

Water plants are dominant.

360 million years ago the first land animals with backbones appear – amphibians that are like fish with strong fleshy fins.

Land

Early reptiles appear, laying eggs with shell

Fern forests appear.

The first land plants appear.

500   400   millions of years ago   300

DNA evidence for evolution

Scientists also compare the DNA from different living things. The more similar the DNA of two living things, the more closely related they are. This information helps scientists to classify them and make sense of the variety of organisms on Earth. They can work out where different species fit on the evolutionary tree.

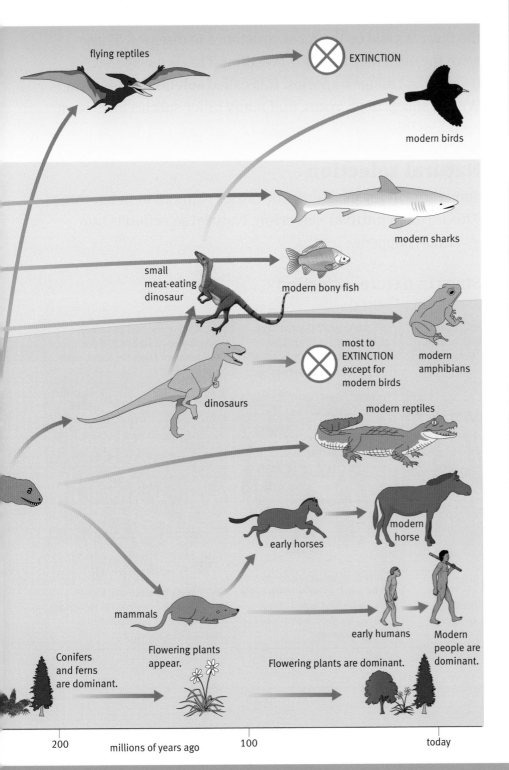

Over 98% of human genes are the same as those of a chimpanzee.

Summary box

✓ **Evolution** is the process of change in living things.
✓ **Fossils and DNA** provide evidence for evolution. They show how living things have changed over time.
✓ **You can tell how closely related organisms are by how similar their DNA is.**

Question

1 Scientists use two types of evidence for evolution. What are they?

Find out about

- ✔ **how evolution happens – natural selection**
- ✔ **how humans have changed some species**

Selective breeding has produced tulips with different coloured flowers.

Evolution is happening now. Scientists can measure the changes in species. They expect evolution will continue in the future. Humans can change the evolution of some species.

Selective breeding

Early farmers noticed differences in their crop plants and animals. Some had the features they wanted, for example, the biggest yield or the most resistance to diseases. These were the ones they used for breeding. This is a way that people can change a species. It is called **selective breeding**. Wheat, sheep, dogs, roses, and many other species have been bred like this.

Natural selection

Something in the environment causes changes in living things. This is called **natural selection**. Natural selection is how evolution happens.

Steps in natural selection

① *Living things in a species are not identical. They have variation.*

Ancestors of modern giraffes had variation in the length of their necks.

② *They compete for things like food, shelter, and a mate. But what if something in the environment changes?*

Food supply became scarce. The giraffes competed for food.

③ *Some will have features that help them to survive. They are more likely to breed. They pass their genes on to their offspring.*

Taller giraffes were able to eat more food, so were more likely to survive and breed. They passed on their features to the next generation.

④ *More of the next generation have the useful feature. If the environment stays the same, even more of the following generation will have the useful feature.*

Over many generations, more giraffes with longer necks were born. The number of taller giraffes in populations increase.

Effects of humans

People have used poisons to kill head lice for many years. In the 1980s, doctors thought that head lice in the UK would soon be wiped out.

But a few headlice survived the poisons. These lice bred. Now there are **populations** or groups of 'superlice' in parts of the country. The poisons do not kill them. They are **resistant**.

Headlice are changing because of humans. But this is another example of natural selection. No-one chose or selected superlice.

Head lice are quite common. They feed on blood.

Question

1 How does evolution happen?

For many years people used the same shampoo to kill head lice.

A few head lice in the population were able to survive. Their cells were probably able to break down the poison.

'Superlouse' was more likely to breed than the head lice killed by the poison.

Eggs laid by 'Superlouse' hatched into lice that also survived the poison.

These lice spread to other people and bred.

The number of resistant lice in the population increased. People couldn't get rid of their head lice.

Scientists developed a new poison to kill the head lice.

The cycle began again – and the species changed a little more.

Summary box

✓ Humans have changed some species by **selective breeding**.

✓ The environment changes some individuals. They pass on their features to their offspring. Over time most individuals have the features. This is **natural selection**. In this way species change. This is **evolution**.

Question

2 Copy and complete the table below to compare selective breeding and natural selection.

Steps in selective breeding	Steps in natural selection
Living things in a species are not all the same.	Living things in a species are not all the same.
Humans choose the individuals with the feature that they want.	
These are the plants or animals that are allowed to breed.	
They pass their genes on to their offspring.	
More of the next generation will have the chosen feature.	
If people keep choosing the same feature, even more of the following generation will have it.	

Today most scientists agree that evolution happens. But evolution wasn't always accepted. A very important person in the story of evolution was Charles Darwin.

Darwin's big idea

Darwin worked out how evolution could happen. He explained how natural selection could produce evolution. But it took many years for him to have this idea.

Charles Darwin was born in 1809. He was always interested in plants and animals. When he was 22, Darwin was given the chance to sail on HMS *Beagle*. The ship was on a five-year, round-the-world trip to make maps.

Journey of the *Beagle*

The *Beagle* stopped at lots of places. At each stop Darwin collected many specimens of plants and animals. He recorded what he saw in notes and pictures.

The *Beagle* stopped at the Galápagos Islands, near South America. Darwin travelled between the different islands. He noticed that there were several species of finches living on the Galápagos Islands. They were different.

Darwin on HMS *Beagle*.

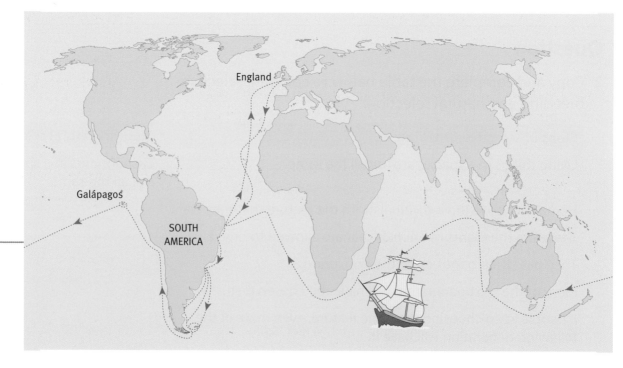

The *Beagle* stopped at different places around the world.

The famous Galápagos finches

Each species of finch seemed to have a different beak. Each beak was suited to eating a different thing. For example, one had a beak like a parrot for cracking nuts. Another had a very tiny beak for eating seeds. It was as if the beaks were adapted to eating the food on each different island.

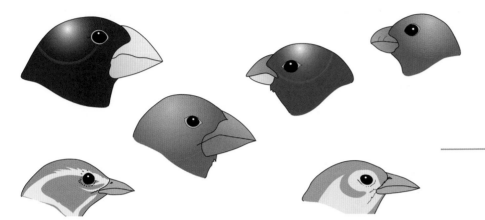

Different species of finch.

In his notes, Darwin started to ask himself a question. Could all the different finches have evolved from just one species?

What was special about Darwin?

Darwin wasn't the first scientist to think that evolution happens. His own grandfather had written about it earlier. But most people at the time didn't agree with evolution. Darwin was the first person to make a strong argument. This changed their minds.

He started by looking at lots of living things. He made many observations. He would use these as evidence for his argument. Then:

- He thought about the evidence in a way that no-one had done before. He was more creative and imaginative.
- He came up with an idea to explain *how* evolution could happen. This was natural selection.

Questions

1 Darwin made many observations about different species. How did he record his data?

2 What personal qualities did Darwin show that helped him develop his explanation of natural selection?

More evidence back home

Darwin worked on his idea of natural selection for 20 years. He exchanged letters with other scientists in different parts of the world. All the time, Darwin was looking for more evidence to support his ideas.

Darwin had some pet pigeons at home. They had many different shapes and colours. But Darwin knew they all belonged to the same species. So he realised that:

• animals or plants from the same species are all different. There is **variation**.

Competition means that many elephants do not survive.

Darwin found more evidence for natural selection at home.

Too many to survive

Next, Darwin realised that:

• there are always too many of any species to survive.

Elephants usually reproduce from age 30 to 90. Darwin worked out that, if they all survived, after 750 years there would be nearly 19 million elephants from just one pair! This does not happen.

All the elephants compete for food and space. A lot of them don't survive.

Darwin put these ideas together. He saw that some animals in a population were better suited to survive than others. They would breed and pass on their features to the next generation. This natural selection could make a species change over time. Darwin had explained how evolution could happen.

Questions

3 How did Darwin try to get more evidence to support his ideas?

4 Natural selection is sometimes described as 'survival of the fittest'. How good a description of natural selection do you think this is?

Same data, different explanations

Other scientists also saw that living things were different. They saw fossils that showed changes in species.

A French scientist called Lamarck wrote a different explanation to Darwin's. He said that animals changed during their lifetime. Then they passed these changes on to their young. He used the example of a giraffe. This was fifty years before Darwin published his ideas.

Why was Darwin's explanation better?

A good explanation does two things:

- it accounts for all the observations
- it explains a link between things that people hadn't thought of before.

Lamarck's explanation said that 'nature' had started with simple living things. At each generation, these got more complicated. If this kept happening, simple living things, like single-celled animals, should disappear. But his idea didn't account for some observations, for example, why simple living things still exist on Earth.

Darwin's idea could better account for these observations. It also linked together variation and competition. This hadn't been done before.

Lamarck's ideas may sound daft now, but he was a good scientist. He tried to explain changes in species.

Why was Darwin worried about his explanation?

Darwin was worried about how people would react. He wrote his idea of natural selection into a book. Then he hid it in a cupboard under the stairs. It stayed hidden for almost 15 years.

The giraffe stretches its neck to reach the food.

The neck becomes longer. MUNCH MUNCH

The giraffe passes its new longer neck on to its offspring.

Giraffe evolution explained by Lamarck.

Summary box

- ✓ Individuals of a species are different. This **variation** means that natural selection can happen. This explains how species can change over time. This is evolution.
- ✓ Members of a species **compete** for resources, like food. Those with the best features survive to reproduce.
- ✓ Darwin's explanation was better than Lamarck's idea. It explains and links all the observations.

Questions

5 What two things make a good explanation?

6 What two things did Darwin link together to work out his explanation of natural selection?

People agreed with Darwin's observations. But they didn't agree with his explanation.

Huxley and Hooker were at the 1860 British Association for the Advancement of Science meeting. They argued in favour of Darwin's theory.

Questions

7 Most people in the 1800s disagreed with natural selection. What evidence did they have against this explanation?

8 Suggest why scientists are sometimes reluctant to give up an accepted explanation, even when new data seems to show it is wrong.

On the Origin of Species

Then, in 1856, Darwin received a letter from another scientist, Alfred Russell Wallace. In it Wallace wrote about the idea of natural selection. Darwin was stunned. He gave Wallace credit for what he had done. Then the two of them published a short report of some of their ideas. But now Darwin wanted to publish his full book.

On the Origin of Species was published in November 1859. This book is now famous. It caused one of the biggest arguments in the history of science.

Many people in Victorian England did not like the idea of natural selection leading to evolution. They were unhappy about the idea that humans were related to apes.

Why did people start to believe in evolution?

In 1860, many scientists argued against Darwin's idea. Darwin's two friends, Thomas Huxley and Joseph Hooker, spoke at a science meeting. They were very good scientists. They helped to change many people's minds about natural selection.

The end of the story?

Natural selection was a good explanation. But there were three big problems with it.

Firstly, he knew that there was not a complete record of fossils in the rocks. New fossil evidence has now been found. It supports the idea of natural selection.

Secondly, in Darwin's time people thought the Earth was about 6000 years old. So there didn't seem to have been enough time for evolution to have taken place. Scientists now have evidence that the Earth is about 4.5 billion years old.

The last problem was in two parts. Darwin could not explain:
- why all the living things in one species were not all the same
- how living things passed features on from one generation to the next.

Where did variation come from?

How do living things inherit features?

Darwin did not know about genes. If he had, he could have answered both these questions.

Gregor Mendel (1822–84) was an Austrian monk. He was breeding pea plants at the same time that Darwin was writing *On the Origin of Species*. From his experiments he discovered dominant and recessive alleles. These are different versions of the same gene. Mendel's work explained how features were passed on. He sent a copy of his work to Darwin. But Darwin didn't realise how important it was.

The debate goes on

People continue to argue about evolution. Many people have strong personal beliefs that are affected by this idea. So the debate is likely to go on for some time.

Summary box
- ✓ People did not like the idea that they are related to apes.
- ✓ Well-respected scientists supported Darwin's ideas.
- ✓ Scientific discoveries since Darwin's time support his ideas.

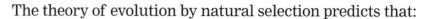

H The birth of species

Find out about

✓ **how new species are formed**

The theory of evolution by natural selection predicts that:
- new species will be formed from existing species
- other species will become extinct.

These events usually happen very slowly. It takes many generations for a new species to form. This is why Darwin was not able to see this happening. Since Darwin's time, scientists have learned a lot about DNA. This has helped them to understand how new species are formed.

Species show variation

At the beginning of this module you saw that a species is a group of organisms that can breed together. Their offspring are fertile. They cannot reproduce successfully with members of different species.

The members of a species are not identical. There is variation.

Mutations

When DNA is copied, sometimes a mistake is made. This is a **mutation**. A mutation might give different coloured flowers or spots on an animal's fur. Mutations happen naturally. They are also caused by some chemicals and ionising radiation.

Mutations cause variation

Mutations produce differences in a species. They cause variation. This is very important for natural selection.

Most mutations have no effect on the plant or animal. They don't harm them or help them survive. Some mutations are harmful. Very, very rarely a mutation causes a change that makes an organism better at surviving. If the mutation is in the organism's sex cells, it can be passed on to its offspring.

A mutation in gene controlling fur makes some tigers have white fur.

Questions

1 Explain what a mutation is.

2 What can cause a mutation?

Living in an uncertain environment

Environments change. When this happens only some of the population will survive. Some individuals will have features that are better suited to the new environment than others. These are better adapted and will survive.

Living in splendid isolation

Some populations are isolated from each other. They have no contact with their neighbours. Organisms will be able to reproduce with other members of their own population. But they will never meet organisms from other populations.

Sometimes one population changes. This will prevent them from reproducing successfully with organisms from populations nearby, even if they met. This is called **reproductive isolation**. The isolated population has become a new species.

Lake Malawi is in East Africa. It contains over 2000 species of brightly coloured cichlid fish. Recently scientists studied their DNA. This DNA evidence showed that they evolved from a single species of fish.

This fish species entered the lake about 1.5 million years ago. This is a long time ago. But for evolution it is very quick.

The populations of cichlids live in the same lake. But they are isolated. This is because different parts of the lake have very different conditions. These differences isolate the populations from each other. If the different species meet they cannot reproduce successfully.

Cichlid fish from Lake Malawi in East Africa.

Question

3 What three processes combine to produce a new species?

Summary box
- ✓ **Mutations are changes in the DNA of a gene.**
- ✓ **Mutation causes variation in a species.**
- ✓ **New species form when their environment changes. This happens because of variation, natural selection, and reproductive isolation.**

Find out about

- ✔ **why it matters if species become extinct**
- ✔ **biodiversity and sustainability**

The dodo was a fat flightless bird. In 1598 sailors arrived on the island where the dodos lived. They brought with them cats, rats, and dogs. These are thought to have attacked the dodos' chicks or eaten their eggs. The sailors may have cut down trees taking away the dodos' habitat. The dodos were not able to survive the changes to their environment. By 1700 the species had became extinct.

There could be over 30 million species on Earth. This includes different animals, plants, fungi, algae, and microorganisms. Within each species is a huge range of genetic variation. This variety of life on Earth is called **biodiversity**.

Does extinction matter?

If new species are being formed, does it matter that some become extinct? Isn't extinction just part of life? Twenty-First Century Science put this question to Georgina Mace of the UK Zoological Society.

Georgina Mace.

"It is true that species have always gone extinct. This is a natural process. But the pattern of extinction today is different from what has been recorded in the past.
- The rate of species extinction today is thousands of times higher than in the past.
- Current extinctions are almost all due to humans."

Human beings can cause other species to become extinct:
- directly, for example, by hunting
- indirectly, for example, by taking away their habitat or bringing other species into the habitat.

Why do we need biodiversity?

If many species become extinct, it shows that the Earth is not a healthy place to live. There will be less variety on Earth. This variety is very important. It helps the environment recover from natural disasters. People depend on other species for many things. Food, fuel, natural fibres (such as cotton and wool), and medicines all come from other species.

Question

1 Give two reasons why it is important that we do not lose biodiversity of life on Earth.

Food crops

Over a long time people have developed wild plants into the food crops we have today. They did this by selective breeding.

The wild relatives are still around. But they are very different to the **domesticated** varieties. For example, wild potatoes are poisonous and wild sugar cane produces very little sugar. Scientists continue to use wild plants and selective breeding to develop new food crops.

Medicines

Many medicines have come from wild plants and animals. New medicines may be found in plants that haven't been found yet. There are still many diseases that need cures.

Natural disaster recovery

Ecosystems cope better with natural disasters when there is high biodiversity. 'Healthy' species have lots of genetic variation. In a drought a species like this is more likely to survive. Some individuals will be better adapted to drier conditions.

Some species will not be able to survive at all. These will become extinct locally.

If there are lots of different species in the ecosystem, some should survive.

Biodiversity and sustainability

To keep biodiversity, we have to use the Earth in a sustainable way. **Sustainability** means meeting the needs of people today without damaging the Earth for people of the future.

We have to make sure the Earth will be a good home for future generations. Making sure other species survive is an important part of this. Keeping biodiversity is about **conservation** of species.

Foxgloves are very poisonous. But they have given us a powerful medicine to treat heart disease.

> ## Question
>
> 2 Explain what is meant by sustainability.

Monoculture crop production helps to maximise yields and profits but reduces biodiversity.

The number of supermarket plastic bags used is falling. But the total packaging of food and other goods is rising. Large-scale packaging use is not sustainable.

Biodegradable plastics are made from starch and cellulose from plants.

Looking after the Earth

Farmers are important people when it comes to biodiversity. They look after much of our land. Farmers produce the food we eat. They have to do this in a sustainable way that will not damage the environment.

Monoculture

Farmers prefer to grow single crops in large fields. This is called a **monoculture**. This makes it easier to harvest crops with machines. Plants in a single crop will all have very similar genes. This helps them to grow at the same rate and be ready to harvest at the same time.

Disadvantages of monoculture

- Pests and diseases are very likely to attack the crop and take hold. This means that the farmer often uses a lot of chemical pesticides to control them.
- If crops had a greater variety of gene types or alleles, some plants would be resistant. The pest or disease would not be able to take hold.
- Monoculture could also threaten our food supply. If there is a natural disaster, like a flood or a drought, it could wipe out the whole crop.

Large fields and the use of pesticides reduce the number of species. This does not help biodiversity. It is not sustainable in the long-term.

Packaging

Packaging is useful. It protects food and other goods. They protect them on the journey from farms or factories to warehouses or shops. Then we take the food or goods home.

Packaging – the problem

Packaging can cause problems for the environment. It is one area that could be made more sustainable. We need to think carefully about how we make things and about how we dispose of the things we no longer need.

In 2008 the UK made about 10.7 million tonnes of packaging. Plastic is light and strong. We use plastics to package about

50% of all goods. All this packaging will end up as waste. In the past the majority of this waste ended up in landfill. Landfill is a huge hole in the ground. It is filled with waste. Then it is covered over and landscaped, hiding the rubbish underground.

Packaging – improving sustainability

Packaging materials such as paper and plant-based plastics are **biodegradable**. This means that bacteria and fungi will break them down with time. You may think that using biodegradable packaging is better for the Earth. They should decompose if put in a landfill site. This would be more sustainable than using oil-based plastics.

But sadly this is not the case. The bacteria that decompose waste need to have oxygen. Landfill sites often lack oxygen. This prevents the breakdown of the waste.

To make things worse, if waste does decompose it releases carbon dioxide. This increases greenhouse gases and could make climate change worse.

Recycling

One solution to the problem would be to recycle packaging waste. In 2008 the UK recycled 61% of its packaging waste. This is a massive increase from the 28% recycled in 1997.

Reduce packaging

It would be even better to use less packaging. To make and transport the original packaging requires resources and energy. These would be reduced. Collecting, transporting, and recycling the waste would no longer be necessary. This would save more energy and cut down carbon dioxide emissions.

Question

3 Explain how the use of packaging can be made more sustainable.

Newspapers dug up after years in a landfill site can still be read.

Summary box

- ✔ **Biodiversity** is the number and variety of different species and genetic variation within a species.
- ✔ **Extinction rate** is increasing.
- ✔ **Humans** can cause extinctions.
- ✔ **Sustainability** is when natural resources are used in such a way that they are available for future generations.
- ✔ **Monoculture** is when only one species is grown. That one species also has very little genetic variation.
- ✔ When something is **biodegradable** it can be broken down by microorganisms.
- ✔ Using less packaging would be more sustainable.

Science Explanations

In this module you will consider different explanations for evolution and learn about natural selection. You will learn how living organisms are dependent on their environment and each other for survival, and you will learn about biodiversity and sustainability.

You should know:

- that a species is a group of breeding organisms, producing fertile offspring
- how a change affecting one species in a food web affects all the other species
- why organisms compete for resources with other species in the same habitat
- how organisms become extinct if they cannot adapt to environmental change, or if a competitor, predator, or disease-causing organism enters the environment
- that the Sun is the ultimate source of energy for nearly all organisms
- how energy transfers through the ecosystem when organisms are eaten or decay
- how energy is lost from a food chain as heat, waste products, and uneaten parts, limiting the length of the food chain
- how carbon cycles through the environment, including the processes of combustion, respiration, photosynthesis, and decomposition
- that the nitrogen cycle involves excretion, decay, and uptake of nitrates by plants
- that life on Earth began 3500 million years ago, evolving from simple living things
- why all individuals of the same species are different and that some variation is genetic
- how mutations increase genetic variation and can be passed on to offspring
- how certain characteristics favour the survival of certain individuals in the process of natural selection
- how humans use selective breeding to choose characteristics in plants and animals
- how new species evolve through mutations, environmental changes, natural selection, and isolation
- that DNA analysis and the fossil record provide evidence for evolution
- how the classification of organisms helps to make sense of biodiversity and shows their evolutionary relationships
- that biodiversity includes the number of different species and variation within and between different species
- that extinction rates are increasing due to human activity
- how maintaining biodiversity is one of the keys to sustainability
- that biodiversity is vital for the development of food crops and medicines
- why large-scale monoculture of a single crop does not maintain biodiversity
- that all packaging materials use raw materials, energy for their production and transport, and create pollution; reducing their use improves sustainability.

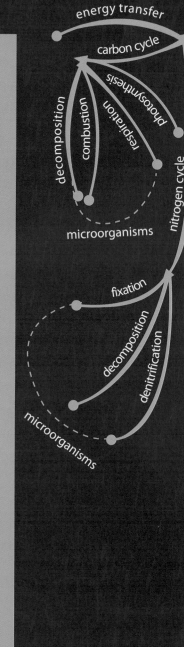

LIFE ON EARTH

adaptation

competition

food chains

food webs

interdependence

observations

creative thought

Darwin

sexual reproduction

variation

mutations

natural selection

evolution

evidence

DNA analysis

fossil record

classification

environmental change

indicators

lichens

mayfly larvae

non-living indicators

number of different species

variation between species

variation within species

biodiversity

ecosystem stability

extinction

human activity

sustainability

biodegradabale

landfill

recycling

developing scientific explanations

data from observations or measurements

creativity

predictions

making decisions

ethical issues

identifying issues

Ideas about Science

Science is about collecting data and using that data creatively to generate explanations. To test whether the explanations are correct, predictions are made and then new experiments or observations are checked against the predictions.

Scientists base their theories and explanations on observations and data. You will need to be able to distinguish between data and explanations and recognise those explanations that involve creative thinking.

Very often, conflicting explanations for the same data are produced. You should be able to suggest why scientists might disagree and to identify the better explanation, giving reasons for your choice. For example, Lamarck thought that characteristics were acquired during life and then passed on to their offspring. By thinking creatively, Darwin produced a new theory; he suggested that organisms evolved due to the process of natural selection. Some scientists disagreed with Darwin because of their personal or religious beliefs.

Scientific explanations can be tested by predictions and comparing the prediction with data obtained from experiments. When the data supports the

prediction our confidence in the explanation is increased. For example, we could predict that when a new antibiotic is produced, bacteria will rapidly evolve resistance to the antibiotic by the process of natural selection. If this were to happen it would increase our confidence in the theory of evolution and the process of natural selection.

Science-based technologies improve the quality of our lives. However, science can sometimes have unintended and undesirable consequences. So the benefits of the new technology need to be weighed against the costs. Humans have introduced new animals into ecosystems with the best of intentions but the consequences have sometimes been terrible, such as the introduction of the rabbit and cane toad into Australia.

You will need to be able to suggest examples of unintended impacts of human activity on the environment, and use ideas and data about sustainability to compare the sustainability of different products or processes, for example, using biodegradable products in packaging.

Review Questions

1 **a** Scientists have gathered evidence to show that life on Earth has evolved.
   Which of the statements below provide the scientists with evidence?
   - ancient manuscripts like the Dead Sea Scrolls
   - stories passed down from one generation to the next
   - the fossil record
   - looking at how life evolved on other planets
   - similarities and differences in DNA
   - using the Internet to research our ancestry.

   b Ideas about evolution have changed with time. Darwin produced his theory of evolution by natural selection. His ideas conflicted with the old explanations that many scientists believed.
   Explain why Darwin's explanation was better than the old ones.

   c Many scientists think that the Earth may warm up in the future.
   This is called climate change. Explain how climate change could produce new species.

2 Look at the food web.

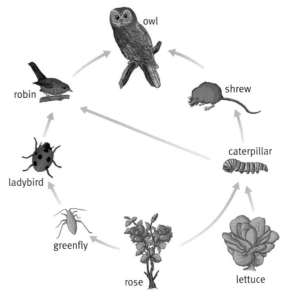

   a Explain the effect on the food web of a farmer spraying the caterpillars with an insecticide.
   b Write down one food chain found in the food web.
   c Explain how energy enters the food chain, how it is transferred along the food chain, and how it is lost from it.

3 Describe two ways a scientist might monitor environmental change in a stream.
   Explain what the scientist might observe if nitrogen fertiliser leaked into the stream.

C3 Chemicals in our lives: Risks and benefits

Why study chemicals in our lives?

You are made up of chemicals, and so is everything around you. Many of the chemicals in the things you buy are natural, others are synthetic. Some chemicals are very good for you, others may be harmful. This Module will help you to understand where some of these chemicals come from and why they are so useful.

What you already know

- Movements of tectonic plates lead to changes in the Earth's surface.

- Chemical reactions rearrange atoms to give products with new properties, which may be either helpful or harmful.

- Alkalis neutralise acids to form salts.

- Crude oil is a valuable source of hydrocarbons, used for fuel and to make synthetic polymers.

- Plasticisers can be used to modify the properties of polymers.

- There are ways to weigh up the risks and benefits of scientific discoveries.

Find out about

- the geological history of Britain, which explains why it is rich in natural resources

- methods chemists use to turn raw materials, such as salt, into many valuable products

- the choices people make to ensure they use chemicals safely and sustainably.

The Science

Science can help to explain why Britain has valuable natural resources including salt, limestone, coal, gas and oil. The chemical industry uses these raw materials to make new chemicals. This has added to the wealth of the country.

Ideas about Science

Manufactured chemicals bring many benefits – but there are also risks. Not all chemicals have been fully tested so the risks are not fully known. Studying all the stages in the life of products helps when choosing which products to use.

Find out about

- ✔ **how Britain came into existence as continents moved**
- ✔ **the different climates Britain has experienced**
- ✔ **magnetic clues that geologists use to track continents**

Moving tectonic plates

The Earth's outer layers (the crust and upper mantle) are divided into a number of **tectonic plates**. The tectonic plates move because of very slow **convection** currents in the mantle beneath the plates.

Movements of the tectonic plates cause oceans to open up slowly between continents in some parts of the world. In other parts of the world, plate movements bring continents together with great force, creating mountain ranges. Most major volcanic eruptions and earthquakes happen in places where tectonic plates meet.

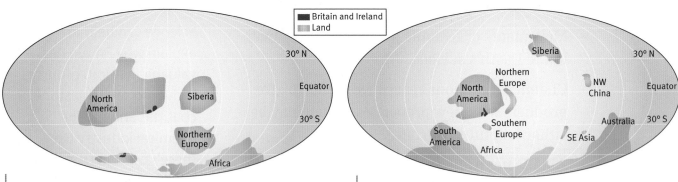

450 million years ago, the two parts of the Earth's crust that would one day make up Britain were both south of the Equator.

360 million years ago, the two parts of Britain collided. The collision created a chain of mountains. The land that would become Britain was at the edge of this chain of mountains in a dry continent.

280 million years ago, Britain was just north of the Equator and had desert-like conditions

65 million years ago, dinosaurs became extinct. Britain was on the edge of the North Atlantic ocean, just south of where it is today.

Magnetic crystals in rocks

In the 1950s, a group of scientists at Imperial College London showed that it is possible to track the very slow movement of the continents by studying **magnetic** minerals, such as magnetite, in rocks.

The mineral magnetite gets its name from its magnetic properties. When the rock forms, the magnetisation lines up in the direction of the Earth's magnetic field, rather like iron filings around a bar magnet.

By studying the angle of the magnetisation in the rocks, geologists can work out where on Earth the rock formed.

Scientists have combined the evidence from magnetism with other clues to track the movement north of the rocks in Britain over millions of years. This movement means that Britain has experienced many different climates during its long history. Evidence for these different climates can be found in the different rocks that now make up the country.

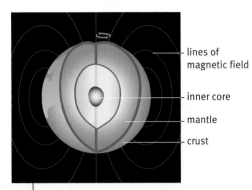

A cutaway diagram showing the Earth's magnetic field. At the Equator the magnetic field is parallel to the ground. Nearer to the Poles it is more steeply angled.

Questions

1 Give two geographical features caused by the movement of tectonic plates.

2 Why do tectonic plates move across the surface of the Earth?

3 What property of the mineral magnetite do geologists study?

4 Do the observations of magnetic minerals made by the scientists at Imperial College conflict with or support the theory of moving tectonic plates?

5 Suggest evidence that geologists might look for in order to test the theory that the northern and southern parts of Britain were once on different continents.

Summary box

✓ Britain came into existence as the tectonic plates moved slowly across the Earth's surface.

✓ As the parts of the Earth's crust that became Britain moved across the Earth's surface, the land experienced different climates, including desert-like conditions.

✓ Geologists track the movement of continents by studying magnetic minerals found in rocks.

Find out about

- ✔ **what geologists can learn by studying rocks**
- ✔ **the origins of some of the rocks in Britain**

Sand dunes in the Namib desert, Namibia. Studying today's sand dunes helps to explain grain sizes and ripples seen in sandstone rocks.

Clues to the past in the rocks

Geologists explain the history of the Earth by looking for clues in rocks. For example, they can find out about the history of a **sedimentary rock** such as sandstone by looking at the shape and size of the sand **grains** in the rock.

Fossilised ripples in sandstone on the Maumturk Mountains, County Galway, Ireland.

The sandstone may have formed from desert sand or river sediment. By comparing the sand grains in the rock with sand grains in deserts and rivers now, geologists can find out about the conditions when the rocks formed. Other clues come from fossilised ripples in rocks, produced by wind or water.

Some sedimentary rocks contain fossilised plants and animals. Geologists use **fossils** to put rock layers in order of their ages. This is possible because rocks may contain fossilised plants and animals from different time periods. Comparing these fossils with plants and animals alive today gives clues about the past environment where the fossilised plants and animals lived.

Different rocks from different climates

There is a rich variety of rocks in Britain. Some are very important economically because they contain useful resources. Salt, coal, and limestone formed in Britain at different times and in different climates.

A chemical industry grew up by the River Mersey in north-west England because all these resources were available nearby.

Summary box

- ✔ **Geologists study the shape and size of the grains in rocks to learn about their history. They also use fossils to work out the ages of rock layers.**
- ✔ **Different rocks in Britain formed at different times and in different conditions. For example, coal formed after the land was covered with swamp.**

Questions

1 How do geologists use fossils?

2 Name three useful resources found in Britain's rocks.

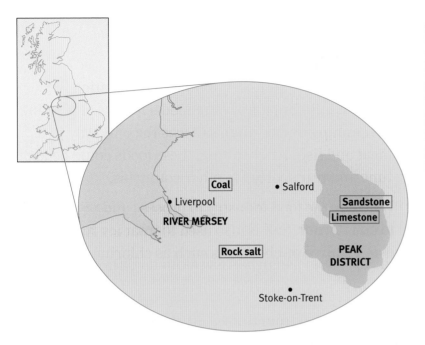

Limestone from a cavern in the Peak District. It contains fossils of crinoid sea lilies. This limestone formed 350 million years ago. When it formed, the land that would become the Peak District lay below a shallow, warm sea that was then just south of the Equator. At the time, the sea was full of living things. As the plants and animals died, they sank to the bottom and formed fossils in the limestone.

Sandstone in the Peak District. About 310 million years ago, the mountains to the north and east of the Peak District were **eroded** by fast-flowing rivers carrying sediments. Sand and small pebbles were deposited in layers, which were then compacted to form coarse sandstones. In the past, this rock was used to make millstones for grinding corn – it is called millstone grit.

Coal shale containing a fossil fern. About 280 million years ago, the river deltas in the area that is now Britain got bigger and created swamp land. Tree ferns grew in the swamps. As the plants died, they formed a layer of peat, which was covered by sediment, compressed, heated, and turned to coal. A period of mountain building followed and the rocks of the Peak District were pushed up towards the surface.

Rock salt mined in Cheshire, consisting mainly of the mineral halite. About 220 million years ago, the sea moved inland. The seawater contained dissolved salt and created a chain of shallow salt marshes across land that is now part of Cheshire. Deposits of rock salt formed as the water in the marshes **evaporated**. This rock salt has a red-yellow coloration. The colour is from sand that blew into the salt marshes from surrounding deserts.

Questions

3 Look at the information on this page.
   a How many years ago was Britain covered in swamp land? Which natural resource formed at this time?

   b How many years ago did the sea move inland across the area that is now Cheshire to create salt marshes?

Find out about

✔ **the uses of salt**

✔ **where salt comes from**

✔ **the methods used to obtain salt**

Salt cod in a fish market in Barcelona.

Salt pans near Mahabalipuram in India. Seawater runs into the pans and evaporates in the hot sunshine. Salt crystals are left behind.

Questions

1 State three uses of salt.

2 Why is large-scale extraction of salt from seawater only economical in hot countries?

The importance of salt

Salt has played an important part in human civilisation for thousands of years. Before there were modern ways of keeping food (such as canning or freezing), salt was the only way to **preserve** meat and fish. After salting, these foods could be kept for a long time and transported to other countries.

Salt is still used by the food industry to process and preserve food, and to add flavour. Salt is also used to treat icy roads in winter and as a source of chemicals such as chlorine.

Sea salt

Salt has been extracted from the sea off the east coast of Essex for over 2000 years. The rainfall in this part of Britain is lower than elsewhere. This means that the concentration of salt in the estuaries and rivers is higher, so less fuel is needed to evaporate the water and leave behind the salt. Small quantities of salt are still obtained in this way for adding to food at home.

Large-scale extraction of salt from the sea is only cost-effective in countries with hot and dry climates. In these places there is no need to burn fuel to evaporate the water, because the energy comes from the Sun.

Rock salt

There are two underground salt mines in England – one in North Yorkshire, the other in Cheshire.

Miners use giant machines to extract rock salt. The rock salt contains about 90% salt mixed with a reddish clay. This salt is mainly used to spread on the roads during freezing weather. Adding salt means that ice and snow melt. The salt used on roads does not need to be pure.

Mining rock salt.

Solution mining

The salt used for the chemical industry in Britain is not mined, it is extracted by pumping water down into the rock. The salt **dissolves** and is carried to the surface in **solution**. The impurities, such as clay, do not dissolve so they stay underground. The solution of salt in water is called **brine**.

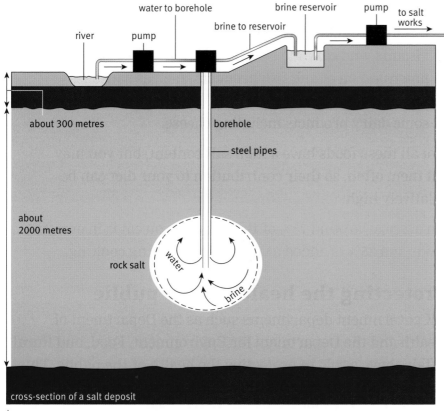

Using water to extract brine from an underground salt deposit.

Salt crystals are recovered from brine by evaporation. The process has to be as efficient as possible to minimise the amount of fuel needed to evaporate the water. The crystals are separated from the remaining brine by **filtering**.

Sudden subsidence

Large-scale pumping to extract salt as brine started in Cheshire in about 1870. This created very large underground holes, which led to widespread **subsidence** where buildings collapsed into the underground holes. Nowadays, pumping is planned so that the holes in the rock are spaced out and separated by pillars of rock. The pillars of rock help to prevent subsidence and stop buildings collapsing.

Summary box

- ✔ **Salt is used in the food industry, as a source of chemicals, and to treat roads in winter.**
- ✔ **Salt can be extracted from the sea by evaporating the water. It can be extracted from underground salt deposits by mining or by dissolving in water.**

Subsidence caused by salt mining in 1891.

Questions

3 What is brine?

4 Why is salt for treating roads extracted in a different way from salt used for food and salt in the chemical industry?

Find out about

- ✔ **why we need salt in our diet**
- ✔ **the possible risks from eating too much salt**
- ✔ **the debate about the evidence for the claims made about salt and health**

The sodium in salt is an essential part of your diet. It is found in your blood, tears, and nerves.

Questions

1. What are the main sources of salt in the diet?

2. A 25 g packet of crisps contains 0.6 g of salt. Do these crisps have a high, medium, or low salt content?

Salt in food

Salt is sodium chloride. The sodium in salt is an essential part of a healthy diet – but you only need a small amount. Salt is used as a **flavouring** and also enhances other flavours present in food. The food industry also uses salt to preserve and process food.

The main sources of salt in the diet are:

- cereal products such as bread, chapattis, breakfast cereals, biscuits, and cakes
- processed meat and fish products, such as sausages and bacon
- some dairy products including cheese.

Not all these foods have a high salt content, but you may eat them often, so their contribution to your diet can be relatively high.

On average, around 75% of the salt that you eat is in everyday foods and 25% is added at the table or during cooking.

Protecting the health of the public

UK government departments such as the Department of Health and the Department for Environment, Food, and Rural Affairs have a role in protecting the health of the public. This role includes carrying out risk assessments concerning chemicals in food. The goverment also advises the public about the effect of food on health.

Health risks from salt

Health experts think most people eat too much salt. The average salt intake in the UK in 2008 was 8.6 g per day. But less than half that, 4 g of salt a day, is enough for nearly everyone.

Government agencies have been working with health experts, consumers, and industry to reduce salt intake to a target of 6 g per day for adults, and less for children.

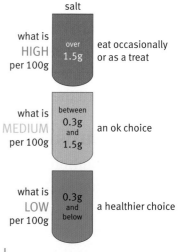

salt

what is HIGH per 100g	over 1.5g	eat occasionally or as a treat
what is MEDIUM per 100g	between 0.3g and 1.5g	an ok choice
what is LOW per 100g	0.3g and below	a healthier choice

The UK government advises shoppers to check the labels on packets and choose foods with less salt.

UK government agencies say that eating too much salt can raise people's blood pressure. This can increase the risk of developing heart disease or having a stroke. People can lower their blood pressure in as little as four weeks by cutting down on salt.

An independent body of experts, set up to advise the government, reviewed over 200 scientific research papers about salt and health. They concluded that 'A reduction in the dietary salt intake of the population would lower the blood pressure risk for the whole population.'

Challenging the salt theory

The European Salt Producers' Association is an industry body representing salt producers across Europe. They have produced a report challenging the **theory** that reducing salt intake brings health benefits for everyone. It suggests that there is no scientific proof for this theory. The report also suggests that a low-sodium diet could be harmful in some cases.

> **Summary box**
> - ✓ Salt in our diet provides sodium, which is found in blood, tears, and nerves.
> - ✓ It is possible that eating too much salt can raise people's blood pressure. This can increase the risk of developing heart disease or having a stroke.
> - ✓ Some people argue that there is no evidence that reducing the amount of salt in diets brings health benefits.

> There is conclusive evidence that moderate sodium reduction lowers blood pressure.

> The research does not support a general recommendation to reduce sodium intake.

> Cutting salt in the diet may be worthwhile for older people with high blood pressure. For people whose blood pressure is normal, the evidence is not strong enough to justify a general reduction in salt levels.

Three separate reviews of research each looked at studies to investigate the effect on blood pressure of salt levels in people's diet, and came to different conclusions.

Questions

3 Why do you think that UK government agencies and the European Salt Producers' Association say different things about the effect of salt on people's health?

4 Why might some people ignore the advice of the government and eat more than the recommended amount of salt?

Traditional alkalis

Before industrialisation, **alkalis** were needed to:

- neutralise acid soils
- convert fats and oils into soap
- make glass
- make chemicals that bind natural dyes to cloth.

Find out about

- ✔ uses of alkalis
- ✔ where alkalis used to come from
- ✔ neutralisation of acids with alkalis

A traditional lime kiln was used to heat chalk and limestone (calcuim carbonate) to break it down and form calcium oxide. Calcium oxide reacts with water to make calcium hydroxide, which is slightly soluble in water and can **neutralise** acids in soils.

Glass is made by melting sand (silicon oxide) with lime (calcium oxide) and soda ash (sodium carbonate).

The old way to make soap. Soap was made by boiling up animal fat with the alkali potash (potassium carbonate).

Alkalis for making alum

One of the first pure chemicals made in Britain was alum. Alum was used for dyeing cloth. It helps dyes stick to cloth so that the colours do not fade too quickly during washing.

Alum was made on the north-east coast of Britain, near Whitby, where rock from the cliffs is rich in aluminium compounds. Workers produced alum using this method:

1 Roast the rock for many months in an open-air fire.

2 Tip the burnt rock into a pit of water and stir with a long wooden pole.

3 Allow the waste rock to settle to the bottom and run the solution on top into lead pans.

4 Boil the solution to get rid of some of the water.

5 Add alkalis to neutralise the acidic solution.

6 Allow the solution to cool and crystals of alum to form.

Questions

1 State four things that alkalis were needed for before industrialisation.

2 Look at the photo of soap being made. What is the name of the alkali used to make soap?

The crystals of alum were sold to the dye industry.

Some of the alkali used in this process was potash (potassium carbonate), from the ash of burnt wood. The rest was ammonia, from stale urine. Local people stored urine in wooden pails and this was collected in large barrels on horse-drawn carts.

So much urine was needed that it was also brought in by sea from London. On the return journey, the ships delivered the bags of alum to dyers in the south of England.

Alkalis and their reactions

All alkalis are soluble in water. When they dissolve, they raise the pH of water above 7. Alkalis are important because they neutralise acids.

Two very corrosive alkalis are sodium hydroxide and potassium hydroxide. When sodium hydroxide neutralises hydrochloric acid, there is a chemical change that produces a salt called sodium chloride. Chemists sometimes call this 'common salt', because it is just one of many different **salts** produced when acids and alkalis react.

This reaction is shown by the **word equation**:

sodium hydroxide + hydrochloric acid $\longrightarrow$ sodium chloride + water

Whenever an alkali neutralises an acid, a salt is produced by the chemical reaction.

Alum is used to help natural dyes stick to cloth so that they do not wash out.

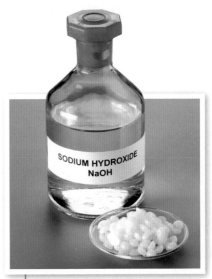

Pure sodium hydroxide is a white solid. It is soluble in water and used in solution as an alkali.

Questions

3 State two sources of the alkalis used in the traditional alum industry.

4 At which stages of the traditional alum industry were the following processes involved?
   a heating
   b evaporation
   c neutralisation
   d crystallisation

5 What product is always produced when an alkali neutralises an acid?

Summary box
✔ Alkalis are used to neutralise acid soils, make chemicals that stick natural dyes to cloth, convert fat and oil to soap, and to make glass.
✔ Alkalis used to come from burnt wood and stale urine.
✔ Alkalis neutralise acids to make chemicals called salts.

Find out about

- ✓ **how alkalis were first manufactured on a large scale**
- ✓ **why this was such a polluting process**
- ✓ **how the government began to regulate the chemical industry**

Air pollution from industry in Widnes in 1895.

Questions

1 Name one industry that used large amounts of alkali in the 1700s.

2 What were the raw materials used in Leblanc's process for making sodium carbonate?

3 Name two gaseous pollutants that were produced by Leblanc's process.

Making alkali on a large scale

During the industrial revolution in the 1700s, there were too few natural sources of alkali to meet demand. In France, large amounts of alkali were used in the glass industry, so in 1791, the French scientist Nicolas Leblanc invented a new process that used chalk or limestone (calcium carbonate), salt (sodium chloride), and coal to make the alkali sodium carbonate. Just three years later, during the French revolution, Leblanc's factory was seized and his process became public property.

A chemical industry began in England based on Leblanc's ideas and grew rapidly. The rural areas of Widnes and Runcorn on the banks of the River Mersey became international centres for new industries based on salt.

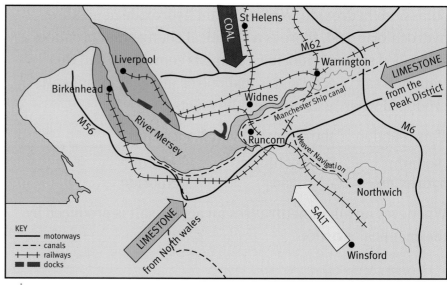

Map showing the region around the River Mersey. A chemical industry grew up around Runcorn and Widnes in the early 1800s.

The **Leblanc process** produced a lot of pollution. For every tonne of the product sodium carbonate, the process created two tonnes of solid waste and almost a tonne of **hydrogen chloride gas**. This acid gas devastated all the land around. The solid waste was dumped in great heaps that slowly gave off toxic **hydrogen sulfide gas**. This gas has a sickening smell of bad eggs. Living and working conditions in the area were appalling.

Starting to regulate the chemical industry

As industrialisation increased in the 1800s, the British public began to demand that the government control pollution. At that time the government was anxious to protect the chemical industry because it brought money to the economy and provided jobs. However, they soon began to pass laws to improve working conditions and control pollution.

In 1863, the government passed the first of the **Alkali Acts**. This Act set up an Alkali Inspectorate to reduce pollution from the chemical industry. Inspectors travelled the country to check that at least 95% of acid fumes were removed from the chimneys of chemical factories.

Tackling the pollution problem

In 1874, Henry Deacon invented a way to use the polluting hydrogen chloride gas from the Leblanc process. He found that it was possible to oxidise the acidic and corrosive hydrogen chloride to **chlorine**. Chlorine is one of the elements in hydrogen chloride but it has very different properties to the compound. Chlorine is useful because it acts as a bleach.

Henry Deacon reacted the hydrogen chloride gas with oxygen. The products were chlorine and steam. The chlorine was used to **bleach** paper and textiles.

The problems of the Leblanc process were eventually solved towards the end of the 1800s, not by government controls, but by developing new methods for making alkalis. The new processes are still in use today.

"…they were ruined when they were required to send labouring children to school; they were ruined when inspectors were appointed to look into their works; they were ruined when such inspectors considered it doubtful whether they were quite justified in chopping people up in their machinery; they were utterly undone when it was hinted that perhaps they need not make so much smoke."

HARD TIMES

CHARLES DICKENS

Dickens mocked industrialists' attitudes to new controls when he wrote *Hard Times* in 1854.

Summary box

- ✓ The Leblanc process used chalk or limestone, salt, and coal to make alkalis.
- ✓ The Leblanc process produced toxic hydrogen chloride and hydrogen sulfide.
- ✓ The UK Government began to regulate the chemical industry and limit pollution by passing laws like the Alkali Acts.

Questions

4 Henry Deacon's solution to the problem of polluting hydrogen chloride gas was to convert it into chlorine. Explain why the chemical industry was pleased with his solution.

5 Suggest reasons why the British Government was slow to bring in laws to control the new chemical industry, despite the serious risks to health, and the unpleasantness for workers and people living nearby.

Find out about

- ✓ **the risks of waterborne diseases**
- ✓ **the benefits of chlorinating drinking water**
- ✓ **worries that some people have about chlorinated water**

A polluted river in Arusha, Tanzania.

This device for filtering drinking water is made locally in Cambodia.

The threat of waterborne disease

Water that is contaminated by sewage can sometimes carry fatal diseases, such as cholera, typhoid, dysentery, and gastroenteritis. The World Health Organisation (WHO) has shown that water quality is still a very serious threat to human health. More than three million people still die each year from drinking unsafe water. Those who die are mainly children in developing countries.

Water treatment with chlorine

Prince Albert, the husband of Queen Victoria, died of typhoid fever in 1861. The poor state of the drains in Windsor Castle may have been to blame. It was only a few years later that it became normal to filter drinking water and then treat it with chlorine to kill **microorganisms**. This process might have saved Prince Albert's life.

Chlorination of drinking water in Britain began in the early twentieth century. This led to a decrease in deaths from typhoid.

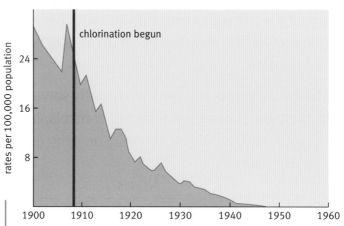

Death rate from typhoid fever in the USA, 1900–1960 (first published in the US Center for Disease Control and Prevention's Summary of Notifiable Diseases 1997).

Questions

1 List four diseases that may be carried in contaminated water.

2 Why is chlorine used to treat water for drinking?

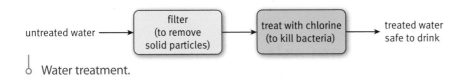

untreated water → filter (to remove solid particles) → treat with chlorine (to kill bacteria) → treated water safe to drink

Water treatment.

Risks of water treatment

Chlorination has helped to prevent the diseases associated with contaminated drinking water. But some scientists are concerned that there might be side effects of chlorination. They are worried that chlorination can cause a group of chemicals known as trihalomethanes (THMs) to form in the water.

THMs can form when chlorine reacts with **organic matter,** such as fragments of leaves, in water. Some organic matter is naturally found in the lakes and rivers used for drinking water. During the water-cleaning process, very small amounts of THMs may form. These may be absorbed into the body when people drink the water.

Some people think that THMs could lead to some types of cancer. However, research studies have not found any evidence to support this idea. The International Agency for Research on Cancer and the World Health Organisation both say there is not enough evidence to prove any strong link between cancer and THMs.

Dr Harriette Chick (1875–1977) studied the factors affecting how quickly chlorine kills bacteria and viruses in water. In 1908 she published her results. Her 'laws of disinfection' helped water companies understand how best to use chlorine.

Questions

3 Use the graph to find the death rate per 100 000 population from typhoid in the USA:
  a in 1900, before chlorination of drinking water began.
  b in 1940, after chlorination of drinking water began.

4 What does chlorine react with to form trihalomethanes (THMs) in water?

5 Explain why some people are concerned about the side effects of chlorination of water.

Summary box
- ✓ **Millions of people each year die as a result of waterborne diseases such as typhoid, cholera, and dysentery.**
- ✓ **Chlorinating drinking water kills microorganisms that cause diseases.**
- ✓ **Some people are concerned that the chlorination process produces trihalomethanes (THMs), which may lead to cancer.**

Find out about

- ✔ the use of electricity to make new chemicals
- ✔ the chemicals made by the electrolysis of brine
- ✔ the environmental impact of the chemical industry based on salt

The Ineos Chlor chemical plant in Runcorn. Chlorine is made here by the electrolysis of brine.

Questions

1 What is brine?

2 State the names of the three products produced by the electrolysis of brine.

Chemicals from salt

Chlorine is now made on a very large scale. Over 10 million tonnes of chlorine are made from salt in Europe each year. Today electricity is used to make chlorine from salt. This process is very much cleaner than the old Leblanc process.

Brine is a solution of salt in water. Chemical changes happen when an electric current flows through brine. The chemical changes convert the salt and water in the brine into three products: chlorine (Cl_2), sodium hydroxide (NaOH), and hydrogen (H_2). The process is called **electrolysis**.

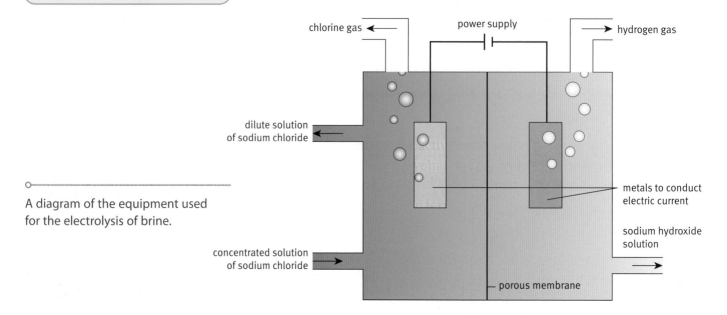

A diagram of the equipment used for the electrolysis of brine.

Uses of chemicals from salt

Chlorine	Sodium hydroxide	Hydrogen
• treating drinking water and waste water • making bleach • making plastics • making hydrochloric acid	• making soap • making paper • making bleach	• fuel • to produce steam • making hydrochloric acid

Some of the many uses of chemicals from salt.

Environmental impacts

Making chemicals from salt by electrolysis needs a lot of energy.

The chemical plant at Runcorn uses as much electricity as a city the size of Liverpool. At the moment, most of the electricity for the electrolysis of brine is generated using fossil fuels. However, the industry is moving towards producing much more of the electricity it needs from renewable sources.

Until recently, the equipment used for the electrolysis of brine often contained mercury, which is **toxic**. Mercury was used as one of the metals to conduct the electricity. However, this method produces products that contain very tiny amounts of mercury. Also, some of the mercury escapes into the environment. As a result, mercury is now very rarely used.

Summary box

✔ **A chemical reaction that happens when electricity flows through a solution is called electrolysis. New chemicals are made.**

✔ **The electrolysis of brine produces three products: chlorine, hydrogen, and sodium hydroxide.**

✔ **The electrolysis of brine uses a large amount of electricity, which is usually generated using fossil fuels. Until recently, the toxic metal mercury was involved in the process.**

Questions

3 Which of the products produced by electrolysis of brine is/are used for:
  a making paper?   c fuel?
  b making bleach?   d making hydrochloric acid?

4 Suggest reasons for cutting down on the use of fossil fuels to generate electricity for the electrolysis of brine.

Greenpeace activists hold banners reading 'Everyday Chemicals Harm My Sperm!' as they demonstrate in front of the Chancellery in Berlin in 2005.

REACH stands for the Registration, Evaluation, and Authorisation of Chemicals.

Synthetic chemicals

Campaigns by environmental groups, such as the World Wide Fund for Nature (WWF) and Greenpeace, have made many people fearful of **synthetic chemicals**. The campaigns have used evidence suggesting that chemicals, such as those found in plastics and pesticides, may cause cancer, or defects in new-born babies.

Most scientists who study toxic chemicals agree that some commonly used synthetic chemicals can be harmful. But not at the amounts usually found in people's bodies. Very sensitive chemical tests have typically found only tiny amounts of these chemicals in human blood. Scientists argue that campaigners are confusing **risks** with hazards. They say there is no evidence that such tiny amounts of them are unsafe.

Laws about chemicals

European industry produces or uses 30 000 different chemicals a year – a tonne or more of each one. But information about their environmental and health effects is available for only a small number of these compounds. European countries and the USA have been safety-testing all new chemicals since 1981, but so far they have only tested about 3% of those in use.

In 2007, the European Union (EU) introduced the REACH system to collect information about the hazards of chemicals and to assess their risks.

Questions

1 What do environmental campaigners say are the health problems associated with some synthetic chemicals?

2 Why do scientists argue that the environmental campaigners are wrong to make people fearful of synthetic chemicals?

3 Why did the European Union bring in the REACH system?

REACH stands for the Registration, Evaluation, and Authorisation of chemicals. REACH made the companies that make or use chemicals responsible for control and safety of these chemicals.

Banned chemicals

There are twelve synthetic chemicals that everyone agrees are harmful even in very small amounts. These are chemicals that do not break down in the environment for a very long time. This means they can spread widely around the world in air and water.

These 12 chemicals are sometimes called the 'dirty dozen'. They build up in the fatty tissues of animals, including humans. So they can harm people and wildlife.

They are a particular problem for people living in the Arctic, where traditional diets are often high in fat. The chemicals build up in fatty tissue of animals, which people then eat.

One of these twelve harmful chemicals is a pesticide called DDT. Like many of the others, it is a compound containing chlorine.

Experts at a conference in Stockholm in 2001 agreed a convention to deal with the dirty dozen chemicals. It became effective in 2004, and about 150 countries have agreed to ban these chemicals.

The diet of those living in Arctic regions is high in fat.

Questions

4 The chemical industry will pay for most of the cost of the REACH system. The cost for the whole European Union will be about €5 billion over the first 11 years of the testing programme. Do you think that such a large cost is justified? Explain your answer.

5 Is it right that the chemical industry should have to organise and pay for the testing? Explain your answer.

Summary box

✓ **Industry produces or uses many chemicals, but information about their environmental or health effects is currently available for only a few.**

✓ **The EU brought in the REACH system to collect hazard information about chemicals and assess their risks.**

✓ **Some harmful chemicals do not break down in the environment, so they can build up in the bodies of animals, which may be eaten by humans.**

Find out about

- ✔ **the stages in the production, use, and disposal of PVC products**
- ✔ **risks involved in making and disposing of PVC**

Poly(vinyl chloride) (PVC) is a synthetic polymer. It is strong, easy to mould and quite cheap. It is also hard-wearing, durable, and can be used to make a wide range of products. The stages in the life of PVC products include production, use, and disposal.

Chemicals from raw materials

Two chemicals are used to make PVC: ethene and chlorine. In the first stage of the process, chlorine and ethene are combined to make a chemical called vinyl chloride. This is a hazardous compound because it can cause cancer.

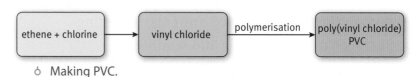

⚬ Making PVC.

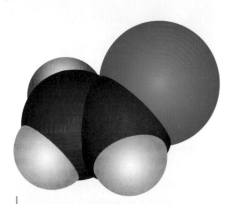

A model of a molecule of vinyl chloride, C_2H_3Cl.

Making PVC from chemicals

Vinyl chloride is a liquid made of small molecules. Polymerisation joins up these small monomer molecules in long chains to make PVC. PVC molecules are made up of three different elements: carbon, hydrogen, and chlorine.

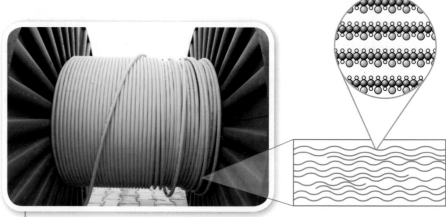

PVC is used to insulate electric cables. PVC is a polymer. The red lines represent the molecule, which are very long chains. These long chains are made up of atoms of carbon, hydrogen, and chlorine. Carbon atoms are shown in black, hydrogen atoms in white, and chlorine atoms in green.

Making products from PVC

PVC is sent to factories to be moulded under heat and pressure. For example, the hot plastic can be made into pipes or bottles.

Questions

1 Which three chemical elements are present in PVC?

2 Why does the chemical industry take care to make sure that workers are not exposed to the chemical vinyl chloride?

Using PVC products

PVC is used to make underground pipes carrying drinking water, sewage, and gas. PVC is also used in building, for gutters and window frames. Many shop signs are made from sheets of PVC.

A softer type of PVC is used in clothing, and to make hoses, and insulation for electric wires. PVC film is used for packaging, blood bags, and the bags for intravenous drips used in hospitals.

Disposing of PVC products

Recycling

The best way of getting rid of old PVC products is recycling. Recycling cuts down the amount of raw materials used to make new PVC. It also reduces the amount of waste produced when PVC products have reached the end of their life.

A big problem with recycling PVC is that it is often mixed with other materials. This can make separating, sorting, and recycling difficult and expensive.

Energy recovery

Some PVC waste can be burnt. The energy released can be used to generate electricity. This is done in special **incinerators**.

Burning PVC can be a problem because this produces acidic hydrogen chloride gas. Acid gases can be removed from the fumes produced by burning before they are released into the air. Burning PVC may also produce other toxic chemicals.

Landfill

Unfortunately, a lot of PVC waste still ends up being tipped into holes in the ground. We call this **landfill**. This really is a waste.

A woman sorting plastic waste in Mumbai, India. She is separating out pieces of PVC by picking the pieces out of a barrel of water. The PVC sinks, unlike some other plastics that are less dense than water.

Summary box

- ✓ PVC is made from the chemical vinyl chloride.
- ✓ PVC is moulded into products such as pipes.
- ✓ PVC products are disposed of by recycling, incineration, or landfill.
- ✓ A risk in making PVC comes from the use of vinyl chloride, a chemical that can cause cancer.
- ✓ A risk in disposing of PVC comes from incineration, which can release acidic hydrogen chloride when the PVC burns.

Questions

3 State five uses of PVC.

4 What are the advantages of recycling products made from PVC?

5 Why is it important that waste incinerators do not release hydrogen chloride into the air?

Find out about

- ✔ **the chemicals used to plasticise PVC**
- ✔ **why plasticisers may be harmful**
- ✔ **what the regulators are doing about the risks**

This child is sliding down a rigid plastic slide into a flexible plastic paddling pool.

Questions

1 Give two reasons why toymakers like to use PVC to make toys.

2 Why do manufacturers add plasticisers to PVC?

3 Why do some people think that plasticisers should be banned?

Worries about plasticisers

Toymakers like to use PVC because:

- it can be either flexible or rigid
- it can be mixed with pigments to give bright colours
- it stands up to rough play
- it is easy to keep clean.

Plasticisers are chemicals that make PVC soft and flexible.

Plasticisers can escape from the plastic and dissolve in liquids in contact with it. For example, plasticisers can escape from a PVC toy into the saliva of a baby that chews it. They can also escape out of the plastic used to make hospital blood bags and enter patients' blood.

Blood from donors is stored in plasticised PVC bags.

This toy duck is free of PVC and plasticisers. It was designed by a sculptor who made toys for his daughter because he was worried about the safety of plastic toys.

Some people argue that some plasticisers should be banned. They think this because of evidence linking plasticisers with health problems such as cancer, liver problems, and infertility.

Makers of PVC and PVC products argue that plasticisers have been in use for over 50 years. They say that, in all that time, there has not been a single known case of anyone being harmed by plasticisers.

What the regulators say

Regulators in Europe and the USA are concerned about the possible effects of plasticisers on young children and newborn babies. The European Union does not allow two common plasticisers to be used in toys that can be placed in the mouth. A third plasticiser (called DEHP) has been banned completely from toys.

Regulators are particularly worried about DEHP because it has been shown to affect the development of the male reproductive system in animals. These effects have not been found in human babies, but it has not been possible to show that there is no risk at all.

Plasticisers in medical equipment

DEHP is the plasticiser used in most medical equipment made from PVC. There are alternatives to DEHP but these are expensive and not always available. DEHP may escape from plastic into liquids used to treat patients. The amount depends on the temperature, how much fat there is in the liquid, and the length of time the liquid is in contact with the plastic.

Seriously ill people often need treatment for a long time. This can increase their exposure to DEHP plasticisers. An example is people who have regular dialysis to treat kidney failure.

The Food and Drugs Administration (FDA) in the USA tells doctors that they should continue to carry out medical treatments using plasticised PVC. They say that the risk of not treating a sick patient is much greater than the risk of exposure to the plasticiser.

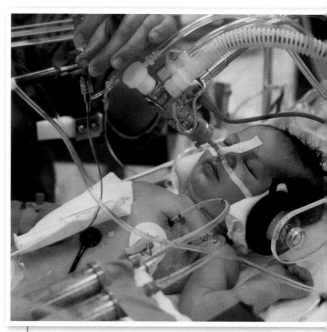

Flexible plastic tubing helps to keep babies alive in intensive care.

Questions

4 How can plasticisers get into the blood of people who are ill?

5 Why are some seriously ill people, who need treatment for a long time, more at risk from plasticisers in PVC?

Summary box
- ✔ Plasticisers are chemicals that make PVC soft and flexible.
- ✔ Plasticisers can escape from PVC products into liquids, including babies' saliva and patients' blood. There is evidence that shows that plasticisers may have harmful effects.
- ✔ Regulators have limited the use of plasticisers in toys that could be put into babies' mouths.

Find out about

✓ **the life of products from cradle to grave**
✓ **the impacts of the products you use**

Summary box

The lives of products have four stages:

✓ **materials are made**
✓ **manufacturers make the product**
✓ **people use the product**
✓ **people throw the product away.**
✓ **The environmental impact of each stage in the life of a product can be assessed in a life cycle assessment. The aim of a life cycle assessment is to protect the environment.**

The life of products

At home, you are surrounded by many different products, such as furniture, clothes, glass, televisions, and mobile phones.

Each of these products has four stages in its life:

1 The materials are made from raw materials.
2 Manufacturers use the materials to make the product.
3 People use the product.
4 People throw away the product.

A 1970s TV set. It contains glass, metals, plastics and wood.

Imagine an old television that was bought in 1970 and thrown away some years ago. It contains glass, metals, plastics, and wood. It is now buried under rock and rubbish in a landfill.

The wood will eventually rot because it is **biodegradable**. But the rest of the materials are there forever. This is not sustainable because the materials cannot be used again.

Once the life of a product is over, its materials should go back into another product. This is recycling.

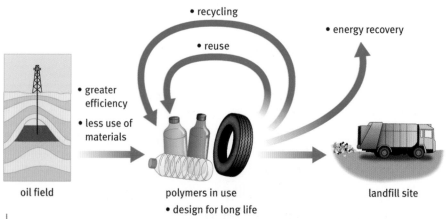

Oil and products from oil, such as polymers, can end up as waste. If the waste can be reused or recycled, this saves energy and raw materials.

Question

1 What are the four stages in the life of a product?

Life cycle assessment

Manufacturers can assess what happens to the materials in their products. This **life cycle assessment** (LCA) helps to protect the environment. The aim is to slow the rate at which we use up natural resources that are not renewable, and use products that are more sustainable.

LCA involves collecting data about each stage in the life of a product, including the use of materials and water, energy inputs and outputs, and environmental impact. An LCA can show, for example, whether it is better to make windows from wood or PVC. Science cannot tell you which of these two materials makes better-looking windows, but it can tell you which is more sustainable.

PVC windows need little maintenance. They are not affected by moisture. However, the raw materials are not renewable and PVC is not biodegradable.

Restoring the paintwork on a wooden window. Wood needs regular painting and can rot if it is not properly looked after. However, wood is a renewable product and is biodegradable.

Stages in the life of products	Environmental impact
1 materials are made	**raw materials** obtained and processed to make useful materials **energy** and **water** used in processing
2 manufacturers make the product	**materials** used to make the product **energy** and **water** used in manufacturing
3 people use the product	**energy** needed to use the product (eg electricity for a computer) **energy** needed to maintain the product (eg cleaning, mending) **water** and **chemicals** needed to maintain it
4 people throw the product away	**energy** needed to dispose of the product **space** needed to store the rubbish

Questions

2 Give two reasons why it is not a good idea to put products into landfill once we have used them.

3 Look at the pictures of the window frames.
   a Give one advantage of using PVC rather than wood for making window frames.
   b Give one advantage of using wood rather than PVC for making window frames.

Science
Explanations

Salt, limestone, coal, gas, and oil have been the basis of the chemical industry for many years. The use of manufactured chemicals has brought many benefits but they are not without risk.

You should know:

- how geologists use observations of processes happening today to help explain the history of the surface of the Earth
- that the parts of the Earth's crust that now make up Britain have moved over the surface of the Earth as a result of plate tectonics
- how magnetic minerals in rocks help geologists track the very slow movement of the continents
- how processes such as mountain building, erosion, sedimentation, dissolving, and evaporation have led to the formation of valuable minerals
- how geologists use clues in rocks, such as fossils, shapes of sand grains, and ripples, to find out about the conditions under which the rocks were formed
- that a chemical industry grew up in northwest England because of all the natural resources nearby
- that salt (sodium chloride) is important for preserving and processing food, as a source of chemicals, and to treat roads in winter
- that salt comes from the sea or from underground salt deposits
- why the methods used to obtain salt may depend on how it is to be used and how pure it needs to be
- why extracting salt may have an impact on the environment
- that before industrialisation, alkalis were used in neutralising acid soils, dying cloth, and making soap and glass
- that the traditional sources of alkali included burnt wood or stale urine
- that alkalis neutralise acids to make salts
- how industrialisation led to an increase in demand for alkali in the 19th century
- why the first process to meet the growing demand for alkali was highly polluting
- how the pollution problems of the old process were reduced by producing useful chemicals such as chlorine
- how using chlorine to kill microorganisms in domestic water supplies has made a major contribution to public health
- that electrolysis is the process now used to make new chemicals, such as sodium hydroxide, chlorine, and hydrogen, from salt solution
- that PVC is a polymer containing chlorine
- how the properties of PVC can be altered by adding plasticisers.

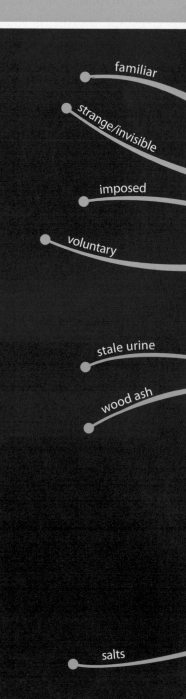

familiar

strange/invisible

imposed

voluntary

stale urine

wood ash

salts

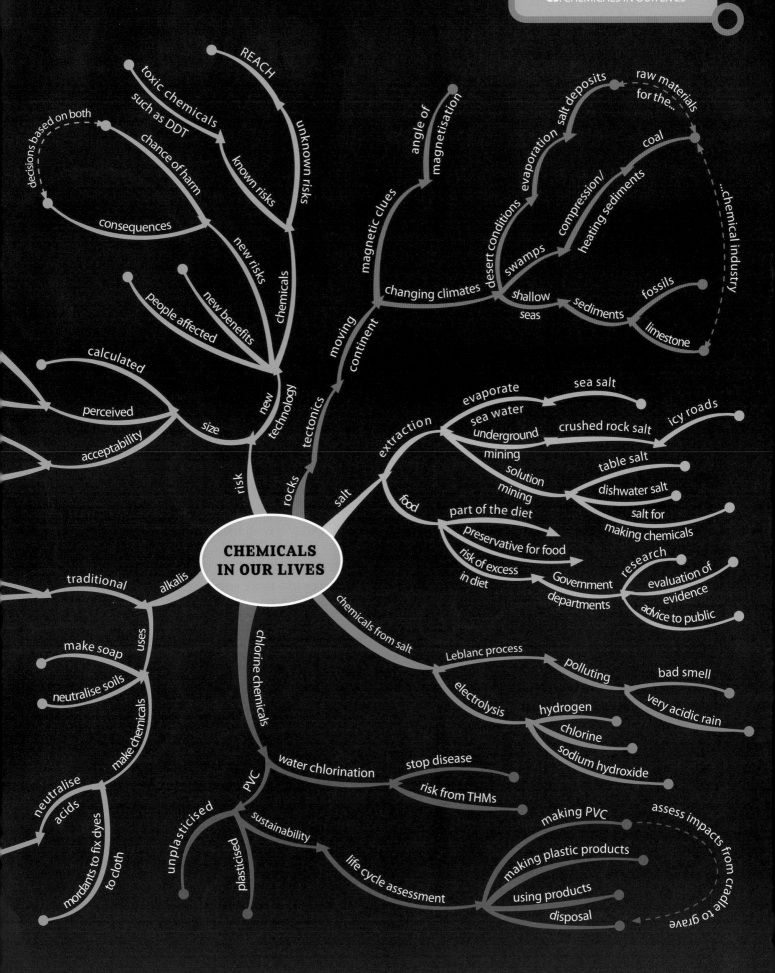

CHEMICALS IN OUR LIVES

- REACH
- toxic chemicals
  - such as DDT
- known risks
- unknown risks
- chance of harm
  - decisions based on both
  - consequences
- new risks
- new benefits
- people affected
- chemicals
- new technology

risk
- size
  - calculated
  - perceived
  - acceptability

rocks
- tectonics
  - moving continent
    - magnetic clues
      - angle of magnetisation
    - changing climates
      - desert conditions
        - evaporation — salt deposits
        - raw materials for the...
      - swamps
        - compression/ heating sediments
        - coal
      - shallow seas
        - sediments
          - fossils
          - limestone
      - ...chemical industry

salt
- extraction
  - sea water
    - evaporate — sea salt
    - underground mining — crushed rock salt — icy roads
    - solution mining
      - table salt
      - dishwater salt
      - salt for making chemicals
- food
  - part of the diet
  - preservative for food
  - risk of excess in diet
    - Government departments
      - research
      - evaluation of evidence
      - advice to public
- chemicals from salt
  - Leblanc process
    - polluting
      - bad smell
      - very acidic rain
  - electrolysis
    - hydrogen
    - chlorine
    - sodium hydroxide

alkalis
- traditional
- uses
  - make soap
  - neutralise soils
  - make chemicals
    - neutralise acids
    - mordants to fix dyes to cloth

chlorine chemicals
- water chlorination
  - stop disease
  - risk from THMs
- PVC
  - unplasticised
  - plasticised
  - sustainability
    - life cycle assessment
      - making PVC
      - making plastic products
      - using products
      - disposal
      - assess impacts from cradle to grave

Ideas about Science

Scientists seek explanations to account for their findings, such as the data collected by studying rocks. You should be able to:

- explain how magnetic data and other clues in rocks support the theory that the continents have moved.

New technologies and processes based on scientific advances sometimes introduce new risks. Some people are worried about the risks of using particular chemicals. You should be able to:

- explain why nothing is completely safe
- identify examples of risks that arise from the use of chemicals
- interpret information on the size of risks, presented in different ways
- describe ways of reducing risks from hazardous chemicals
- discuss a given risk, taking into account both the chances of it happening and the consequences if it did
- identify risks and benefits, for the different individuals and groups involved, arising from uses of chemicals
- suggest why people accept (or reject) the risk of a certain activity, for example, eating a diet with more salt than is recommended
- recognise that people's perception of the size of a risk is often very different from the scientific assessment of the risk
- illustrate the idea that people tend to overestimate the risk of unfamiliar things and things that have an invisible effect.

Governments and public bodies assess what level of risk is acceptable. Treaties, regulations, and laws control scientific research and the applications of science. The decision to regulate may be controversial, especially if those most at risk are not those who benefit. You should understand that governments and regulators are responding to concerns that:

- many people are putting their health at risk by eating too much salt

- there are possible disadvantages of chlorinating drinking water, including possible health problems
- some toxic chemicals persist in the environment; they can be carried over large distances and may accumulate in food and human tissues
- the plasticisers added to PVC can leach out from the plastic into the surroundings where they may have harmful effects.

Science helps to find ways of using natural resources in a more sustainable way. You should understand that:

- a life cycle assessment (LCA) tests a material's fitness for purpose and the effects of using material products from production to final disposal
- an LCA involves consideration of the use of resources including water, the energy input or output, and the environmental impact, of each of these stages:
  - making materials from natural raw materials
  - making useful products from materials
  - using the products
  - disposing of the products.

When given appropriate information from an LCA, you should be able to compare and evaluate the use of different materials for the same job.

Review Questions

1 **a** The table shows the mass of salt in different foods.

Food	Mass of salt in 100 g of the food (g)
White bread	1.2
Cornflakes	1.8
Ham	3.1
Crisps	2.5
Chocolate muffin	1.7

  i Which food in the table contains the most salt in 100 g?

  ii Ben eats a 100 g chocolate muffin. How many grams of salt has he eaten?

  iii Emma eats a 50 g packet of crisps. How many grams of salt has she eaten?

  iv Who has eaten more salt?

 b Health experts recommend that adults should eat no more than 6 g of salt each day.

  i Identify two risks linked to eating too much salt.

  ii Suggest why some people eat more than 6 g of salt each day, even though they know about the risks of eating too much salt.

2 **a** Cholera is a disease that is caused by a microorganism. It spreads through contaminated water. Its victims may die. In 1991, there was an outbreak of cholera in South America. The table shows data from the time of the outbreak.

Village	Number of people who caught cholera	Did the village add chlorine to its drinking water?
A	0	no
B	27	no
C	1	yes
D	31	no
E	42	no

Vincent suggests an explanation for the data. He says that adding chlorine to water kills the microorganism that causes cholera.

  i In which villages would Vincent expect there to be deaths from cholera?

  ii In which village would Vincent expect there to be no deaths from cholera?

  iii Data from which villages is accounted for by Vincent's explanation?

  iv Data from which villages conflicts with Vincent's explanation?

 b Describe one possible disadvantage of adding chlorine to water.

 c Give the name of the process by which chlorine is produced from salt (sodium chloride).

3 In the 18th century farmers in Yorkshire used lime kilns to heat limestone (calcium carbonate). The new product was mixed with water to make slaked lime (calcium hydroxide).

 a Why did farmers spread the slaked lime onto acidic soil?

 b What chemical process was taking place?

4 Rocks contain a lot of evidence about how and where they were formed.

 a Give the letter of the information provided by the following types of evidence.

  i Pieces of shell.

  ii Data on the direction of magnetism.

  iii Types of fossilised plants or animals.

	Information
A	The latitude at which (how far north or south) the rocks were originally formed.
B	Whether the rock was formed under the sea.
C	The age of the rock.

 b Which other piece of information do fossils provide evidence for?

P3 Sustainable energy

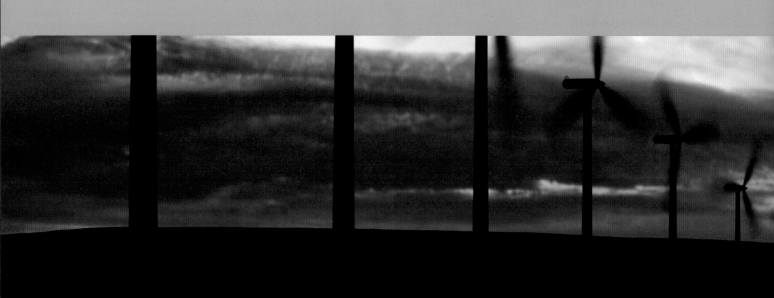

Why study energy?

Our energy supply provides the fuel we need for transport, heating, and to generate electricity. Modern society needs a large supply of energy. Most of us take electricity for granted. But today's power stations are becoming old and will soon need replacing. How should we generate electricity in the future? Can we reduce our impact on the environment without reducing our quality of life?

What you already know

- When energy is transferred the total amount of energy remains constant.

- Whenever energy is used some of it spreads out into the surroundings.

- Electricity is a useful way of transferring energy long distances.

- Electricity is generated in power stations.

- Electric current transfers energy from the power supply to lamps and other devices in the circuit.

Find out about

- how much energy we use, as individuals, as a country, and across the world

- how we could use energy more efficiently

- how electricity is generated in a power station

- the choices for generating electricity in the future.

The Science

Energy cannot be made or destroyed. Whenever we use it some is lost to the surroundings. We need ways of using energy more efficiently.
Most UK electricity is generated by burning gas and coal to drive generators. All the methods of generating electricity have advantages and drawbacks.

Ideas about Science

Nothing is completely safe; there are different risks of using each energy source. But who should be making the decisions? How can you have your say?

Find out about

✔ **energy sources**
✔ **why we need to be concerned about energy supplies**

People need energy to keep them alive, warm, and moving. We use much more energy now than in the past because:

*   there are more people in the world and the population is still increasing
*   modern transport, buildings, possessions, and communications need more energy than ever before
*   people travel further and faster and have a different lifestyle.

Understanding about the energy sources available is important when making choices.

Most UK electricity is generated by burning fossil fuels.

Modern living can demand large amounts of energy.

Energy sources

Energy is **conserved**. This means it can not be created or destroyed. The energy we use for heat, movement, and light must all come from an **energy source**. For example, we can release energy by burning fuels, or we can use energy carried by radiation from the Sun.

A **primary energy source** is one that is found naturally. Examples include fuels such as coal, oil, natural gas, and wood, and wind, waves, and sunlight.

Electricity is a **secondary energy source**. It must be generated using a primary source.

Question

1   Write down three things that you do during a day that use:
    a   a primary energy source
    b   a secondary energy source.

Types of fuels

Fossil fuels

A **fossil fuel** is one that has built up over millions of years by the decay of plant and animal remains. Coal, crude oil, and natural gas are all fossil fuels. We are using them up far more quickly than they can form.

When they burn, fossil fuels produce carbon dioxide (CO_2) and other **pollutants**, such as carbon particles. The amount of CO_2 in the atmosphere has risen over the past two hundred years and is affecting the Earth's climate.

Biofuel

A **biofuel** is one that has recently come from living material (biomass). Wood, straw, sewage, and sugar are all used as biofuels. Like fossil fuels, biofuels produce CO_2 when they burn. Unlike fossil fuels, biofuels are produced quickly.

Nuclear fuel

Nuclear fuel releases energy without burning so it does not make CO_2. Nuclear fuels are not found in the UK so any that we use must be imported.

Sustainable energy

Sustainable energy means using energy sources in a way that will allow people in the future to use as much as we do and live in the same environment. But some of the energy sources we use are running out, and some of our energy use is damaging the environment. This is not sustainable. To decide what to do, we need to know some facts about the amount of energy we use.

Crude oil is an oily mixture of solid, liquid, and gas. Petrol, oil, and diesel fuel are all made from crude oil.

Can wind power supply enough energy?

Summary box
- ✓ **Primary energy sources include fuels.**
- ✓ **Electricity is a secondary energy source.**
- ✓ **We use energy in a way that is not sustainable.**
- ✓ **Some sources will run out and we are damaging the environment.**

Question

2 List two reasons for reducing our use of fossil fuels.

Find out about

- ✓ **what is measured on a domestic electricity meter**
- ✓ **how to calculate the energy used by an electrical appliance**
- ✓ **how to calculate the cost of the electrical energy used**
- ✓ **how electric power is related to current and voltage**

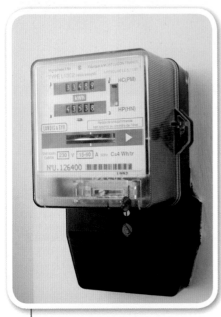

The electricity meter in your home measures the number of kilowatt-hours of electrical energy that you buy.

Meter: 326565		Tariff: **Domestic**	
cost of energy	number of units used	unit charges	total
13.25	2213	first 227 at 13.25p	£30.08
		next 661 at 7.88p	£52.08
			£82.16

Measuring energy

The energy used by an electrical appliance is measured with a meter. This energy depends on:

- the power of the appliance
- the time it is on for.

The **power** is the amount of energy used each second. An appliance with a power of 1 **watt** (1 W) uses 1 **joule** of energy (1 J) every second. But 1 joule is a tiny amount of energy.

Many domestic appliances have powers of a few kilowatts. One kilowatt is one thousand watts. For domestic appliances we use the **kilowatt-hour** as the unit of energy. It is the energy used by a 1 kW appliance switched on for one hour.

1 kWh = 3 600 000 J

energy used	=	power	×	time
(joule, J)(watt, W)		(second, s)		
(kilowatt-hour, kWh)		(kilowatt, kW),		(hour, h)

Paying for energy

On an electricity bill, '1 unit' means 1 kilowatt-hour. To find the cost of the energy, multiply the number of units by the cost of one unit.

cost of energy = number of units used × price of one unit

(pence, p)　　　　(kilowatt-hours, kWh)　　　(pence per kilowatt-hour, p per kWh)

Power, current and voltage

When an electrical appliance is switched on, electric **current** passes through it and energy is transferred to the appliance and its surroundings.

The power is worked out from current and **voltage.**

power　　=　voltage　×　current
(watt, W)　　(volt, V)　　(amp, A)

In the UK, the mains electricity voltage is 230V. Battery voltages are usually up to 12 V.

Appliances that include motors, or are used for heating, usually need quite large currents. They take a high power and are expensive to run.

The power of an electrical appliance tells you how much energy it uses each second when it is switched on.

Worked example

Working out the power

A heater has a current of 10 A.

$$\text{power} = \text{voltage} \times \text{current}$$

For all UK mains appliances the operating voltage is 230 V.

$$\text{power} = 230\,\text{V} \times 10\,\text{A}$$

$$\text{power} = 2300\,\text{W} = 2.3\,\text{kW}$$

Working out the cost

The heater power is 2.3 kW. It is used for 2 hours.

Electricity costs 10 p per unit.

Energy used = 2.3 kW × 2 h = 4.6 kWh

Cost = 4.6 kWh × 10 p / kWh = 46 p

Summary box

✓ **Energy is measured in joules and in kilowatt-hours.**

✓ **Power is the energy transferred per second and is measured in watts.**

Question

1 Look at each of the tasks in the table on the right that use electricity.

   a Calculate the number of kilowatt-hours that each task uses.

   b Electricity costs 10p per unit. Calculate the cost of each task.

Task	Appliance used	Power rating (W)	Time for which it is on
watch television for the evening	television	300	5 hours
make a pot of tea	electric kettle	2000	4 minutes
write a homework assignment	computer	250	2 hours
listen to music	mp3 player	0.2	2 hours
wash a load of dirty clothes	washing machine	1850	$1\frac{1}{2}$ hours
play a game	games console	190	1 hour

Find out about

✓ the energy we need for our daily lives

A large, less economical car uses about 0.8 kWh per km.

Transport	Energy per passenger-km (kWh / passenger-km)
Bus	0.19
Train	0.06
Aircraft	0.51
Boat	0.57

Question

1 Look at the transport table.
A bus uses more fuel than a car to travel the same distance. Explain why the energy per passenger-kilometre is less for a bus.

We use a lot more energy in a day than is accounted for by the electricity bill at the end of the month.

Heating and cooking

Most of the energy you use at home is probably supplied by electricity. For some tasks you might use another source such as gas or oil, but the energy needed will be the same.

Task	Energy (kWh)
Bath (about 100 litres of hot water)	5
Shower (about 30 litres of hot water)	1.4
Gas cooker (for 1 hour)	1.5
Room heater, such as radiator (for 1 hour)	1
Air conditioning unit (for 1 hour)	0.6
Patio heater (for 1 hour)	15

Transport

Different means of transport use different amounts of energy.

Burning 1 litre of petrol in a car releases enough energy for an economical car to travel about 10 miles. 10 miles = 16 km. The car uses about 0.6 kWh per km.

Travelling alone in a car uses much more energy than sharing public transport. So figures for public transport are based on people sharing. The table lists energy per **passenger-kilometre**, which is each passenger's share of the energy used to travel 1 km.

Worked example

Calculating the energy used

A student travels 5 km to school in the car.

energy used (kWh) = distance travelled (miles) × energy per km (kWh per km)

energy used = 5 miles × 0.6 kWh per km = 3 kWh

Food and drink

Growing and producing food uses energy. Some of that energy is stored in the food and passed on to you when you eat it. The table lists the energy needed to produce some fresh foods. Processed foods use more energy.

Food	Energy (kWh) for production
1 egg	0.5
1 pint of milk	0.8
50 g cheese	0.8
100 g meat (eg beef, chicken, pork)	4
100 g fruit or vegetables	0.5

Other stuff

Everything you use has an energy cost. The table lists the energy needed to make and transport some items that you might buy or use.

Item	Energy (kWh)
Drinks can	0.6
Plastic bottle	0.7
AA battery	1.4
Magazine	1
Computer	1800

A person in the UK uses about 160 litres of clean water each day. The energy needed to treat and distribute this amount of water is the **energy cost** of the water. In the UK the energy cost of our daily water use is about 0.4 kWh.

On average each person in the UK throws away 400 g of packaging per day with an energy cost of about 4 kWh.

Questions

2 Suggest reasons why producing processed food needs more energy than fresh food.

3 Someone wants to change their lifestyle and use less energy. Use information from these pages to suggest what they might do.

Summary box

✓ **In addition to electricity, we use energy for:**
  - **heating and cooking**
  - **transport**
  - **growing and producing food**
  - **producing the things we buy and their packaging.**

Find out about

- ✔ **how public services and activities contribute to our energy use**
- ✔ **how people's daily energy use varies between countries**

Energy we use in the UK

In the UK, the average energy use is about 110 kWh per person per day. A diary of your own energy use probably given less than this.

$$\text{Average daily energy use} = \frac{\text{total energy used in the UK in a day}}{\text{number of people in the UK}}$$

The bigger picture

Some of the energy uses in the UK are shared between everybody in the country.

The armed forces work for everyone in the country. Our share of their energy use is about 4 kWh per person per day.

Supermarkets use about 0.5 kWh per person per day.

Building homes uses about 1 kWh per person per day. Building and maintaining roads uses about 2 kWh per person per day.

Computer servers are at the core of many businesses and at the heart of the internet. They need energy to drive the computers and even more energy to cool them. Servers across the UK use about 0.5 kWh per person per day.

Question

1 Suggest at least two more energy-using activities that are shared between everyone in the UK.

Energy use in other countries

The map shows the average energy use per person in different parts of the world. 1 megawatt-hour = 1000 kWh

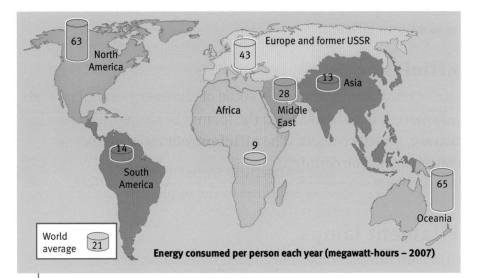

Industrial countries have higher living standards and use more energy. Energy use in India and China is growing fast.

Country	Average daily energy use (kWh per person per day)
Australia	190
China	50
India	20
Japan	130
Poland	80
Turkey	40
UK	110
USA	250

Energy use per person 2007. Source: World Bank.

The table shows the average daily energy use for people in various countries.

Rich and poor countries

In general, richer countries use more energy per person than poorer ones. If people have more money they can buy more goods, live in larger, more comfortable houses, and travel more. All these things use energy.

But the figures for daily energy use still do not tell the whole story, because they only include energy used within each country. They do not include energy used to make imported goods. To take account of all the UK imports, we should add about 40 kWh per person per day to the UK energy figure.

These jeans are made in China but sold in the UK. The energy used to grow the cotton, weave the cloth, and make the jeans contributes to the average energy use in China, not the UK.

Question

2 a Which three countries in the table have the highest daily energy use per person per day?

b Which three countries have the lowest energy use per person per day?

Summary box

✓ Some of the energy use in the UK is shared by everyone, for example, road building.

✓ Energy use per person per day varies across the world.

Find out about

✔ **what is meant by 'efficiency'**
✔ **how to use a Sankey diagram to show energy transfer**

We can use less energy by:
- switching off appliances
- using appliances that don't waste energy – appliances that are more efficient.

Efficiency

In electrical appliances, only some of the energy supplied ends up where it is wanted and in the form it is wanted. The rest is wasted, usually as heat. The **efficiency** of an appliance is:

$$\text{efficiency} = \frac{\text{energy usefully transferred}}{\text{energy supplied to the appliance}} \times 100\%$$

Filament lamps

Filament lamps, sometimes called light bulbs, are very inefficient. They get very hot. Most of the energy from the electricity supply is wasted as heat. Only a small amount of energy is transferred as light.

The CFL on the left needs less energy than the filament lamp on the right to produce the same light output per second. It is more efficient.

Worked example

In one second 100 J of energy is supplied to a 100 W filament lamp but only about 10 J of energy is usefully transferred as light.

Efficiency $= \frac{10\text{ J}}{100\text{ J}} \times 100\% = 10\%$

The other 90% is wasted as heat. This is why the EU has banned sales of new filament lamps.

Summary box

✔ **Efficiency tells you how much energy supplied is used in a useful way.**
✔ **If a lot of energy is wasted as heat, this is inefficient.**
✔ **Sankey diagrams show how energy is transferred.**

Question

1 A 20 W CFL gives a light output of 11 W.
   a How much energy is used each second by the lamp?
   b How much of this energy is useful?
   c Calculate the efficiency of the lamp.

More efficient lighting

CFLs (compact fluorescent lamps), halogen lamps, and LEDs (light-emitting diodes) are more efficient. They waste less energy as heat.

Sankey diagrams

In a **Sankey diagram**, branching arrows show how energy is transferred. Their width indicates the amount of energy. The total width stays the same because energy cannot be lost or gained overall.

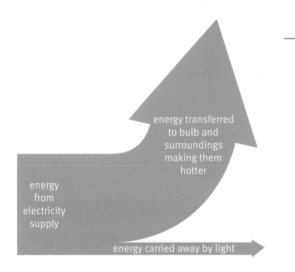

The efficiency of a light bulb is about 10%.

Electrical appliances are labelled with an efficiency rating to help people choose which to buy.

Questions

2 Draw a Sankey diagram for an electric kettle.

3 a Which of these televisions is more efficient?
  b Explain how you know.

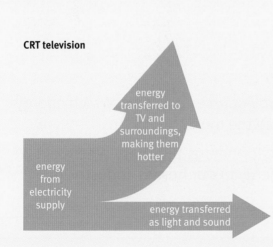

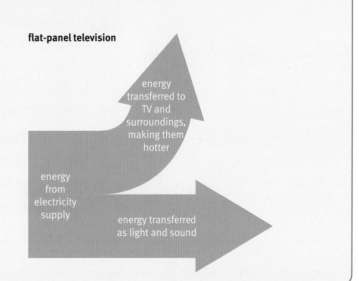

What are our sources of energy?

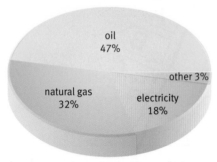

UK energy sources 2008.

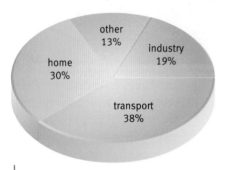

Main users of energy in the UK 2008.

What fuel do we use and where

Each year the UK government publishes information about the country's energy use. They tell us about our use of:

- electricity
- natural gas, oil including petrol, diesel, and other fuels made from oil
- other fuels, including coal and wood.

The main UK energy users are industry, transport, and homes. These tables show their different energy use.

Energy use by UK industry 2008.			
Electricity	Gas	Petroleum	Other
33%	38%	21%	8%

Energy use by UK transport 2008.			
Electricity	Gas	Petroleum	Other
1%	0%	97%	2%

UK domestic energy use 2008.			
Electricity	Gas	Petroleum	Other
22%	69%	7%	2%

Questions

1 Look at the tables of energy use. Which energy source is used most:
   a in the home?
   b by UK industry?
   c for transport?

2 Look at the energy-sources pie chart. Which energy source did we use the most?

3 Look at the users-of-energy pie chart. Where did we use the most energy in our homes, industry, or transport?

Using electricity

In our homes, we might use gas, oil or other fuels for heating and cooking. For almost everything else we use a secondary source – electricity. Electricity can be used for many different tasks and it is easy to distribute using cables and wires.

Generating electricity

If the mains electricity is cut off a battery will supply low power. High-power appliances, like washing machines need a generator.

Generators work on the principle of **electromagnetic induction**.

A current can be generated by moving a magnet into, or out of, a coil. The movement of the magnet causes an induced voltage across the ends of the coil. 'Induced' means that it is caused by something else – in this case, the movement of the magnet.

You need three things to generate electricity:
- a magnet to induce the voltage
- a coil, or wire, in which to induce the voltage
- a change in the magnetism — usually by moving the magnet or the coil.

If the coil is part of a complete circuit, the induced voltage makes a current flow.

Electricity reaches last village in Britain

In May 2003 Cym Brefi in Wales became the last village in Britain to get a mains electricity supply.

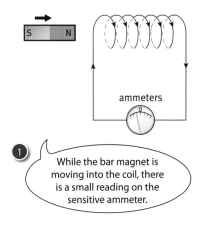

1 While the bar magnet is moving into the coil, there is a small reading on the sensitive ammeter.

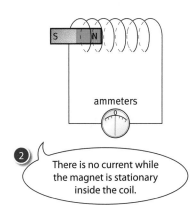

2 There is no current while the magnet is stationary inside the coil.

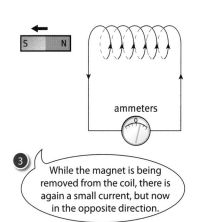

3 While the magnet is being removed from the coil, there is again a small current, but now in the opposite direction.

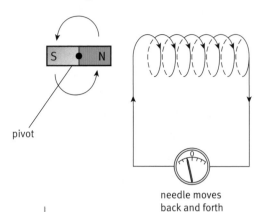

rotate magnet

S • N

pivot

needle moves
back and forth

A rotating magnet generates
a current in the coil.

The technician is constructing this
generator. Wires are wound
around the outside to make the
coil. Magnets rotate in the centre.

Summary box
✓ **A moving magnet
induces a voltage in
a coil.**

How to keep the current flowing

To keep the current flowing, the magnetism must keep changing. If a magnet keeps moving in and out of a coil, or rotated close to a coil, a continuous current can be generated. This is what happens inside a shake torch, a wind-up radio, some bicycle light systems, and in large-scale electricity generators.

More powerful generators use more fuel.

Eternity FlashLight

Shaking this torch moves a magnet in and out of a coil to generate an electric current.

front light

rear light

moving
magnet

generator

This bicycle has a small generator to power the lights. The generator uses the movement of the wheel to produce a current.

Questions

4 In a shake torch, how will the current change as the torch is shaken more vigorously?

5 Suggest a situation where a wind-up radio would be more convenient than an ordinary radio with batteries.

How much energy to turn the generators?

Human power

Instead of using mains electricity from power stations, we could try to power all our appliances ourselves.

Pedal power station

In 2009, the BBC television programme 'Bang Goes the Theory' set up a human power station. 70 cyclists pedalled bicycles to generate electricity. The electricity was used to power appliances in a family house.

As high-power appliances were switched on, the cyclists found it harder to pedal enough to supply the power. The oven and the power shower were the most difficult appliances to run with cycle power. The greater the current supplied by the generator, the harder the cyclists had to pedal.

The cyclists got their energy from eating and drinking. They became tired, hot, and sweaty.

Generating electricity is never 100% efficient. Only some of the energy from the food they had eaten was used to produce electricity. Quite a lot was carried away as heat.

Find out about

✓ **how human power can be used to generate electricity**
✓ **how many people you would need to supply the energy you use each day**

Each bicycle in the human power station was fixed in place with the back wheel connected to a small generator.

Worked example

A fit cyclist can produce an output power of 200 W.

If they keep this up for 24 hours non-stop, their energy output is 200 W × 24 h ÷ 1000 = 4.8 kWh.

If you use 125 kWh per day, you need 120 kWh ÷ 4.8 kWh = 25 cyclists to be your 'slaves'.

Summary box

✓ **Humans can produce electricity, but only a small amount.**

Question

6 Sketch a Sankey diagram for a cyclist in the human power station. The input is the energy stored in their body from the food they have eaten, and the useful output is the energy carried by the electricity. On your diagram label the wasted energy.

Find out about

- how fossil fuels and biomass fuels can be used to produce electricity
- the sequence of events inside a power station
- why power stations are always less than 100% efficient

Fuel used in power stations

Electricity is a secondary energy source. Energy companies generate and distribute it. When you boil a kettle, the electricity may have come from any type of primary source.

Burning fuel

In a fossil-fuel power station, coal, gas, or oil is burned to boil water and make high-pressure steam. Biofuels, such as wood, can be used in the same way. Any power station that works like this is known as a **thermal power station**.

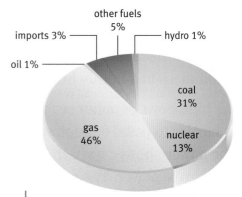

In the UK, most electricity is generated by burning fossil fuels.

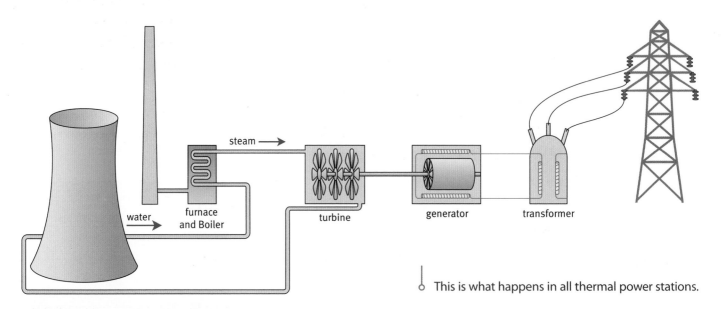

This is what happens in all thermal power stations.

Summary box

- A thermal power station burns fossil fuels or biofuels. Steam turns the turbines. Turbines turn the generators.

Thermal power station

In a thermal power station, steam passes through a **turbine**. The turbine rotates a generator to produce electricity. After passing through the turbines, the steam condenses to water. It can be fed back into the boiler and used again.

This turbine has small blades that are driven round by the steam.

Regular maintenance keeps the generators running smoothly.

Steam collects in cooling towers where it condenses back to water.

Reducing waste

In a fossil-fuel or biofuel power station, only some of the energy from the burning fuel is transferred electrically. A lot of energy is wasted because it is carried away as heat in steam and exhaust gases.

Burning fuels produce CO_2 and other waste products. Some of these are removed from the exhaust gases before they can escape into the atmosphere.

One way of reducing the amount of CO_2 produced is to use more efficient power stations. But there are arguments both for and against building more gas-fired power stations.

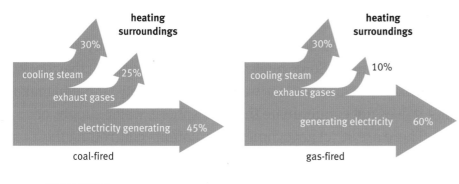

coal-fired

gas-fired

Weighing the arguments – should we build more gas-fired power stations?

Questions

1 Look at the pie chart. What percentage of UK electricity is generated using:
   a nuclear fuels?
   b fossil fuels?

2 Look at the Sankey diagrams. What is the typical efficiency of:
   a a coal-fired power station?
   b a gas-fired power station?

Sankey diagrams show what happens to all the energy. Less energy is wasted in a gas-fired power station.

Summary box

✓ **In a thermal power station energy is wasted as heat.**

Find out about

- ✔ **what happens in a nuclear power station**
- ✔ **why nuclear waste must be handled carefully**
- ✔ **some benefits and risks of nuclear power**

Is more nuclear power the right choice?

There are ten nuclear power stations in the UK. Some of these are coming towards the end of their working lives. In 2009 the government proposed that another ten should be built by 2020.

Nuclear power stations

Nuclear power stations use solid fuel that contains uranium. In a nuclear reactor, uranium atoms split. This releases energy, so the nuclear fuel becomes very hot. The hot fuel boils water to make steam that drives turbines. The nuclear fuel gradually becomes solid nuclear waste.

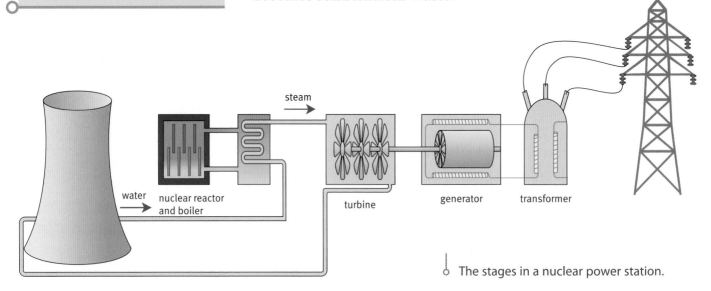

steam

water   nuclear reactor and boiler   turbine   generator   transformer

The stages in a nuclear power station.

Nuclear fuel and waste

Nuclear fuel and nuclear waste are **radioactive**. They give out ionising radiation. Some nuclear waste will be radioactive for thousands of years. Nuclear waste must be safely stored to make sure it does not contaminate the atmosphere, water supply, or soil. There are strict government regulations controlling the way radioactive materials are used and stored.

Summary box

- ✔ **Nuclear power stations use heat from nuclear fuel to produce steam.**
- ✔ **Nuclear fuel and nuclear waste are radioactive.**

Question

1 Compare the diagram of a nuclear power station with the thermal power station on page 270.

   List the parts that are   **a** the same   **b** different.

Contamination and irradiation

Radioactive **contamination** occurs when radioactive material lands on or inside something. Exposure to ionising radiation is called **irradiation**. Limits for irradiation are set by law.

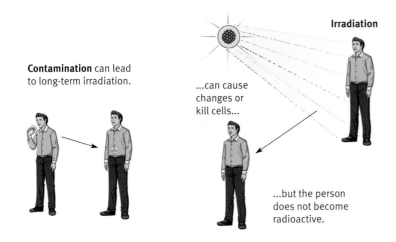

Contamination can lead to long-term irradiation.

Irradiation

...can cause changes or kill cells...

...but the person does not become radioactive.

Uranium mines contain enough fuel for hundreds of years.

Benefits and risks

Benefits of nuclear power are

- Nuclear fuel releases far more energy than fossil fuels. 1 g of uranium fuel can provide as much energy as 8 kg of fossil fuel.
- A nuclear power station produces much less waste than a fossil fuel power station.
- A nuclear reactor does not burn fuel, so no CO_2 is produced.

These people are concerned about the risks.

We can't see radiation, how can we judge the risk?

Suppose there is an accident and fuel leaks out?

There are no uranium mines in Britain. I am worried about relying an imports.

Why should we be exposed to risks so that everyone can have cheap electricity?

What if nuclear waste falls into the hands of terrorists?

They can't store waste at Sellafield, with sea levels rising. It's on the coast!

Summary box

✓ **Contamination is more dangerous than a short period of irradiation from a radioactive source. This is because it can cause long-term irradiation.**

Questions

2 Why might drinking a glass of water, contaminated by radioactive waste, be more dangerous than being irradiated by the glass of water?

3 Make a table of benefits and risks of nuclear power.

PV panels on south-facing roofs in the UK.

The Nant y Moch dam is part of a hydroelectric scheme in Wales. The power output from this scheme is 55 megawatts.

Question

1 Draw a labelled Sankey diagram for a PV panel with 10% efficiency.

Should we use more renewable energy sources?

A **renewable** energy source is one that can be used without running out. We already use some renewable energy sources in the UK.

Solar power

Electromagnetic radiation from the Sun provides **solar power**. In the UK, we use some solar **thermal** panels that use the Sun's radiation to heat water or buildings directly. We also use a different kind of solar panel that uses the Sun's radiation to generate a voltage; these are called **photovoltaic** (PV) panels.

Hydroelectric power

Water heated by the Sun evaporates, and then falls as rain. Rain falling on high ground can be stored behind a dam. Then it can be used to turn turbines in a **hydroelectric** power station as it flows downhill. In the UK there are hydroelectric power stations in Scotland and Wales. They are in places where hills allow faster-flowing water.

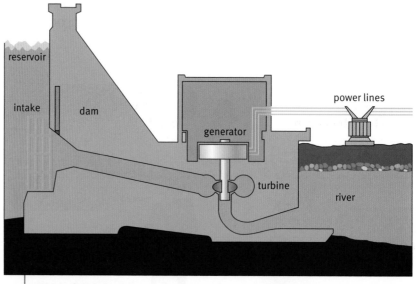

Water from the reservoir turns turbines, which turn the generator.

Wind power

The Sun affects the weather and causes winds. Wind energy can be used to to turn a turbine that drives an electricity generator. But the wind does not blow all the time. A wind farm is a group of wind turbines.

We could build wind farms all around the coast of the UK. This would be more difficult and expensive than building them on land.

Power from waves and tides

The pull of gravity between the Earth and Moon causes the tides. The wind produces waves.

Water movement due to tides and waves can drive turbines. We could build tidal generators and wave generators because the UK is surrounded by sea. They have to be designed so that they are not damaged in storms.

Biofuels

Biofuels are renewable because they can be replaced quickly. Some biofuels could replace oil fuels for transport. Biofuels could be burned in thermal power stations.

The Whitelee wind farm near Glasgow.

A Pelamis generator uses **wave power** to produce electricity.

Miscanthus grass is grown for fuel and burned in power stations.

In a geothermal power station energy from hot rocks is used to produce steam to drive turbines.

Questions

2 A student says 'All our energy comes from the Sun.' Explain why this is true for:
   a hydroelectric power   c wave power
   b wind power   d biomass fuels

3 Give an advantage and a drawback of:
   a hydroelectric power   c wave power
   b wind power

Summary box
- ✓ Renewable sources of energy are ones that will not run out.
- ✓ Renewable sources are:
  - biomass
  - solar
  - wind
  - water (includes waves, tides, and hydroelectric).

Find out about

- ✔ **why we need a National Grid**
- ✔ **why the National Grid uses very high voltages**
- ✔ **why transformers are used to alter the voltage of an electricity supply**

Power stations are built close to their energy source or where there is plenty of cooling water. But that is not always where the electricity is needed. So the electricity is distributed to the users by the National Grid.

National Grid

All the power stations in the UK are connected to the **National Grid**, and so are all the electricity users. This is so that power stations can be switched on and off without cutting off your electricity supply. The photograph shows the wires, and a pylon used by the Grid.

High voltage

The National Grid covers large distances so there is a lot of wire.

When an electric current flows in a wire, the wire gets hot. This means that some energy is wasted as heat. It is not getting to the user.

But there is a way to reduce the wasted energy. This is to use a very high voltage.

It is more efficient to use a high voltage to distribute electricity. The higher the voltage, the smaller the current needed for the same power output to the user. With a smaller current, less energy is lost heating the wires.

In the UK the mains voltage is 230 V but you can see in the diagram that parts of the grid transmit at 275 000 V.

Transformers

The voltage of an a.c. electricity supply can be altered using a **transformer**.

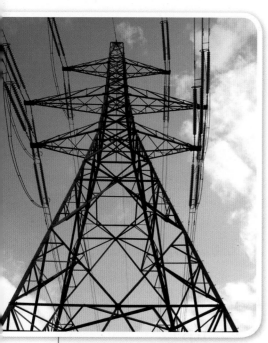

The high-voltage wires of the Grid are supported by tall pylons.

Questions

1 What is the mains voltage in the UK?

2 Explain why the National Grid uses a high voltage.

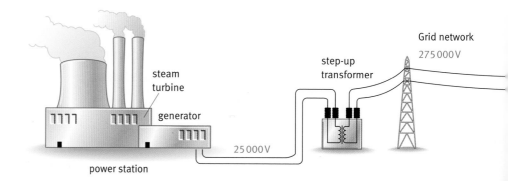

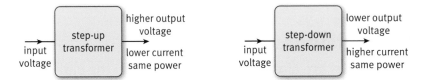

The National Grid uses step-up transformers to increase the voltage for transmission of electricity. A step-down transformer in the local substation reduces the voltage.

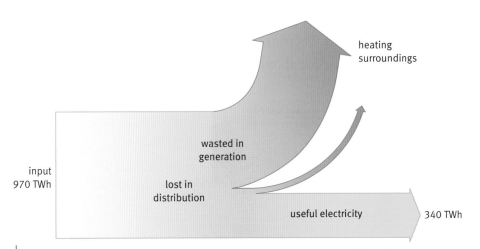

In 2008 the UK used about 970 TWh of energy to supply 340 TWh of electricity, 40 TWh was lost in the distribution process. 1 TWh is one thousand million kWh.

This transformer is about to be installed in a substation.

Questions

3 What does a step-up transformer do to the voltage?

4 Use the Sankey diagram to calculate the overall efficiency of electricity generation and distribution in the UK.

5 a Where would you find a step-down transformer in the National Grid?
   b Explain why it is used.

Summary box

✔ **All power stations and users are connected to the National Grid.**

✔ **Electricity is distributed at high voltage to reduce the energy wasted as heat.**

✔ **Mains voltage is 230V.**

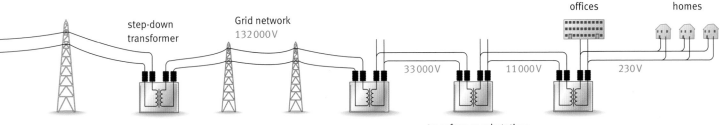

Find out about

✓ arguments for and against using various energy sources

Summary box

✓ There are advantages and disadvantages of using all energy sources.
✓ Governments and society have to decide which energy sources to use and how to use them.

The energy debate

Nuclear

Making decisions

Old power stations are closed down as they reach the end of their useful lives. The buildings must be taken apart and made safe. This is called **decommissioning**. New power stations must be built to replace them.

Energy companies have all the primary energy sources to choose from; their choices take into account government policy and public opinion. You can make your views heard by writing to your MP or your local paper.

Taking apart Berkley nuclear power station in Gloucestershire. Electricity costs take in the whole life of a power station, from start to finish.

YES

Nuclear power is the only energy source that can meet a large electricity demand. It releases no damaging carbon dioxide.

The best way to use uranium is as fuel in nuclear power stations to generate electricity. Otherwise it can be used for making nuclear weapons.

UK nuclear power stations use tried-and-tested technology. Safety systems meet high standards. Waste disposal is a problem that we can solve.

NO

Nuclear power stations may release little CO_2 while operating. But large amounts of CO_2 are released when they are built and decommissioned. Most importantly, they produce radioactive waste that lasts for years.

New reactors would take about 10 years to build and cost roughly £2 billion each. Insurance companies will not cover their risks. If anything goes wrong the public will have to pay.

Renewable energy sources

NO

Renewable energy is unreliable. Winds don't always blow. The Sun doesn't always shine.

Renewable sources would not provide enough energy for this country.

Wind farms should not be built where people live and work. Wind turbines are huge noisy machines.

Wave and tidal generators harm wildlife. Large hydroelectric schemes damage the countryside.

The main renewable energy sources are not in the same place as power stations. We would have to connect them using more power lines across the countryside.

YES

The UK should use its own energy sources and not rely on imports. Recent studies suggest that renewable energy sources could provide the UK with a reliable supply of electricity.

What we need is a full range of generators – very big to very small – at sites all around the country. Building wind generators and solar cells on the rooftops of many offices and homes will be relatively cheap and easy.

Using power from the Sun and winds releases little CO_2.

Use less energy – for and against

YES

The energy used by the UK rises year by year. In your lifetime, you are likely to use as much energy as all four of your grandparents put together. This is not sustainable it is using up energy sources and damaging the environment. We must save energy or the sources will run out. There are ways of saving energy without changing our lifestyle. Every energy saving you can make will help.

The government can help by making sure that:
- new buildings use less energy for heating and lighting
- grants help householders improve heat and power systems
- new appliances are energy efficient
- fossil fuels are more highly taxed

NO

Energy improves our standard of living and our health. We can't give up improvements and return to the way our grandparents lived. In the UK we need energy for technology to feed, clothe, and house our large population. And everyone has a right to a good standard of living at home.

Questions

1 What does 'a sustainable supply of energy' mean?

2 Look at the arguments for and against each energy source.

   Draw balance diagrams for each option, listing statements on each side.

3 The cost of decommissioning adds to the price of electricity. It is much larger for nuclear power stations than for stations burning fossil fuels. Explain why.

Science Explanations

Energy comes from many different sources, including fossil fuels, nuclear power, and renewable sources such as solar power. This energy is also used to generate electricity, which has become essential in our daily lives.

You should know:

- that the demand for energy is continually increasing, and that this raises issues about the availability of sources and the environmental effect of using them
- the main primary energy sources
- why electricity is called a secondary energy source and why it is convenient to use
- which renewable energy sources are used for generating electricity
- that burning carbon fuels in power stations produces carbon dioxide
- that power is the amount of energy transferred each second
- that electrical energy transferred = power × time
- that electric power = voltage × current
- that joules and kilowatt hours are both units of energy
- how to interpret and construct Sankey diagrams
- that efficiency of electrical appliances and power stations can be calculated using the equation:

$$\text{efficiency} = \frac{\text{energy usefully transferred}}{\text{total energy supplied}}$$

- that mains electricity is produced by generators, which contain coils of wire and spinning magnets
- that thermal power stations use a primary energy source to heat water to drive a turbine and generator, but that many renewable sources of energy drive a turbine directly
- how to label a block diagram showing the main parts of power stations
- that nuclear power stations produce radioactive waste, which emits ionising radiation
- the difference between contamination and irradiation by a radioactive material
- that electricity is distributed through the National Grid at high voltages, although the mains supply voltage to our homes is 230 V
- how to evaluate energy sources, using data where appropriate, in terms of where they are used (home, work place, or nationally)
- factors that affect the choice of the source (the environment, economics, waste products produced)
- the advantages and disadvantages of different non-renewable and renewable power stations (fossil fuel, nuclear, biomass, solar, wind, and water).

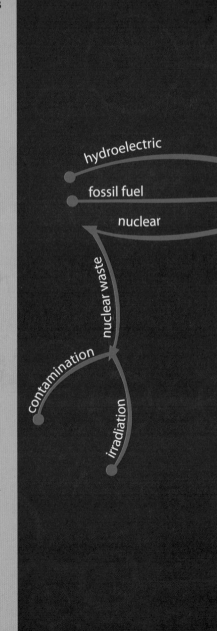

hydroelectric

fossil fuel

nuclear

nuclear waste

contamination

irradiation

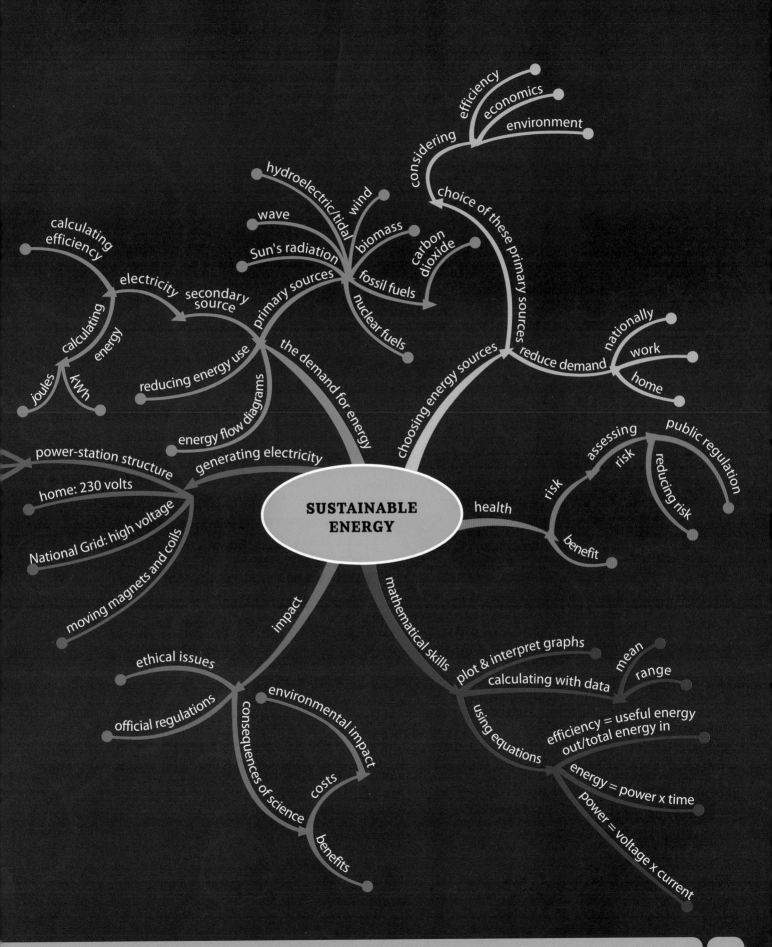

SUSTAINABLE ENERGY

considering
- efficiency
- economics
- environment

choice of these primary sources

hydroelectric/tidal
wind
wave
biomass
Sun's radiation
carbon dioxide
primary sources
fossil fuels
nuclear fuels

calculating efficiency

electricity — secondary source

calculating energy
- joules
- kWh

reducing energy use

the demand for energy

choosing energy sources

reduce demand
- nationally
- work
- home

energy flow diagrams

power-station structure
home: 230 volts
National Grid: high voltage
moving magnets and coils

generating electricity

health
- risk
  - assessing risk
    - public regulation
    - reducing risk
- benefit

impact

ethical issues
official regulations
consequences of science
- costs
- benefits
environmental impact

mathematical skills

plot & interpret graphs

calculating with data
- mean
- range

using equations
- efficiency = useful energy out/total energy in
- energy = power x time
- power = voltage x current

Ideas about Science

In addition to developing an understanding of the use and generation of electricity, it is important to assess the risks and benefits associated with the chosen methods of energy use, and to appreciate the issues involved in making decisions about the use of science and technology.

Everything we do carries some risk, and new technologies often introduce new risks. It is important to assess the chance of a particular outcome happening, and the consequences if it did. Something that benefits us will often also have risks, so the benefits must be weighed against the risks.

You should be able to:
- explain why it is impossible for anything to be completely safe
- identify risks arising from scientific or technological advances
- suggest ways of reducing a given risk
- discuss how risk should be regulated by governments and other public bodies.

Science-based technology provides people with many things they value. However, some applications of science can have undesirable effects on quality of life and on the environment. Benefits need to be weighed against costs.

In the context of the sustainable energy, you should be able to:
- identify the groups affected, and the main benefits and costs of a course of action for each group
- identify examples of unintended impacts of human activity on the environment
- explain the idea of sustainability, and use it to compare the sustainability of different processes
- know about the official regulation of the application of scientific knowledge
- in cases where an ethical issue is involved, say clearly what the issue is and summarise different views that may be held
- understand ethical arguments based on 'the best outcome for the greatest number of people'.
- understand that certain things are right or wrong whatever the circumstances.

Review Questions

1

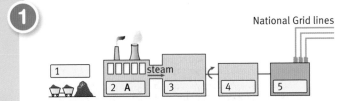

National Grid lines

steam

a Copy and label the diagram of a coal-fired power station.
Put the letters **A**, **B**, **C**, **D**, and **E** in the correct boxes on the diagram above. One has been done for you.

A	furnace
B	transformer
C	fuel
D	turbine
E	generator

b Power stations use a carbon-based fuel. Which greenhouse gas will definitely be produced when the fuel is burnt?

c Coal is a non-renewable energy source. Which two of the following are **renewable** energy sources that are used to generate electricity?

natural gas   **nuclear fuel**
wind power   **oil**   **wave power**

2 The diagram shows the efficiency of a modern power station.

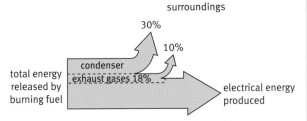

heating the surroundings
30%
10%
condenser
total energy released by burning fuel
exhaust gases 18%
electrical energy produced

a Use the diagram to calculate the efficiency of the power station in producing electrical energy.

b Half of the heat energy from the condenser is used to heat homes and businesses near the power station.
  i Draw a new Sankey diagram to show:
    the % electrical energy produced
    the % energy released as exhaust gases
    the % energy wasted in the condenser
    the % energy used to heat homes and businesses.
  ii Use your diagram to work out the efficiency of the power station in providing useful energy output.

3 An electric heater draws a current of 10 A from a 230 V power supply.
a Calculate the input power, in watts and in kilowatts, to the heater.
b Calculate the cost of using the heater for five hours, if one kilowatt-hour of electrical energy costs 8 p.

4 It costs £400 million to set up and operate a wind farm. The pie chart below shows how these costs are shared out between different factors.

Which one of the following is the best estimate of the cost of the turbines?

£40 million   **£75 million**
£150 million   **£200 million**

maintenance and operating cost
rent of land/ sea area
turbines
£75 million
cables and connection to the National Grid
foundations and other buildings
Total cost = £400 million

Glossary

absorb (radiation) The radiation that hits an object and is not reflected, or transmitted through it, is absorbed (for example, black paper absorbs light). Its energy makes the object gets a little hotter.

accumulate To collect together and increase in quantity.

accuracy How close a quantitative result is to the true or 'actual' value.

actual risk Risk calculated from reliable data.

adaptation A feature that helps an organism survive in its environment.

ADH A hormone that makes kidney tubules more permeable to water, causing greater re-absorption of water.

aerial A wire, or arrangement of wires, that emits radio waves when there is an alternating current in it, and in which an alternating current is induced by passing radio waves. So it acts as a source or a receiver of radio waves.

alcohol The intoxicating chemical in wine, beer, and spirits. Causes changes in behaviour and may create long-term addiction.

Alkali Acts The Acts of Parliament passed in the UK in order to control levels of pollution. They led to the formation of an Alkali Inspectorate, which checked that at least 95% of acid fumes were removed from the chimneys of chemical factories.

alkali A compound that dissolves in water to give a solution with a pH higher than 7. An alkali can be neutralised by an acid to form a salt.

allele Different versions of the same gene.

allergic People with an allergy suffer symptoms when they eat some foods that most people find harmless. Symptoms can include itchy skin, shortness of breath, and an upset stomach.

ammeter A meter that measures the size of an electric current in a circuit.

ampere (amp, for short) The unit of electric current.

amplitude For a mechanical wave, the maximum distance that each point on the medium moves from its normal position as the wave passes. For an electromagnetic wave, the maximum value of the varying electric field (or magnetic field).

analogue signal Signals used in communications in which the amplitude can vary continuously.

antibiotic resistant Microorganisms that are not killed by antibiotics.

antibiotics Drugs that kill or stop the growth of bacteria and fungi.

antibodies A group of proteins made by white blood cells to fight dangerous microorganisms. A different antibody is needed to fight each different type of microorganism. Antibodies bind to the surface of the microorganism, which triggers other white blood cells to digest them.

antigens The proteins on the surface of a cell. A cell's antigens are unique markers.

artery A blood vessel that carries blood away from the heart.

asexual reproduction When a new individual is produced from just one parent.

assumption A piece of information that is taken for granted without sufficient evidence to be certain.

asteroid A dwarf rocky planet, generally orbiting the Sun between the orbits of Mars and Jupiter.

atmosphere The layer of gases that surrounds the Earth.

atom The smallest particle of an element. The atoms of each element are the same as each other and are different from the atoms of other elements.

best estimate When measuring a variable, the value in which you have most confidence.

big bang An explosion of a single mass of material. This is currently the accepted scientific explanation for the start of the Universe.

biodegradable Materials that are broken down in the environment by microorganisms. Most synthetic polymers are *not* biodegradable.

biodiversity The great variety of living things, both within a species and between different species.

biofuel A renewable fuel that uses biological material, such as recently living plant materials and animal waste.

bleach A chemical that can destroy unwanted colours. Bleaches also kill bacteria. A common bleach is a solution of chlorine in sodium hydroxide.

blind trial A clinical trial in which the patient does not know whether they are taking the new drug, but their doctor does.

blood pressure The pressure exerted by blood pushing on the walls of a blood vessel.

blood transfusion Transfer of blood from one person to another.

branched chain A chain of carbon atoms with short side branches.

brine A solution of sodium chloride (salt) in water. Brine is produced by solution mining of underground salt deposits.

capillary The smallest blood vessel. Its walls are only one cell thick and allow substances to diffuse between the blood and the cells.

carbon cycle The cycling of the element carbon in the environment between the atmosphere, biosphere, hydrosphere, and lithosphere. The element exists in different compounds in these spheres. In the atmosphere it is mainly present as carbon dioxide.

carrier Someone who has the recessive allele for a characteristic or disease but who does not have the characteristic or disease itself.

carrier wave A steady stream of radio waves produced by an RF oscillator in a radio to carry information.

catalyst A chemical that speeds up a chemical reaction but is not used up in the process.

catalytic converter A device fitted to a vehicle exhaust that changes the waste gases into less harmful ones.

cause When there is evidence that changes in a factor produce a particular outcome, then the factor is said to cause the outcome. For example, increases in the pollen count cause increases in the incidence of hayfever.

centrifuge A piece of equipment used to separate a mixture of liquids and solids by spinning the mixture very fast.

ceramic Solid material such as pottery, glass, cement, and brick.

chemical change/chemical reaction A change that forms a new chemical.

chemical equation A summary of a chemical reaction showing the reactants and products with their physical states (see balanced chemical equation).

chemical formula A way of describing a chemical that uses symbols for atoms. It gives information about the number of different types of atom in the chemical.

chlorination The process of adding chlorine to water to kill microorganisms, so that it is safe to drink.

chlorine A greenish toxic gas, used to bleach paper and textiles, and to treat water.

CFCs Liquids that used to be used in refrigerators and aerosols. Their vapour damages the ozone layer.

chromosome Long, thin, threadlike structure in the nucleus of a cell made from a molecule of DNA. Chromosomes carry the genes.

classification Putting living things into groups based on their shared characteristics.

climate Average weather in a region over many years.

clinical trial When a new drug is tested on humans to find out whether it is safe and whether it works.

clone A new cell or individual made by asexual reproduction. A clone has the same genes as its parent.

coding (in communications) Converting information from one form to another, for example, changing an analogue signal into a digital one.

combustion The process of burning a substance that reacts with oxygen to produce heat and light.

comet A rocky lump, held together by frozen gases and water, that orbits the Sun.

competition Different organisms that require the same resource, such as water, food, light, or space, must compete for the resource.

compression A material is in compression when forces are trying to push it together and make it smaller.

concentration The quantity of a chemical dissolved in a stated volume of solution. Concentrations can be measured in grams per litre.

condensed The change of state from a gas to a liquid,, for example, water vapour in the air condenses to form rain.

conservation of atoms   All the atoms present at the beginning of a chemical reaction are still there at the end. No new atoms are created and no atoms are destroyed during a chemical reaction.

conservation of energy   The principle that the total amount of energy at the end of any process is always equal to the total amount of energy at the beginning – though it may now be stored in different ways and in different places.

conservation of mass   The total mass of chemicals is the same at the end of a reaction as at the beginning. No atoms are created or destroyed and so no mass is gained or lost.

consumer   An organism that eats others in a food chain. This is all the organisms in a food chain except the producer(s).

contamination   Having a radioactive material inside the body, or having it on the skin or clothes.

continental drift   A theory that describes the extremely slow movements of the continents across the Earth.

control   In a clinical trial, the control group is people taking the currently used drug. The effects of the new drug can then be compared to this group.

convection   The movement that occurs when hot material rises and cooler material sinks.

core   The Earth's core is made mostly from iron, solid at the centre and liquid above.

coronary artery   The artery that supplies blood carrying oxygen and glucose directly to the muscle cells of the heart.

correlation   A link between two things. For example, if an outcome happens when a factor is present, but not when it is absent, or if an outcome increases or decreases when a factor increases. For example, when pollen count increases hayfever cases also increase.

cross-link   A link or bond joining polymer chains together.

crude oil   A dark, oily liquid found in the Earth, which is a mixture of hydrocarbons.

crust   A rocky layer at the surface of the Earth, 10–40 km deep.

crystalline polymer   A polymer with molecules lined up in a regular way as in a crystal.

crystallise   To form crystals, for example, by evaporating the water from a solution of a salt.

cystic fibrosis   An inherited disorder. The disorder is caused by recessive alleles.

decoding   In communications, converting information back into its original form, for example, changing a digital signal back into an analogue one.

decommissioning   Taking a power station out of service at the end of its lifetime, dismantling it, and disposing of the waste safely.

decomposer bacteria   Microorganisms that break down the organic compounds in dead plants and animals and waste.

decomposition   The process of breaking down dead plants and animals and waste by microorganisms.

deforestation   Cutting down trees from an area of land.

denitrification   The removal of nitrogen from soil. Bacteria break down nitrates in the soil, converting them back to nitrogen.

denitrifying bacteria   Bacteria that break down nitrates in the soil, releasing nitrogen into the air.

density   A dense material is heavy for its size. Density is mass divided by volume.

detritivore   An organism that feeds on dead organisms and waste. Woodlice, earthworms, and millipedes are examples of detritivores.

digest   To break down larger, insoluble molecules into small, soluble molecules.

digital code   A string of 0s and 1s that can be used to represent an analogue signal, and from which that signal can be reconstructed.

digital signal   Signals used in communications in which the amplitude can take only one of two values, corresponding to the digits 0 and 1.

disease   A condition that impairs normal functioning of an organism's body, usually associated with particular signs and symptoms. It may be caused by an infection or by the dysfunction of internal organs.

dissolve   Some chemicals dissolve in liquids (solvents). Salt and sugar, for example, dissolve in water.

DNA (deoxyribonucleic acid)   The chemical that makes up chromosomes. DNA carries the genetic code, which controls how an organism develops.

dominant   Describes an allele that will show up in an organism even if a different allele of the gene is present. You only need to have one copy of a dominant allele to have the feature it produces.

double-blind trial   A clinical trial in which neither the doctor nor the patient knows whether the patient is taking the new drug.

durable   A material is durable if it lasts a long time in use. It does not wear out.

duration   How long something happens for. For example, the length of time someone is exposed to radiation.

dwarf planet   A round, planetlike object with a similar orbit to the eight planets but too small to clear its orbit of other small objects.

earthquake   An event in which rocks break to allow tectonic plate movement, causing the ground to shake.

Ecstasy   A recreational drug that increases the concentration of serotonin at the synapses in the brain, giving pleasurable feelings. Long-term effects may include destruction of the synapses.

effector   The part of a control system that brings about a change to the system.

efficiency   The percentage of the energy supplied to a device that is transferred to the desired place, or in the desired way.

electric charge   A fundamental property of matter. Electrons and protons are charged particles.

electric current   A flow of charge around an electric circuit.

electrolysis   Splitting up a chemical into its elements by passing an electric current through it.

electromagnetic induction   The name of the process in which a potential difference (and hence often an electric current) is generated in a wire, when it is in a changing magnetic field.

electromagnetic spectrum   The 'family' of electromagnetic waves of different frequencies and wavelengths.

electromagnetic wave   A wave consisting of vibrating electric and magnetic fields, which can travel in a vacuum. Visible light is one example.

electron   A tiny, negatively charged particle, which is part of an atom. Electrons are found outside the nucleus. Electrons have negligible mass and one unit of charge.

embryo   The earliest stage of development for an animal or plant. In humans the embryo stage lasts for the first two months.

emission   Something given out by something else, for example, the emission of carbon dioxide from combustion engines.

emit   Give out (radiation).

endangered   A species that is at risk of becoming extinct.

energy cost   The amount of energy used to produce something or to do something.

environment   Everything that surrounds you. This is factors like the air and water, as well as other living things.

enzyme   A protein that catalyses (speeds up) chemical reactions in living things.

epidemiological study   A scientific study that examines the causes, spread, and control of a disease in a human population.

erode   The movement of solids at the Earth's surface (for example, soil, mud, and rock) caused by wind, water, ice, and gravity, and living organisms.

ethics   A set of principles that may show how to behave in a situation.

evaporate   The change of state from a liquid to a gas.

evolution   The process by which species gradually change over time. Evolution can produce new species.

excretion   The removal of waste products of chemical reactions from cells.

extinct   A species is extinct when all the members of the species have died out.

extruded   A plastic is shaped by being forced through a mould.

factor   A variable that changes and may affect something else.

false negative   A wrong test result. The test result says that a person does not have a medical condition but this is incorrect.

false positive   A wrong test result. The test result says that a person has a medical condition but this is incorrect.

fertile   An organism that can produce offspring.

fibres   Long thin threads that make up materials such as wool and polyester. Most fibres used for textiles consist of natural or synthetic polymers.

filtering   Separating a solid from a liquid by passing it through a filter paper.

flavouring   Mixtures of chemicals that give food, sweets, toothpaste, and other products their flavours.

flexible   A flexible material bends easily without breaking.

food chain   In the food industry this covers all the stages from where food grows, through harvesting, processing, preservation, and cooking to being eaten.

food web   A series of linked food chains showing the feeding relationships in a habitat – 'what eats what'.

formula (chemical)   A way of describing a chemical that uses symbols for atoms. A formula gives information about the numbers of different types of atom in the chemical. The formula of sulfuric acid, for example, is H_2SO_4.

fossil   The stony remains of an animal or plant that lived millions of years ago, or an imprint it has made (for example, a footprint) in a surface.

fossil fuel   Natural gas, oil, or coal.

fraction   A mixture of hydrocarbons with similar boiling points that have been separated from crude oil by fractional distillation.

fractional distillation   The process of separating crude oil into groups of molecules with similar boiling points called fractions.

frequency   The frequency of a wave is the number of waves that pass any point each second.

functional protein   Proteins that take part in chemical reactions, for example, enzymes.

fungi   A group of living things, including some microorganisms, that cannot make their own food.

galaxy   A collection of thousands of millions of stars held together by gravity.

gamma radiation (gamma rays)   The most penetrating type of ionising radiation, produced by the nucleus of an atom in radioactive decay. The most energetic part of the electromagnetic spectrum.

gene   A section of DNA giving instructions for a cell about how to make one kind of protein.

generator   A device used to produce electricity by spinning a magnet near a coil of wire (or a coil near a magnet).

genetic screening   Testing a population for a particular allele.

genetic study   A scientific study of the genes carried by people in a population to look for alleles that increase the risk of disease.

genetic test   A test to find whether a person has a particular DNA sequence or allele.

genetic variation   The differences between individuals caused by differences in their genes. Gametes show genetic variation – they all have different genes.

genotype   A description of the genes an organism has.

grain   A relatively small particle of a substance, for example, grains of sand.

greenhouse effect   The atmosphere absorbs infrared radiation from the Earth's surface and radiates some of it back to the surface, making it warmer than it would otherwise be.

greenhouse gas   A gas that contributes to the greenhouse effect, including carbon dioxide, methane, and water vapour.

habitat   The place where an organism lives.

hard   A material that is difficult to dent or scratch.

heart disease   A disease where the coronary arteries become increasingly blocked with fatty deposits, restricting the blood flow to the heart muscle. The risk of this is increased by a high fat diet, smoking, and drinking excess alcohol.

homeostasis   Keeping a steady state inside your body.

human trial   The stage of the trial process for a new drug where the drug is taken by healthy volunteers to see if it is safe, and then by sick volunteers to check that it works.

Huntington's disease   An inherited disease of the nervous system. The symptoms do not show up until middle age.

hydrocarbon   A compound of hydrogen and carbon only. Ethane, C_2H_6, is a hydrocarbon.

hydroelectric power station   A power station that uses water stored behind a dam to drive turbines to generate electricity.

hydrogen chloride gas   An acid gas that is toxic and corrosive, and is produced by the Leblanc process.

hydrogen sulfide gas   A poisonous gas that smells of rotten eggs.

immune   Able to react to an infection quickly, stopping the microorganisms before they can make you ill, usually because you've been exposed to them before.

immune system   A group of organs and tissues in the body that fight infections.

incinerator   A factory for burning rubbish and generating electricity.

indirectly   When something humans do affects another species, but this wasn't the reason for the action. For example, a species habitat is destroyed when land is cleared for farming.

infectious   A disease that can be caught. The microorganism that causes it is passed from one person to another through the air, through water, or by touch.

infertile   An organism that cannot produce offspring.

information (in a computer)   Data stored and processed. It is measured in bytes.

infrared   Electromagnetic waves with a frequency lower than that of visible light, beyond the red end of the visible spectrum.

inherited   A feature that is passed from parents to offspring by their genes.

intensity   the intensity of a beam of electromagnetic radiaiton is the energy is arriving at a square metre of surface each second

interdependence   The relationships between different living things that they rely on to survive.

ion   An electrically charged atom, or group of atoms.

ionising radiation   Radiation with photons of sufficient energy to remove electrons from atoms in its path. Ionising radiation, such as ultraviolet, X-rays, and gamma rays, can damage living cells.

irradiation   Being exposed to radiation from an external source.

joule   A unit used to measure energy.

kidneys   Organs in the body that removes waste urea from the blood, and balances water and blood plasma levels. People are usually born with two kidneys.

kilowatt-hour   A unit used to measure energy. It is equivalent to using energy at a rate of 1 kilowatt for 1 hour. Power (kW) × time (hours).

landfill   Disposing of rubbish in holes in the ground.

latitude   The location of a place on Earth, north or south of the equator.

leach   The movement of the plasticisers in a polymer into water, or another liquid, that is flowing past the polymer or is contained by it.

Leblanc process   A process that used chalk (calcium carbonate), salt (sodium chloride) and coal to make the alkali, sodium carbonate. The Leblanc process was highly polluting.

lichen   An organism consisting of a fungus growing with a simple photosynthetic organism called an alga. Lichens grow very slowly are often found growing on walls and roofs.

life cycle assessment   A way of analysing the production, use, and disposal of a material or product to add up the total energy and water used and the effects on the environment.

lifestyle   The way in which people choose to live their lives, for example, what they choose to eat, how much exercise they choose to do, how much stress they experience in their job.

lifestyle disease   a disease that is not caused by microorganisms. They are triggered by other factors, for example, smoking, diet, and lack of exercise.

light pollution   Light created by humans, for example, street lighting, that prevents city dwellers from seeing more than a few bright stars. It also causes problems for astronomers.

light-year   The distance travelled by light in one year.

long-chain molecule   Polymers are long-chain molecules. They consist of long chains of atoms.

longitudinal wave   A wave in which the particles of the medium vibrate in the same direction as the wave is travelling. Sound is an example.

macroscopic   Large enough to be seen without the help of a microscope.

magnetic   A material that is attracted to a magnet. For example, iron is magnetic.

mantle   A thick layer of rock beneath the Earth's crust, which extends about halfway down to the Earth's centre.

match   Some studies into diseases compare two groups of people. People in each group are chosen to be as similar as possible (matched) so that the results can be fairly compared.

mayfly larvae   Mayflies spend most of their lives (up to three years) as larvae (also called mayfly nymphs). They live and feed in aquatic environments. The adult insects live on the wing for a short time, from a few hours to a few days.

mean value   A type of average, found by adding up a set of measurements and then dividing by the number of measurements. You can have more confidence in the mean of a set of measurements than in a single measurement.

mechanism   A process that explains why a particular factor causes an outcome.

medium (plural media)   A material through which a wave travels.

melting point   The temperature at which something melts.

memory cell   A long-lived white blood cell, which is able to respond very quickly (by producing antibodies to destroy the microorganism) when it meets a microorganism for the second time.

metal   Metals are materials with characteristic properties: they are shiny when polished and they conduct electricity.

microorganism   A living organism that can only be seen through a microscope. They include bacteria, viruses, and fungi.

microwave radiation   The radio wave with the highest frequency (shortest wavelength), used for mobile phones and satellite TV.

Milky Way   The galaxy in which the Sun and its planets including Earth are located. It is seen from the Earth as an irregular, faintly luminous band across the night sky.

mixture   Two or more different chemicals, mixed but not chemically joined together.

modulate   To vary the amplitude or frequency of the carrier waves produced in a radio so that they carry the information in a sound wave.

molecule   A group of atoms joined together. Most non-metals consist of molecules. Most compounds of non-metals with other non-metals are also molecular.

monoculture   The continuous growing of one type of crop.

monomer   A small molecule that can be joined to others like it in long chains to make a polymer.

mountain chain   A group of mountains that extend along a line, often hundreds or even thousands of kilometres. Generally caused by the movement of tectonic plates.

mutation   A change in the DNA of an organism. It alters a gene and may change the organism's characteristics.

nanometre   A unit of length 1 000 000 000 times smaller than a metre. 1 nm = 0.001 μm = 0.000001 mm.

nanoparticle   A very tiny particle, whose size can be measured in nanometres.

nanotechnology   The use and control of structures that are very small (1 to 100 nanometres in size)

National Grid   A network of cables and transformers that connects power stations to the consumers who use the electricity.

natural polymer   A polymer that occurs naturally but may need processing to make it useful, such as silk, cotton, leather, and asbestos.

natural selection   When certain individuals are better suited to their environment they are more likely to survive and breed, passing on their features to the next generation.

negative feedback   A system where any change results in actions that reverse the original change.

neutralisation   A reaction in which an acid reacts with an alkali to form a salt. During neutralisation reactions, the hydrogen ions in the acid solution react with hydroxide ions in the alkaline solution to make water molecules.

neutralise   An acid will neutralise an alkali to form a salt. This is called a neutralisation reaction.

nitrogen cycle   The continual cycling of nitrogen, which is one of the elements essential for life. By being converted to different chemical forms, nitrogen is able to pass between the atmosphere, lithosphere, hydrosphere, and biosphere.

nitrogen fixation   When nitrogen in the air is converted into nitrates in the soil by bacteria.

nitrogen-fixing bacteria   Bacteria found in the soil and in swellings (nodules) on the roots of some plants (legumes), such as clover and peas. These bacteria take in nitrogen gas and make nitrates, which plants can absorb and use to make proteins.

noise   Unwanted electrical signals that get added on to radio waves during transmission, causing additional modulation. Sometimes called 'interference'.

non-ionising radiation   Radiation with photons that do not have enough energy to ionise molecules.

nuclear fuel   In a nuclear reactor, uraniums atom splits and releases energy when hit by a neutron.

nuclear fusion   The process in which two small nuclei combine to form a larger one, releasing energy. An example is hydrogen combining to form helium. This happens in stars, including the Sun.

nucleus (plural nuclei)   The central core of the atom. It is made up of protons and neutrons.

nucleus   The central structure in a cell containing genetic material. It controls the function and characteristics of the cell.

oceanic ridge   A line of underwater mountains in an ocean, where new seafloor constantly forms.

open-label trial   A clinical drug test in which both the patient and their doctor knows whether the patient is taking the new drug.

optical fibre   A thin glass fibre, down which a light beam can travel. The beam is reflected at the sides so very little escapes. Used in modern communications, for example, to link computers in a building to a network.

organic matter   Material that has come from dead plants and animals.

outcome   A variable that changes as a result of something else changing.

outlier   A measured result that seems very different from other repeat measurements, or from the value you would expect, which you therefore strongly suspect is wrong.

oxidation   A reaction that adds oxygen to a chemical.

ozone layer   A thin layer in the atmosphere, about 30 km up, where oxygen is in the form of ozone molecules. The ozone layer absorbs ultraviolet radiation from sunlight.

parallax   The apparent shift of an object against a more distant background, as the position of the observer changes. The further away an object is, the less it appears to shift. This can be used to measure how far away an object is, for example, to measure the distance to stars.

parallax angle   When observed at an interval of six months, a star will appear to move against the background of much more distant stars. Half of its apparent angular motion is called its parallax angle.

particulate   A tiny bit of a solid.

passenger-kilometre   A unit used to compare different transport systems to take account of how many passengers are carried. Number of passengers × distance travelled in km.

peer review   The process whereby scientists who are experts in their field critically evaluate a scientific paper or idea before and after publication.

persistent organic pollutant (POP)   A POP is an organic compound that does not break down in the environment for a very long time. POPs can spread widely around the world and build up in the fatty tissue of humans and animals. They can be harmful to people and the environment.

phenotype   A description of the physical characteristics that an organism has (often related to a particular gene).

photon   A tiny 'packet' of electromagnetic radiation. All electromagnetic waves are emitted and absorbed as photons. The energy of a photon is proportional to the frequency of the radiation.

photosynthesis   A chemical reaction that happens in green plants using the energy in sunlight. The plant takes in water and carbon dioxide, and uses sunlight to convert them to glucose (a nutrient) and oxygen.

photovoltaic (PV) panel   A device that uses the Sun's radiation to generate electricity.

phthalate   A chemical that is used as a plasticiser, added to polymers to make them more flexible.

phytoplankton   Single-celled photosynthetic organisms found in an ocean ecosystem.

pituitary gland   The part of the human brain that coordinates many different functions, for example, release of ADH.

placebo   Occasionally used in clinical trials, this looks like the drug being tested but contains no actual drug.

planet   A very large, spherical object that orbits the Sun, or other star.

plasticiser   A chemical (usually a small molecule) added to a polymer to make it more flexible.

pollutant   Waste matter or chemical that contaminates the water, air, or soil.

polymer   A material made of very long molecules formed by joining lots of small molecules, called monomers, together.

population   A group of animals or plants of the same species living in the same area.

potential difference (p.d.)   The difference in potential energy (for each unit of charge flowing) between any two points in an electric circuit.

power   In an electric circuit, the rate at which work is done by the battery or power supply on the components in a circuit. Power is equal to current × voltage.

predator   An animal that kills other animals (its prey) for food.

pre-implantation genetic diagnosis (PGD)   This is the technical term for embryo selection. Embryos fertilised outside the body are tested for genetic disorders. Only healthy embryos are put into the mother's uterus.

preservative   A chemical added to food to stop it going bad.

primary energy source   A source of energy not derived from any other energy source, for example, fossil fuels or uranium.

principal frequency   The frequency that is emitted with the highest intensity.

processing centre   The part of a control system that receives and processes information from the receptor, and triggers action by the effectors.

producer   The organism found at the start of a food chain. Producers are autotrophs, able to make their own food.

product   A new chemical formed during a chemical reaction.

properties   The physical or chemical characteristics of a chemical. The properties of a chemical are what make it different from other chemicals.

proportional   Two variables are proportional if there is a constant ratio between them.

protein   Chemicals in living things that are polymers made by joining together amino acids.

pulse rate   The rate at which the heart beats. The pulse is measured by pressing on an artery in the neck, wrist, or groin.

P-wave   A longitudinal seismic wave through the Earth, produced during an earthquake.

radiation   A flow of energy from a source. Light and infrared are examples. Radiation spreads out from its source, and may be absorbed or reflected by objects in its path. It may also go (be transmitted) through them.

radio wave   Electromagnetic wave of a much lower frequency than visible light. Radio waves can be made to carry signals and are widely used for communications.

radioactive   Used to describe a material, atom, or element that produces ionising radiation.

radiotherapy   Using radiation to treat a patient.

random   Of no predictable pattern.

range   The difference between the highest and the lowest of a set of measurements.

reactant   A chemical on the left-hand side of an equation. These chemicals react to form the products.

reacting mass   The masses of chemicals that react together, and the masses of products that are formed. Reacting masses are calculated from the balanced symbol equation using relative atomic masses and relative formula masses.

reactive metal   A metal with a strong tendency to react with chemicals such as oxygen, water, and acids. The more reactive a metal, the more strongly it joins with other elements such as oxygen. So reactive metals are hard to extract from their ores.

receptor   The part of a control system that detects changes in the system and passes this information to the processing centre.

recessive   An allele that will only show up in an organism when a dominant allele of the gene is not present. You must have two copies of a recessive allele to have the feature it produces.

recycling   A range of methods for making new materials from materials that have already been used.

redshift   When radiation is observed to have longer wavelengths than expected. (Red light has the longest wavelength of visible light.)

reducing agent   A chemical that removes oxygen from another chemical. For example, carbon acts as a reducing agent when it removes oxygen from a metal oxide. The carbon is oxidised to carbon monoxide during this process.

reduction   A reaction that removes oxygen from a chemical.

reference material   A known chemical used in analysis for comparison with unknown chemicals.

regulation   A rule that can be enforced by an authority, for example, the government. The law that says that all vehicles that are three years old and older must have an annual exhaust emission test is a regulation that helps to reduce atmospheric pollution.

renewable energy source   A resource that can be used to generate electricity without being used up, such as the wind, tides, and sunlight.

repeatable   A quality of a measurement that gives the same result when repeated under the same conditions.

reproduction   The production of offspring through a sexual or asexual process.

reproductive isolation   Two populations are reproductively isolated if they are unable to breed with each other.

respiration   A series of chemical reactions in cells that release energy for the cell to use.

risk   The probability of an outcome that is seen as undesirable, associated with some behaviour or process.

risk factor   A variable linked to an increased risk of disease. Risk factors are linked to disease but may not be the cause of the disease.

rock cycle   Continuing changes in rock material, caused by processes such as erosion, sedimentation, compression, and heating.

rubber   A material that is easily stretched or bent. Natural rubber is a natural polymer obtained from latex, the sap of a rubber tree.

salt   A compound formed when an acid neutralises an alkali.

sampling   In the context of physics, measuring the amplitude of an analogue signal many times a second in order to convert it into a digital signal.

Sankey diagram   A flow diagram used to show what happens to energy during a process. The width of the arrows are proportional to the energy flow.

seafloor spreading   The process of forming new ocean floor at oceanic ridges.

secondary energy source   Energy in a form that can be distributed easily but is manufactured by using a raw energy resource such as a fossil fuel or wind. Examples of secondary energy sources are electricity, hot water used in heating systems, and steam.

sedimentary rock   Rock formed from layers of sediment.

seismic wave   A wave produced by the vibrations caused by an earthquake.

selective absorption   Some materials absorb some forms of electromagnetic radiation but not others. For example, glass absorbs infrared but is transparent to visible light.

selective breeding   Choosing parent organisms with certain characteristics and mating them to try to produce offspring that have these characteristics.

sensitivity   The ability to detect small changes, for example, radiation or temperature.

sex cells   Cells produced by males and females for reproduction – sperm cells and egg cells. Sex cells carry a copy of the parent's genetic information. They join together at fertilisation.

sexual reproduction   Reproduction where the sex cells from two individuals fuse together to form an embryo.

shielding   Materials used to absorb radiation.

signal   Information carried through a communication system, for example, by an electromagnetic wave with variations in its amplitude or frequency, or being rapidly switched on and off.

social context   The situation of people's lives.

soft   A material that is easy to dent or scratch.

solar power   Power supplied by electromagnetic radiation from the Sun.

Solar System   The Sun and objects that orbit around it – planets and their moons, comets, and asteroids.

solution   Formed when a solid, liquid, or gas dissolves in a solvent.

source   An object that produces radiation.

specialised   A specialised cell is adapted for a particular job.

species   A group of organisms that can breed to produce fertile offspring.

speed of light   300 000 kilometres per second – the speed of all electromagnetic waves in a vacuum.

stem cell   An unspecialised animal cell that can divide and develop into a specialised cell.

stiff   A material that is difficult to bend or stretch.

strong   A material that is hard to pull apart or crush.

structural   Making up the structure (of a cell or organism).

structural protein   A protein that is used to build cells.

subsidence   The sinking of the ground's surface when it collapses into a hole beneath it.

Sun   The star nearest Earth. Fusion of hydrogen in the Sun releases energy, which makes life on Earth possible.

surface area   How much exposed surface a solid object has.

sustainability   Using resources and the environment to meet the needs of people today without damaging Earth or reducing the resources for people in the future.

sustainable   Meeting the needs of today without damaging the Earth for future generations.

S-wave   A transverse seismic wave through the Earth, produced during an earthquake.

symptom   What a person has when they have a particular illness, for example, a rash, high temperature, or sore throat.

synthetic   A material made by a chemical process, not naturally occurring.

tectonic plates   Giant slabs of rock (about 12, comprising crust and upper mantle) that make up the Earth's outer layer.

telescope   An instrument that gathers electromagnetic radiation to form an image or to map data, from astronomical objects such as stars and galaxies. It makes visible things that cannot be seen with the naked eye.

tension   A material is in tension when forces are trying to stretch it or pull it apart.

termination   When medicine or surgical treatment is used to end a pregnancy.

theory   A scientific explanation that is generally accepted by the scientific community.

thermal panel   A device that uses the Sun's radiation to heat water.

thermal power station   A power station that heats water to produce steam to drive turbines.

tidal power station   A power station that uses the tides to drive turbines to generate electricity.

toxic   A chemical that may lead to serious health risks, or even death, if breathed in, swallowed, or taken in through the skin.

transformer   An electrical device, consisting of two coils of wire wound on an iron core. An alternating current in one coil causes an ever-changing magnetic field that induces an alternating current in the other. Used to 'step' voltage up or down to the level required.

transmitted (transmit)   When radiation hits an object, it may go through it. It is said to be transmitted through it. We also say that a radio aerial transmits a signal. In this case, transmits means 'emits' or 'sends out'.

transverse wave   A wave in which the particles of the medium vibrate at right angles to the direction in which the wave is travelling. Water waves are an example.

turbine   A device that is made to spin by a flow of air, water, or steam. It is used to drive a generator.

ultraviolet radiation (UV)   Electromagnetic waves with frequencies higher than those of visible light, beyond the violet end of the visible spectrum.

uncertain   Describes measurements where scientists know that they may not have recorded the true value.

uncertainty   The amount by which a measurement could differ from the true value.

Universe   All things (including the Earth and everything else in space).

unspecialised   A cell that has not yet developed into one particular type of cell.

vaccination   Introducing to the body a chemical (a vaccine) used to make a person immune to a disease. A vaccine contains weakened or dead microorganisms, or parts of the microorganism, so that the body makes antibodies to the disease without being ill.

variation   Differences between living organisms. This could be differences between species. There are also differences between members of a population from the same species.

vein   A blood vessel that carries blood towards the heart.

vibrate   To move rapidly and repeatedly back and forth.

virus   A microorganism that can only live and reproduce inside living cells.

volcano   A vent in the Earth's surface that erupts magma, gases, and solids.

voltage   The voltage marked on a battery or power supply is a measure of the 'push' it exerts on charges in an electric circuit. The 'voltage' between two points in a circuit means the 'potential difference' between these points.

vulcanisation   A process for hardening natural rubber by making cross-links between the polymer molecules.

watt   The unit used to measure power: 1 watt = 1 joule/second.

wave power   Using the sea waves to drive turbines to generate electricity.

wave speed   The speed at which waves move through a medium.

wavelength   The distance between one wave crest (or wave trough) and the next.

white blood cell   A cell in the blood that fights microorganisms. Some white blood cells digest invading microorganisms. Others produce antibodies.

wind farm   A power station that uses the wind to drive turbines to generate electricity.

word equation   A summary in words of a chemical reaction.

X-ray   Electromagnetic waves with high frequency, well above that of visible light.

XX chromosomes   The pair of sex chromosomes found in a human female's body cells.

XY chromosomes   The pair of sex chromosomes found in a human male's body cells.

Index

Appendices

Useful relationships, units, and data

Relationships

You will need to be able to carry out calculations using these mathematical relationships.

P1 The Earth in the Universe

distance travelled by a wave = wave speed × time

wave speed = frequency × wavelength

P3 Sustainable energy

energy transferred = power × time

power = voltage × current

Units that might be used in the Science course

length: metres (m), kilometres (km), centimetres (cm), millimetres (mm), micrometres (μm), nanometres (nm)

mass: kilograms (kg), grams (g), milligrams (mg)

time: second (s), millisecond (ms)

temperature: degrees Celsius (°C)

area: cm^2, m^2

volume: cm^3, dm^3, m^3, litres (l), millilitres (ml)

speed: m/s, km/s, km/h

energy: joules (J), kilojoules (kJ), megajoules (MJ), kilowatt-hours (kWh), megawatt-hours (MWh)

power: watts (W), kilowatt (kW), megawatt (MW)

frequency: hertz (Hz), kilohertz (kHz)

information: bytes (B), kilobytes (kB), megabytes (MB)

Prefixes for units

nano	micro	milli	kilo	mega	giga	tera
one thousand millionth	one millionth	one thousandth	× thousand	× million	× thousand million	× million million
0.000000001	0.000001	0.001	1000	1000 000	1000 000 000	1000 000 000 000

Useful data

C1 Air quality

Approximate proportions of the main gases in the atmosphere:
78% nitrogen, 21% oxygen, 1% argon

P1 The Earth in the Universe

Speed of light = 300 000 km/s

P2 Radiation and life

Electromagnetic spectrum in increasing order of frequency:
radio waves, microwaves, infrared, visible light, ultraviolet,
X-rays, gamma rays

P3 Sustainable energy

Mains supply voltage: 230 V

Chemical formulae

C1 Air quality

carbon dioxide CO_2

carbon monoxide CO

sulfur dioxide SO_2

nitrogen monoxide NO

nitrogen dioxide NO_2

water H_2O

OXFORD
UNIVERSITY PRESS

Great Clarendon Street, Oxford OX2 6DP

Oxford University Press is a department of the University of Oxford. It furthers the University's objective of excellence in research, scholarship, and education by publishing worldwide in

Oxford   New York

Auckland   Cape Town   Dar es Salaam   Hong Kong   Karachi
Kuala Lumpur   Madrid   Melbourne   Mexico City   Nairobi
New Delhi   Shanghai   Taipei   Toronto

With offices in
Argentina   Austria   Brazil   Chile   Czech Republic   France   Greece
Guatemala   Hungary   Italy   Japan   Poland   Portugal   Singapore
South Korea   Switzerland   Thailand   Turkey   Ukraine   Vietnam

Oxford is a registered trade mark of Oxford University Press
in the UK and in certain other countries.

British Library Cataloguing in Publication Data.

Data available.

ISBN 978 019 913813-5

10 9 8 7 6 5 4 3 2 1

Printed in Great Britain by Bell and Bain, Glasgow.

Paper used in the production of this book is a natural, recyclable product made from wood grown in sustainable forests. The manufacturing process conforms to the environmental regulations of the country of origin.

Acknowledgements
The publisher and authors would like to thank the following for their permission to reproduce photographs and other copyright material:
P13: Chris Schmidt/Istockphoto; **P14:** Alan Schein Photography/Corbis; **P16l:** Monkey Business Images/Shutterstock; **P16r:** Luca DiCecco/Alamy; **P17:** Richard J. Green/Science Photo Library; **P18:** Kenneth Sponsler/Shutterstock; **P19:** St. Felix School, Suffolk; **P22:** CNRI/Science Photolibrary; **P23l:** BSIP Astier Science Photo Library; **P23r:** David Crausby/Alamy; **P25l:** Dan Sinclair/Zooid Pictures; **P25m:** Zooid Pictures; **P28:** Ian Miles-Flashpoint Pictures/Alamy; **P29:** BSIP, Laurent/Science Photo Library; **P30:** Ariel Skelley/Corbis; **P31:** Counsyl; **P34t:** BSIP, Laurent H.Americain/Science Photo Library; **P34b:** Pascal Goetgheluck/Science Photo Library; **P35t:** David Scharf/Science Photo Library; **P35b:** Claude Nuridsany & Marie Perennou/Science Photo Library; **P36:** Dr Yorgos Nikas/Science Photo Library; **P37:** Yoav Levy/Phototake Inc./Alamy; **P40t:** BSIP, Laurent/Science Photo Library; **P40b:** David Scharf/Science Photo Library; **P42:** Kelly Redinger/Design Pics/Corbis; **P44t:** Charles D. Winters/Science Photo Library; **P44b:** NASA/Zooid Pictures; **P45:** M.T. Mangan/USGS; **P46:** David Hardy/Science Photo Library; **P47t:** Russell Shively/Shutterstock; **P47bl:** George Steinmetz/Science Photo Library; **P47br:** Dirk Wiersma/Science Photo Library; **P48t:** John Wilkinson/Ecoscene/Corbis; **P48b:** Harvey Pincis/Science Photo Library; **P51:** Victor De Schwanberg/Science Photo Library; **P56tl:** Mate 3rd Class Daniel Scott/U.S. Navy photo; **P56tr:** Raoux John/Orlando Sentinel/Sygma/Corbis; **P56b:** Cordelia Molloy/ Science Photo Library; **P58:** Nick Hawkes/Ecoscene/Corbis; **P59:** Andrew Lambert Photography/Science Photo Library; **P60t:** Burkard Manufacturing Co. Limited; **P60m:** Andy Harmer /Science Photo Library; **P60b:** Philippe Plailly/Eurelios/Science Photo Library; **P61:** Garo/Phanie/Rex Features; **P62:** Ian Hooton/Science Photo Library; **P63:** Action Press/Rex Features; **P64:** RPL Carburettor and Injection Centre; **P65:** Spencer Grant/Science Photo Library; **P66:** Simon Fraser/Science Photo Library; **P67:** Caroline Penn/Corbis; **P70:** George Steinmetz/Science Photo Library; **P72:** Johan Ramberg/Istockphoto; **P76l:** Frank Zullo/Science Photo Library; **P76r:**

Detlev Van Ravenswaay/Science Photo Library; **P77t:** NASA/CXC/STScI/JPL-Caltech/Science Photo Library/**P77b:** Mark Garlick/Science Photo Library; **P78:** Jerry Lodriguss/Science Photo Library; **P79:** Zooid Pictures; **P80:** Chris Butler/ Science Photo Library; **P81t:** Tony Hallas/Science Photo Library; **P81b:** NASA/ ESA/STSCI/R.Williams, Hdf Team/ Science Photo Library; **P83:** Colin Cuthbert/ Science Photo Library; **P84l:** Jack Sullivan/Alamy; **P84m:** Enzo & Paolo Ragazzini/Corbis; **P84r:** Sinclair Stammers/Science Photo Library; **P86:** Bettmann/Corbis; **P90:** Marta/Fotolia; **P91:** James Wardell/Rex Features; **P100t:** NASA/ESA/STSCI/R.Williams, Hdf Team/ Science Photo Library; **P100b:** AZPworldwide/Shutterstock; **P102:** Bjorn Svensson/Science Photo Library; **P104l:** Science Photo Library; **P104r:** Guzelian Photographers; **P105:** Guzelian Photographers; **P110:** BSIP Laurent & Gille/Science Photo Library; **P111t:** Getty Images News/Getty Images; **P111b:** Philip Wolmuth/Alamy; **P112:** Robert Pickett/Corbis; **P113:** Paul A. Souders/Corbis; **P114t:** Donald R. Swartz/ Shutterstock; **P114b:** Pete Saloutos/Corbis; **P115t:** Simon Fraser/Mrc Unit, Newcastle General Hospital/Science Photo Library; **P115b:** Ed Kashi/Corbis; **P116:** Dr P. Marazzi/Science Photo Library; **P119l:** Science Photo Library; **P119m:** Biophoto Associates/Science Photo Library; **P119r:** Guzelian Photographers; **P120:** AVAVA/Shutterstock; **P121tl:** Bettmann/Corbis UK Ltd.; **P121tr:** Sipa Press/Rex Features; **P121b:** Matt Meadows, Peter Arnold Inc./ Science Photo Library; **P123:** Janine Wiedel Photolibrary/Alamy; **P124:** Dimitri Iundt/Corbis UK Ltd.; **P125:** Publiphoto Diffusion/Science Photo Library; **P126:** Martyn F. Chillmaid; **P127:** Getty Images; **P130:** Simon Fraser/Mrc Unit,Newcastle General Hospital/Science Photo Library; **P132:** FotografiaBasica/ Istockphoto; **P134:** Peter Menzel/Science Photo Library; **P136tl:** Danish Khan/ Istockphoto; **P136tm:** PeskyMonkey/Istockphoto; **P136tr:** Lee Torrens/ Istockphoto; **P136bl:** Yuri Arcurs/Shutterstock; **P136bm:** Danish Khan/ Istockphoto; **P136br:** Arpi/Shutterstock; **P137t:** PhotoCuisine/Corbis UK Ltd.; **P137ml:** David Constantine/Science Photo Library; **P137mm:** K.M. Westermann/Corbis; **P137mr:** Empics; **P137b:** Yves Forestier/Sygma/Corbis; **P138tl:** David Keith Jones/Images of Africa Photobank/Alamy; **P138tr:** Dennis Gilbert/VIEW Pictures Ltd/Alamy; **P138bl:** Tom Tracy Photography/Alamy; **P138br:** Rich Carey/Shutterstock; **P139t:** Masterfile; **P139b:** Duncan Moody/ Istockphoto; **P140:** J & P Coats Ltd; **P141:** Studio 1One/Shutterstock; **P142l:** Tina Chang/Photolibrary; **P142m:** Andrew Syred/Science Photo Library; **P142r:** Eye Of Science/ Science Photo Library; **P145:** akva/Shutterstock; **P146t:** Dan Sinclair/Zooid Pictures; **P146b:** Taryn Cass/Zooid Pictures; **P147:** Tim Pannell/ Corbis; **P148l:** Zooid Pictures; **P148r:** ABACA/Empics; **P149:** Thayer Allyson Gowdy/The Image Bank/Getty Images; **P150:** W. L. Gore & Associates, Ltd.; **P151t:** Du Pont (UK) Ltd; **P151b:** Eye Of Science/Science Photo Library; **P152:** Paul Rapson/Science Photo Library; **P154b:** Wiscan/Dreamstime; **P154b:** David Buffington/Photolibrary; **P155:** Dr P. Marazzi/Science Photo Library; **P156t:** irabel8/Shutterstock; **P156bl:** Charles M. Ommanney/Rex Features; **P156br:** Back Page Images/Rex Features; **P157:** fact fact/Photolibrary; **P160t:** fact fact/ Photolibrary; **P160b:** PeskyMonkey/Istockphoto; **P162:** Gustoimages/Science Photo Library; **P164:** Trevor Worden/Photolibrary; **P166:** Terraxplorer/ Istockphoto; **P167t:** NASA/Science Photo Library; **P167b:** Solent News And Photos/Rex Features; **P168t:** David Turnley/Corbis; **P168m:** Silver-john/ Shutterstock; **P168b:** CNRI/Science Photo Library; **P169:** Mike Hill/Alamy; **P170t:** Image Source/Alamy; **P170b:** Astier - Chru Lille/Science Photo Library; **P171:** University of Oxford- Division of Public Health and Primary Health Care; **P173t:** Janine Wiedel/Janine Wiedel Photolibrary/Alamy; **P173b:** Ted Kinsman/ Science Photo Library; **P177t:** Philip Lange/Shutterstock; **P177bl:** Martin Muránsky/Shutterstock; **P177bm:** KJ Pictures/The Flight Collection/Alamy; **P177br:** Martin Bond/Photofusion Picture Library/Alamy; **P178:** George Steinmetz/Science Photo Library; **P179tl:** Victor De Schwanberg/Science Photo Library; **P179tr:** pinecone/Shutterstock; **P179m:** Jon Van De Grift, Visuals Unlimited/Science Photo Library; **P179b:** ricardoazoury/Istockphoto; **P183:** lebanmax/Shutterstock; **P184:** Loskutnikov/Shutterstock; **P190t:** Silver-john/ Shutterstock; **P190b:** lebanmax/Shutterstock; **P192:** Nancy Nehring/ Istockphoto; **P194l:** Michael Prince/Corbis; **P194r:** Wayne Bennett/Corbis; **P195t:** Kit Houghton/Corbis; **P195m:** Corbis; **P195bl:** EuToch/Shutterstock; **P195bm:** Stephen Ausmus/US Department Of Agriculture/Science Photo Library; **P195br:** Will & Deni McIntyre/Corbis; **P196:** Niall Benvie/Corbis; **P198t:** Pakhnyushcha/Shutterstock; **P198b:** HartmutMorgenthal/Shutterstock; **P199:** Dr Morley Read/Science Photo Library; **P202:** Wim Van Egmond, Visuals Unlimited/Science Photo Library; **P203l:** Dr Keith Wheeler/Science Photo Library; **P203m:** Pedro Salaverria/Shutterstock; **P203r:** Duncan Shaw/Science Photo Library;**P205t:** Oxford University Press; **P205b:** Tom Brakefield/Corbis; **P206:** Holt Studios International; **P207:** VVG/Science Photo Library; **P210:** Mary Evans Picture Library; **P214:** Konrad Wothe/LOOK-foto/Photolibrary; **P215:** Andreas Gradin/Shutterstock; **P217:** bl0ndie/Shutterstock; **P218t:** Collpicto/ Shutterstock; ; **P218b:** Paul Rapson/Science Photo Library; **P219:** Serhiy Zavalnyuk/Istockphoto; **P222t:** bl0ndie/Shutterstock; **P222b:** Pakhnyushcha/ Shutterstock; **P224:** Joan Vicent Cantó Roig/Istockphoto; **P228t:** Vincent Lowe/ Alamy; **P228b:** Kaido Karner/Shutterstock; **P229t:** Andrew J. Martinez/Science Photo Library; **P229bl:** Martin Bond/Photolibrary; **P229bm:** Dirk Wiersma/ Science Photo Library; **P229br:** James King-Holmes/Science Photo Library; **P230t:** Unclesam/Fotolia; **P230m:** Pascal Goetgheluck/Science Photo Library; **P230b:** Winsford Rock Salt Mine; **P231:** Geographical; **P232:** benicce/ Shutterstock; **P234l:** Patrick Frilet/Rex Features; **P234m:** Richard Watson/ Photolibrary; **P234r:** Timur Kulgarin/Shutterstock; **P235t:** Syagci/Istockphoto **P235b:** Martyn F. Chillmaid/Science Photo Library; **P236:** © Catalyst; **P238t:** Samrat35/Dreamstime; **P238b:** Sean Sprague/Photolibrary; **P239:** American

Chemistry Council, Inc.; **P240:** Robert Brook/Science Photo Library; **P241l:** News (UK) Ltd/Rex Features; **P241m:** Lea Paterson/Science Photo Library; **P241r:** Martyn F. Chillmaid/Science Photo Library; **P242:** Tobias Schwarz/ Reuters; **P243:** Caroline Penn/Corbis; **P244:** Kodda/Shutterstock; **P245:** Bob Edwards/Science Photo Library; **P246l:** Craig Holmes Premium/Alamy; **P246m:** AJ Photo/Science Photo Library; **P246r:** Aikotel/Shutterstock; **P247:** Peter Ryan/Science Photo Library; **P248:** ginosphotos/Istockphoto; **P249t:** Gordon Ball LRPS/Shutterstock; **P249b:** Ton Kinsbergen/Science Photo Library; **P252:** Kaido Karner/Shutterstock; **P254:** Stephen Strathdee/Istockphoto; **P256l:** ronfromyork/Shutterstock; **P256r:** Christopher Walker/Shutterstock; **P257t:** Tonylady/Shutterstock; **P257b:** Jeffrey Van Daele/Shutterstock; **P258:** Cecile Degremont/Look At Sciences/Science Photo Library; **P259:** Martin Moxter/Photolibrary; **P260:** ben smith/Shutterstock; **P261t:** Ilya Akinshin/ Shutterstock; **P261b:** Foment/Shutterstock; **P262tl:** Rex Features; **P262tr:** Htjostheim/Dreamstime; **P262bl:** Jonathan Feinstein/Shutterstock; **P262br:** Olexa/Fotolia; **P264:** Ieva Geneviciene/Shutterstock; **P265:** Sheila Terry/ Science Photo Library; **P267:** Barry Batchelor/PA Photos; **P268t:** B. S. Merlin/ Alamy; **P268m:** Paul Rapson/Alamy; **P268b:** © freelights.co.uk 2010; **P269:** © 2009 Dragonfly; **P271l:** Sean Gallup/Getty Images News/Getty Images; **P271m:** Ron Giling/Photolibrary; **P271r:** Mark Sykes/Science Photo Library; **P273:** Ria Novosti/Science Photo Library; **P274t:** marco mayer/Shutterstock; **P274b:** Pearl Bucknall/Robert Harding/Rex Features; **P275t:** D. Kusters/Shutterstock; **P275ml:** hjschneider/Shutterstock; **P275m:** Rhoberazzi/Istockphoto; **P275r:** Pool/Joao Abreu Miranda/AFP Photo; **P276:** Victor De Schwanberg/Science Photo Library; **P277:** Penimages/Dreamstime; **P278:** Martin Bond/Science Photo Library; **P282t:** Htjostheim/Dreamstime; **P282b:** Foment/Shutterstock.

Illustrations by IFA Design, Plymouth, UK, Clive Goodyer, and Q2A Media.

Project Team acknowledgements
These resources have been developed to support teachers and students undertaking the OCR suite of specifications GCSE Science Twenty First Century Science. They have been developed from the 2006 edition of the resources.

We would like to thank David Curnow and Alistair Moore and the examining team at OCR, who produced the specifications for the Twenty First Century Science course.

Authors and editors of the first edition
We thank the authors and editors of the first edition, David Brodie, Jenifer Burden, Peter Campbell, Anne Daniels, Anne Fullick, John Holman, Andrew Hunt, John Lazonby, Jean Martin, Robin Millar, Peter Nicolson, Cliff Porter, David Sang, Charles Tracy, and Jane Wilson.

Many people from schools, colleges, universities, industry, and the professions contributed to the production of the first edition of these resources. We also acknowledge the invaluable contribution of the teachers and students in the pilot centres.

The first edition of Twenty First Century Science was developed with support from the Nuffield Foundation, The Salters Institute, and the Wellcome Trust.

A full list of contributors can be found in the Teacher and Technician Resources.

The continued development of *Twenty First Century Science* is made possible by generous support from:
- The Nuffield Foundation
- The Salters' Institute